Mathematics I

Volume 1

Randall I. Charles
Basia Hall
Dan Kennedy
Laurie E. Bass
Allan E. Bellman
Sadie Chavis Bragg
William G. Handlin
Art Johnson
Stuart J. Murphy
Grant Wiggins

PEARSON

ston, Massachusetts • Chandler, Arizona • Glenview, Illinois • Upper Saddle River, New Jersey

Acknowledgments appear on page Z60, which constitutes an extension of this copyright page.

PEARSON

ISBN-13:   978-0-13-323461-9
ISBN-10:   0-13-323461-4

17   20

From the *Authors*

Welcome

Math is a powerful tool with far-reaching applications throughout your life. We have designed a unique and engaging program that will enable you to tap into the power of mathematics and mathematical reasoning. This award-winning program has been developed to align fully to the Common Core State Standards.

Developing mathematical understanding and problem-solving abilities is an ongoing process—a journey both inside and outside the classroom. This course is designed to help make sense of the mathematics you encounter in and out of class each day and to help you develop mathematical proficiency. .

You will learn important mathematical principles. You will also learn how the principles are connected to one another and to what you already know. You will learn to solve problems and learn the reasoning that lies behind your solutions. You will also develop the key mathematical practices of the Common Core State Standards.

Each chapter begins with the "big ideas" of the chapter and some essential questions that you will learn to answer. Through this question-and-answer process you will develop your ability to analyze problems independently and solve them in different applications.

Your skills and confidence will increase through practice and review. Work through the problems so you understand the concepts and methods presented and the thinking behind them. Then do the exercises. Ask yourself how new concepts relate to old ones. Make the connections!

Everyone needs help sometimes. You will find that this program has built-in opportunities, both in this text and online, to get help whenever you need it.

The problem-solving and reasoning habits and problem-solving skills you develop in this program will serve you in all your studies and in your daily life. They will prepare you for future success not only as a student, but also as a member of a changing technological society.

Best wishes,

Series *Authors*

Randall I. Charles, Ph.D., is Professor Emeritus in the Department of Mathematics at San Jose State University, San Jose, California. He began his career as a high school mathematics teacher, and he was a mathematics supervisor for five years. Dr. Charles has been a member of several NCTM committees including the writing team for the Curriculum Focal Points. He is the former Vice President of the National Council of Supervisors of Mathematics. Much of his writing and research has been in the area of problem solving. He has authored more than 90 mathematics textbooks for kindergarten through college.

Dan Kennedy, Ph.D., is a classroom teacher and the Lupton Distinguished Professor of Mathematics at the Baylor School in Chattanooga, Tennessee. A frequent speaker at professional meetings on the subject of mathematics education reform, Dr. Kennedy has conducted more than 50 workshops and institutes for high school teachers. He is coauthor of textbooks in calculus and precalculus, and from 1990 to 1994 he chaired the College Board's AP Calculus Development Committee. He is a 1992 Tandy Technology Scholar and a 1995 Presidential Award winner.

Basia Hall currently serves as Manager of Instructional Programs for the Houston Independent School District. With 33 years of teaching experience, Ms. Hall has served as a department chair, instructional supervisor, school improvement facilitator, and professional development trainer. She has developed curricula for Algebra 1, Geometry, and Algebra 2 and co-developed the Texas state mathematics standards. A 1992 Presidential Awardee, Ms. Hall is past president of the Texas Association of Supervisors of Mathematics and is a state representative for the National Council of Supervisors of Mathematics (NCSM).

Consulting *Authors*

Stuart J. Murphy is a visual learning author and consultant. He is a champion of helping students develop visual learning skills so they become more successful students. He is the author of MathStart, a series of children's books that presents mathematical concepts in the context of stories, and *I See I Learn*, a Pre-Kindergarten and Kindergarten learning initiative that focuses on social and emotional skills. A graduate of the Rhode Island School of Design, he has worked extensively in educational publishing and has been on the authorship teams of a number of elementary and high school mathematics programs. He is a frequent presenter at meetings of the National Council of Teachers of Mathematics, the International Reading Association, and other professional organizations.

Grant Wiggins, Ed.D., is the President of Authentic Education in Hopewell, New Jersey. He earned his B.A. from St. John's College in Annapolis and his Ed.D. from Harvard University Dr. Wiggins consults with schools, districts, and state education departments on a variety of reform matters; organizes conferences and workshops; and develops print materials and web resources on curricular change. He is perhaps best known for being the coauthor, with Jay McTighe, of *Understanding by Design* and *The Understanding by Design Handbook*[1], the award-winning and highly successful materials on curriculum published by ASCD. His work has been supported by the Pew Charitable Trusts, the Geraldine R. Dodge Foundation, and the National Science Foundation.

[1]ASCD, publisher of the "Understanding by Design Handbook" co-authored by Grant Wiggins and registered owner of the trademark "Understanding by Design", has not authorized or sponsored this work and is in no way affiliated with Pearson or its products.

Program *Authors*

Algebra Topics

Allan E. Bellman, Ph.D., is an Associate Professor of Mathematics Education at the University of Mississippi. He previously taught at the University of California, Davis for 12 years and in public school in Montgomery County, Maryland for 31. He has been an instructor for both the Woodrow Wilson National Fellowship Foundation and the Texas Instruments' T^3 program. Dr. Bellman has expertise in the use of technology in education and assessment-driven instruction and speaks frequently on these topics. He is a recipient of the Tandy Award for Teaching Excellence and has twice been listed in Who's Who Among America's Teachers.

Sadie Chavis Bragg, Ed.D., is Senior Vice President of Academic Affairs and professor of mathematics at the Borough of Manhattan Community College of the City University of New York. She is a past president of the American Mathematical Association of Two-Year Colleges (AMATYC). In recognition for her service to the field of mathematics locally, statewide, nationally, and internationally, she was awarded AMATYC's most prestigious award, The Mathematics Excellence Award for 2010. Dr. Bragg has coauthored more than 60 mathematics textbooks for kindergarten through college.

William G. Handlin, Sr., is a classroom teacher and Department Chair of Mathematics and former Department Chair of Technology Applications at Spring Woods High School in Houston, Texas. Awarded Life Membership in the Texas Congress of Parents and Teachers for his contributions to the well-being of children, Mr. Handlin is also a frequent workshop and seminar leader in professional meetings.

Geometry Topics

Laurie E. Bass is a classroom teacher at the 9–12 division of the Ethical Culture Fieldston School in Riverdale, New York. A classroom teacher for more than 30 years, Ms. Bass has a wide base of teaching experiences, ranging from Grade 6 through Advanced Placement Calculus. She was the recipient of a 2000 Honorable Mention for the Radio Shack National Teacher Awards. She has been a contributing writer for a number of publications, including software-based activities for the Algebra 1 classroom. Among her areas of special interest are cooperative learning for high school students and geometry exploration on the computer. Ms. Bass is a frequent presenter at local, regional, and national conferences.

Art Johnson, Ed.D., is a professor of mathematics education at Boston University. He is a mathematics educator with 32 years of public school teaching experience, a frequent speaker and workshop leader, and the recipient of a number of awards: the Tandy Prize for Teaching Excellence, the Presidential Award for Excellence in Mathematics Teaching, and New Hampshire Teacher of the Year. He was also profiled by the Disney Corporation in the American Teacher of the Year Program. Dr. Johnson has contributed 18 articles to NCTM journals and has authored over 50 books on various aspects of mathematics.

Using **Your Book** with Success

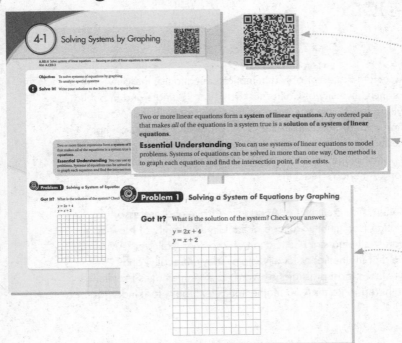

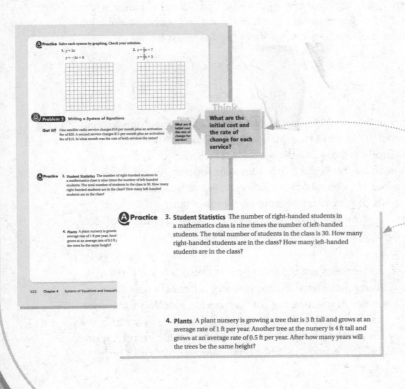

4-1 Solving Systems by Graphing

Two or more linear equations form a **system of linear equations**. Any ordered pair that makes *all* of the equations in a system true is a **solution of a system of linear equations**.

Essential Understanding You can use systems of linear equations to model problems. Systems of equations can be solved in more than one way. One method is to graph each equation and find the intersection point, if one exists.

Problem 1 Solving a System of Equations by Graphing

Got It? What is the solution of the system? Check your answer.

$y = 2x + 4$
$y = x + 2$

Think
What are the initial cost and the rate of change for each service?

Practice 3. **Student Statistics** The number of right-handed students in a mathematics class is nine times the number of left-handed students. The total number of students in the class is 30. How many right-handed students are in the class? How many left-handed students are in the class?

4. **Plants** A plant nursery is growing a tree that is 3 ft tall and grows at an average rate of 1 ft per year. Another tree at the nursery is 4 ft tall and grows at an average rate of 0.5 ft per year. After how many years will the trees be the same height?

● You will find a QR code on each lesson opener. Each code links to a unique instructional video develope by **Virtual Nerd**™.

● The **Essential Understandin** presents the key concept of lesson and connects to the E Ideas that are introduced in Chapter Opener.

● After working through the Problem in the Interactive D Path, you complete a **Got It** exercise in your book. For exercises that require graph a blank grid is provided.

● The **Think** and **Plan** boxes suggest questions to help yo make sense of the problem develop a solution plan.

● Each **Got It?** exercise is foll by additional exercises that focus on the same math co and skill. You complete thes exercises in your book.

You can use the instructional summaries in the **Take Note** boxes to review concepts when completing homework or studying for an assessment.

At the end of each lesson is a **Lesson Check** that you complete in your book. The Do you know HOW? section focuses on skills and the Do you UNDERSTAND? section targets your understanding of the math concepts related to the skills.

Each lesson ends with **More Practice and Problem Solving** exercises. You will complete these exercises in your homework notebook or on a separate sheet of paper.

The exercises with the **Common Core logo** help you become more proficient with the standards for Mathematical Practice. Those with the STEM logo provide practice with science, technology, or engineering topics.

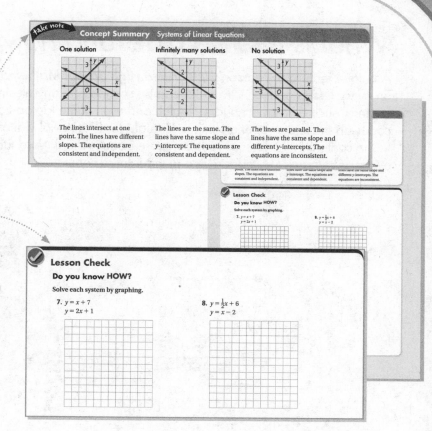

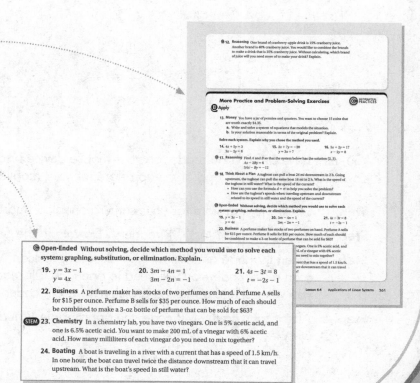

take note

Concept Summary   Systems of Linear Equations

One solution	Infinitely many solutions	No solution

The lines intersect at one point. The lines have different slopes. The equations are consistent and independent.

The lines are the same. The lines have the same slope and y-intercept. The equations are consistent and dependent.

The lines are parallel. The lines have the same slope and different y-intercepts. The equations are inconsistent.

Lesson Check

Do you know HOW?

Solve each system by graphing.

7. $y = x + 7$
$y = 2x + 1$

8. $y = \frac{1}{2}x + 6$
$y = x - 2$

More Practice and Problem-Solving Exercises

B Apply

13. **Money** You have a jar of pennies and quarters. You want to choose 15 coins that are worth exactly $4.35.
   a. Write and solve a system of equations that models the situation.
   b. Is your solution reasonable in terms of the original problem? Explain.

Solve each system. Explain why you chose the method you used.

14. $4x + 3y = 3$
$3x - 2y = 8$

15. $2x + 7y = -20$
$y = 3x + 7$

16. $5x + 2y = 17$
$x - 2y = 8$

17. **Reasoning** Find A and B so that the system below has the solution $(2, 3)$.
$Ax - 2By = 4$
$3Ax - By = -12$

18. **Think About a Plan** A tugboat can pull a boat 24 mi downstream in 2 h. Going upstream, the tugboat can pull the same boat 16 mi in 2 h. What is the speed of the tugboat in still water? What is the speed of the current?
   • How can you use the formula $d = rt$ to help you solve the problem?
   • How are the tugboat's speeds when traveling upstream and downstream related to its speed in still water and the speed of the current?

Open-Ended Without solving, decide which method you would use to solve each system: graphing, substitution, or elimination. Explain.

19. $y = 3x - 1$
$y = 4x$

20. $3m - 4n = 1$
$3m - 2n = -1$

21. $4s - 3t = 8$
$t = -2s - 1$

22. **Business** A perfume maker has stocks of two perfumes on hand. Perfume A sells for $15 per ounce. Perfume B sells for $35 per ounce. How much of each should be combined to make a 3-oz bottle of perfume that can be sold for $63?

STEM 23. **Chemistry** In a chemistry lab, you have two vinegars. One is 5% acetic acid, and one is 6.5% acetic acid. You want to make 200 mL of a vinegar with 6% acetic acid. How many milliliters of each vinegar do you need to mix together?

24. **Boating** A boat is traveling in a river with a current that has a speed of 1.5 km/h. In one hour, the boat can travel twice the distance downstream that it can travel upstream. What is the boat's speed in still water?

What is a **QR code** and how do I use it?

A unique feature of Pearson's *Integrated High School Mathematics* is the QR code on every lesson opener. QR codes can be scanned by any electronic device with a camera, such as a smart phone, tablet, and even some laptop computers. The QR codes on the lesson openers link to Virtual Nerd™ tutorial videos that directly relate to the content in the lesson. To learn more about Virtual Nerd tutorial videos and its exclusive dynamic whiteboard, go to virtualnerd.com.

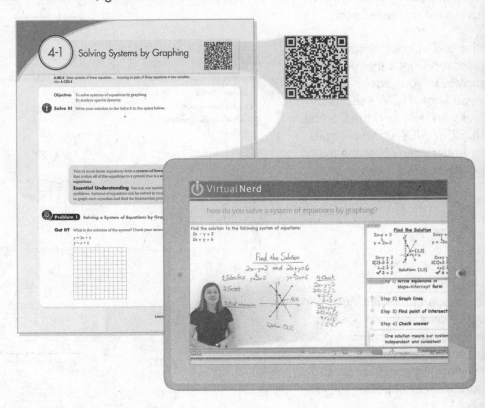

You must have a QR code reader on your mobile device or computer. You can download a QR reader app at the app store for your mobile device.

Step 1: Go to the app store for your camera-enabled smart phone or tablet.

Step 2: Search for "QR" or "QR readers". Download the QR reader app.

Step 3: Open that app and follow the instructions to scan. Whenever you want to scan a QR code, you will need to open the QR reader app first, otherwise you will just end up taking a picture of a QR code.

Step 4: After scanning the QR code, the appropriate Virtual Nerd tutorial video will play.

What **Resources** can I use when studying?

Pearson's *Integrated High School Mathematics* offers a range of resources that you can use out of class.

Student Worktext Your book is more than a textbook. Not only does it have important summaries of key math concepts and skills, it will also have your worked-out solutions to the *Got It?* and *Practice* exercises and your own notes for each lesson or problem. Use your book to:

Refer back to your worked-out solutions and notes.

Review the key concepts of each lesson by rereading the *Essential Understanding* and *Take Note* boxes.

Access video tutorials of the concepts addressed in the lesson by scanning the QR codes.

Pearson SuccessNet You have full access to all of the resources on Pearson SuccessNet, including the **Interactive Digital Path** where you will find all of the *Solve Its!* and Problems presented in class. Revisit the animated, stepped-out problems presented in-class to clarify and solidify your math knowledge. Additional resources available to you include:

Interactive Student Worktext
Homework Video Tutors in English and Spanish
Online Glossary with audio in English and Spanish
MathXL for School Interactive Math Practice
Math Tools and Online Manipulatives
Multilingual Handbook
Assessments with immediate feedback

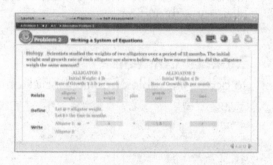

Mobile eText You may wish to access your student book on the go, either online or offline via download. Pearson's *Integrated High School Mathematics* also offers you a complete mobile etext of the Student Worktext.

Use the notes, highlight, and bookmark features to personalize your eText.

Watch animated problem videos with step-by-step instruction for every lesson.

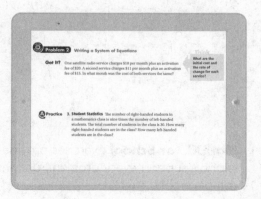

Pearson SuccessNet

Pearson SuccessNet is the gateway to all of the digital components of the program. You can use the online content to review the day's lesson, complete lessons independently, get help with your homework assignments, and prepare for and/or take an assessment. You will be given a username and password to log into www.pearsonsuccessnet.com.

The Homepage

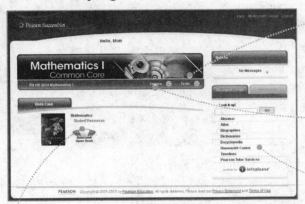

The **To Do** tab contains a list of assignments that you need to complete. You can also access your gradebook and review past assignments.

The **Explore** tab provides you access to the Table of Contents and all of the digital content for the program.

You can also access the following student resources: Practice Worksheets, Homework Video Tutors, and a Multilingual Handbook

Your eText includes links to animated lesson videos, highlighting and note taking tools, and a visual glossary with audio.

Table of Contents

To access the Table of Contents, click on *Explore* from your Homepage.

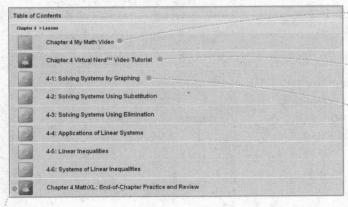

Student-developed videos bring real-life context to mathematics.

Step-by-step video tutorials offer additional support for every lesson

Digital lessons include access to animated problems, math tools, homework exercises, and self-assessments.

MathXL for School exercises provide additional practice. Examples and tutorials support every problem, and instant feedback is provided as you complete each exercise.

Interactive Digital Path

To access the **Interactive Digital Path**, click on the appropriate lesson from the Table of Contents.

Math Tools help you explore and visualize concepts.

You'll find opportunities to review formulas, properties, and other key concepts.

Interactive Glossary is available in English and Spanish with audio.

Every lesson includes the following:

Launch: Interactive lesson opener connects the math to real-world applications.

Instruction: All lesson problems are stepped out with detailed instruction. You can complete the subsequent *Got It?* exercises in your Student Worktext.

Practice: Exercises from your Student Worktext are available for view.

Self-Assessment: You can take the self-check lesson quiz, and then check your answers on the second screen.

MathXL for School

To access *MathXL for School*, click on the Chapter Review and Practice link from the Table of Contents.

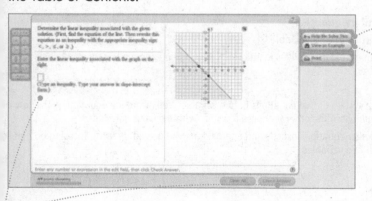

Select **Help Me Solve This** for an interactive step-by-step tutorial.

Select **View an Example** to see a similar worked out problem.

Input your answer and select **Check Answer** to get immediate feedback. After completing the exercise, a new exercise automatically regenerates, so you have unlimited practice opportunities.

Common Core *State Standards*
Mathematics I

Hi, I'm Max. Here is a list of the Common Core State Standards that Integrated Mathematics I addressess.

Number and Quantity

Quantities

Reason quantitatively and use units to solve problems

N.Q.1 Use units as a way to understand problems and to guide the solution of multi-step problems; choos and interpret units consistently in formulas; choose and interpret the scale and the origin in graphs data displays.

N.Q.2 Define appropriate quantities for the purpose of descriptive modeling.

N.Q.3 Choose a level of accuracy appropriate to limitations on measurement when reporting quantities.

Algebra

Seeing Structure in Expressions

Interpret the structure of expressions

A.SSE.1.a Interpret expressions that represent a quantity in terms of its context.★ Interpret parts of an expression, such as terms, factors, and coefficients.

A.SSE.1.b Interpret expressions that represent a quantity in terms of its context.★ Interpret complicated expressions by viewing one or more of their parts as a single entity.

Write expressions in equivalent forms to solve problems

A.SSE.3.c Choose and produce an equivalent form of an expression to reveal and explain properties of the quantity represented by the expression.★ Use the properties of exponents to transform expression exponential functions.

Creating Equations★

Create equations that describe numbers or relationships

A.CED.1 Create equations and inequalities in one variable and use them to solve problems. Include equation arising from linear and exponential functions.

A.CED.2 Create equations in two or more variables to represent relationships between quantities; graph equations on coordinate axes with labels and scales.

A.CED.3 Represent constraints by equations or inequalities, and by systems of equations and/or inequalities, and interpret solutions as viable or nonviable options in a modeling context.

A.CED.4 Rearrange formulas to highlight a quantity of interest, using the same reasoning as in solving equations.

Reasoning with Equations and Inequalities

Solve equations and inequalities in one variable

A.REI.3 Solve linear equations and inequalities in one variable, including equations with coefficients represented by letters.

Solve systems of equations

A.REI.5 Prove that, given a system of two equations in two variables, replacing one equation by the sum of equation and a multiple of the other produces a system with the same solutions.

A.REI.6 Solve systems of linear equations exactly and approximately (e.g., with graphs), focusing on pairs c linear equations in two variables.

★ Indicates a modeling standard

Represent and solve equations and inequalities graphically

A.REI.10   Understand that the graph of an equation in two variables is the set of all its solutions plotted in the coordinate plane, often forming a curve (which could be a line).

A.REI.11   Explain why the x-coordinates of the points where the graphs of the equations $y = f(x)$ and $y = g(x)$ intersect are the solutions of the equation $f(x) = g(x)$; find the solutions approximately, e.g., using technology to graph the functions, make tables of values, or find successive approximations. Include cases where $f(x)$ and/or $g(x)$ are linear and exponential functions. ★

A.REI.12   Graph the solutions to a linear inequality in two variables as a half-plane (excluding the boundary in the case of a strict inequality), and graph the solution set to a system of linear inequalities in two variables as the intersection of the corresponding half-planes.

Functions

Interpreting Functions

Understand the concept of a function and use function notation

F.IF.1   Understand that a function from one set (called the domain) to another set (called the range) assigns to each element of the domain exactly one element of the range. If f is a function and x is an element of its domain, then $f(x)$ denotes the output of f corresponding to the input x. The graph of f is the graph of the equation $y = f(x)$.

F.IF.2   Use function notation, evaluate functions for inputs in their domains, and interpret statements that use function notation in terms of a context.

F.IF.3   Recognize that sequences are functions, sometimes defined recursively, whose domain is a subset of the integers.

Interpret functions that arise in applications in terms of the context

F.IF.4   For a function that models a relationship between two quantities, interpret key features of graphs and tables in terms of the quantities, and sketch graphs showing key features given a verbal description of the relationship. *Key features include: intercepts; intervals where the function is increasing, decreasing, positive, or negative; relative maximums and minimums; symmetries; end behavior; and periodicity.* ★

F.IF.5   Relate the domain of a function to its graph and, where applicable, to the quantitative relationship it describes. ★

F.IF.6   Calculate and interpret the average rate of change of a function (presented symbolically or as a table) over a specified interval. Estimate the rate of change from a graph. ★

Analyze functions using different representations

F.IF.7.a   Graph functions expressed symbolically and show key features of the graph, by hand in simple cases and using technology for more complicated cases. ★ Graph linear functions and show intercepts, maxima, and minima.

F.IF.9   Compare properties of two functions each represented in a different way (algebraically, graphically, numerically in tables, or by verbal descriptions).

Building Functions

Build a function that models a relationship between two quantities

F.BF.1.a   Write a function that describes a relationship between two quantities. ★ Determine an explicit expression, a recursive process, or steps for calculation from a context.

F.BF.2   Write arithmetic and geometric sequences both recursively and with an explicit formula, use them to model situations, and translate between the two forms. ★

Linear, Quadratic, and Exponential Models

Construct and compare linear and exponential models and solve problems.

F.LE.1.a   Distinguish between situations that can be modeled with linear functions and with exponential functions. Prove that linear functions grow by equal differences over equal intervals, and that exponential functions grow by equal factors over equal intervals.

Look at the domains in bold and the cluster to get a good idea of the topics you'll study this year.

F.LE.1.b   Distinguish between situations that can be modeled with linear functions and with exponential functions. Recognize situations in which one quantity changes at a constant rate per unit interval relative to another.

F.LE.1.c   Distinguish between situations that can be modeled with linear functions and with exponential functions. Recognize situations in which a quantity grows or decays by a constant percent rate per interval relative to another.

F.LE.2   Construct linear and exponential functions, including arithmetic and geometric sequences, given a graph, a description of a relationship, or two input-output pairs (include reading these from a table).

F.LE.3   Observe using graphs and tables that a quantity increasing exponentially eventually exceeds a quantity increasing linearly.

Interpret expressions for functions in terms of the situation they model

F.LE.5   Interpret the parameters in a linear or exponential function in terms of a context.

Geometry

Congruence

Experiment with Transformations in the Plane

G.CO.1   Know precise definitions of angle, circle, perpendicular line, parallel line, and line segment, based on undefined notions of point, line, distance along a line, and distance around a circular arc.

G.CO.2   Represent transformations in the plane using, e.g., transparencies and geometry software; describe transformations as functions that take points in the plane as inputs and give other points as outputs. Compare transformations that preserve distance and angle to those that do not (e.g., translation versus horizontal stretch).

G.CO.3   Given a rectangle, parallelogram, trapezoid, or regular polygon, describe the rotations and reflections that carry it onto itself.

G.CO.4   Develop definitions of rotations, reflections, and translations in terms of angles, circles, perpendicular lines, parallel lines, and line segments.

G.CO.5   Given a geometric figure and a rotation, reflection, or translation, draw the transformed figure using, e.g., graph paper, tracing paper, or geometry software. Specify a sequence of transformations that will carry a given figure onto another.

Understand congruence in terms of rigid motions

G.CO.6   Use geometric descriptions of rigid motions to transform figures and to predict the effect of a given rigid motion on a given figure; given two figures, use the definition of congruence in terms of rigid motions to decide if they are congruent.

G.CO.7   Use the definition of congruence in terms of rigid motions to show that two triangles are congruent if and only if corresponding pairs of sides and corresponding pairs of angles are congruent.

G.CO.8   Explain how the criteria for triangle congruence (ASA, SAS, and SSS) follow from the definition of congruence in terms of rigid motions.

Prove geometric theorems

G.CO.9   Prove theorems about lines and angles. *Theorems include: vertical angles are congruent; when a transversal crosses parallel lines, alternate interior angles are congruent and corresponding angles are congruent; points on a perpendicular bisector of a line segment are exactly those equidistant from the segment's endpoints*

G.CO.10   Prove theorems about triangles. *Theorems include: measures of interior angles of a triangle sum to 180°; base angles of isosceles triangles are congruent; the segment joining midpoints of two sides of a triangle is parallel to the third side and half the length; the medians of a triangle meet at a point.*

G.CO.11   Prove theorems about parallelograms. *Theorems include: opposite sides are congruent, opposite angles are congruent, the diagonals of a parallelogram bisect each other and conversely, rectangles are parallelograms with congruent diagonals.*

Statistics and Probability★

Interpreting Categorical and Quantitative Data

Summarize, represent, and interpret data on a single count or measurement variable

S.ID.1   Represent data with plots on the real number line (dot plots, histograms, and box plots).

S.ID.2   Use statistics appropriate to the shape of the data distribution to compare center (median, mean) and spread (interquartile range, standard deviation) of two or more different data sets.

S.ID.3   Interpret differences in shape, center, and spread in the context of the data sets, accounting for possible effects of extreme data points (outliers).

Summarize, represent, and interpret data on two categorical and quantitative variables

S.ID.5   Summarize categorical data for two categories in two-way frequency tables. Interpret relative frequencies in the context of the data (including joint, marginal, and conditional relative frequencies). Recognize possible associations and trends in the data.

S.ID.6.a Represent data on two quantitative variables on a scatter plot, and describe how the variables are related. Fit a function to the data; use functions fitted to data to solve problems in the context of the data. Use given functions or choose a function suggested by the context. Emphasize linear and exponential models.

S.ID.6.c Represent data on two quantitative variables on a scatter plot, and describe how the variables are related. Fit a linear function for a scatter plot that suggests a linear association.

Interpret linear models

S.ID.7   Interpret the slope (rate of change) and the intercept (constant term) of a linear model in the context of the data.

S.ID.8   Compute (using technology) and interpret the correlation coefficient of a linear fit.

S.ID.9   Distinguish between correlation and causation.

BIGideas

These Big Ideas are the organizing ideas for the study of important areas of mathematics: algebra, geometry, and statistics.

Stay connected! These Big Ideas will help you understand how the math you study in high school fits together.

Algebra

Properties
- In the transition from arithmetic to algebra, attention shifts from arithmetic operations (addition, subtraction, multiplication, and division) to the use of the *properties* of these operations.
- All of the facts of arithmetic and algebra follow from certain properties.

Variable
- Quantities are used to form expressions, equations, and inequalities.
- An expression refers to a quantity but does not make a statement about it. An equation (or an inequality) is a statement about the quantities it mentions.
- Using variables in place of numbers in equations (or inequalities) allows the statement of relationships among numbers that are unknown or unspecified.

Equivalence
- A single quantity may be represented by many different expressions.
- The facts about a quantity may be expressed by many different equations (or inequalities).

Solving Equations & Inequalities
- Solving an equation is the process of rewriting the equation to make what it says about its variable(s) as simple as possible.
- Properties of numbers and equality can be used to transform an equation (or inequality) into equivalent, simpler equations (or inequalities) in order to find solutions.
- Useful information about equations and inequalities (including solutions) can be found by analyzing graphs or tables.
- The numbers and types of solutions vary predictably, based on the type of equation.

Proportionality
- Two quantities are *proportional* if they have the same ratio in each instance where they are measured together.
- Two quantities are *inversely proportional* if they have the same product in each instance where they are measured together.

Function
- A function is a relationship between variables in which each value of the input variable is associated with a unique value of the output variable.
- Functions can be represented in a variety of ways, such as graphs, tables, equations, or words. Each representation is particularly useful in certain situations.
- Some important families of functions are developed through transformations of the simplest form of the function.
- New functions can be made from other functions by applying arithmetic operations or by applying one function to the output of another.

Modeling
- Many real-world mathematical problems can be represented algebraically. These representations can lead to algebraic solutions.
- A function that models a real-world situation can be used to make estimates or predictions about future occurrences.

Statistics and Probability

Data Collection and Analysis
- Sampling techniques are used to gather data from real-world situations. If the data are representative of the larger population, inferences can be made about that population.
- Biased sampling techniques yield data unlikely to be representative of the larger population.
- Sets of numerical data are described using measures of central tendency and dispersion.

Data Representation
- The most appropriate data representations depend on the type of data—quantitative or qualitative, and univariate or bivariate.
- Line plots, box plots, and histograms are different ways to show distribution of data over a possible range of values.

Probability
- Probability expresses the likelihood that a particular event will occur.
- Data can be used to calculate an experimental probability, and mathematical properties can be used to determine a theoretical probability.
- Either experimental or theoretical probability can be used to make predictions or decisions about future events.
- Various counting methods can be used to develop theoretical probabilities.

Geometry

Visualization
- Visualization can help you see the relationships between two figures and help you connect properties of real objects with two-dimensional drawings of these objects.

Transformations
- Transformations are mathematical functions that model relationships with figures.
- Transformations may be described geometrically or by coordinates.
- Symmetries of figures may be defined and classified by transformations.

Measurement
- Some attributes of geometric figures, such as length, area, volume, and angle measure, are measurable. Units are used to describe these attributes.

Reasoning & Proof
- Definitions establish meanings and remove possible misunderstanding.
- Other truths are more complex and difficult to see. It is often possible to verify complex truths by reasoning from simpler ones using deductive reasoning.

Similarity
- Two geometric figures are similar when corresponding lengths are proportional and corresponding angles are congruent.
- Areas of similar figures are proportional to the squares of their corresponding lengths.
- Volumes of similar figures are proportional to the cubes of their corresponding lengths.

Coordinate Geometry
- A coordinate system on a line is a number line on which points are labeled, corresponding to the real numbers.
- A coordinate system in a plane is formed by two perpendicular number lines, called the x- and y-axes, and the quadrants they form. The coordinate plane can be used to graph many functions.
- It is possible to verify some complex truths using deductive reasoning in combination with the distance, midpoint, and slope formulas.

1

Solving Equations and Inequalities

Number and Quantity

Quantities
  Reason quantitatively and use units to solve problems

Algebra

Seeing Structure in Expressions
  Interpret the structure of expressions

Creating Equations
  Create equations that describe numbers or relationships

Reasoning with Equations and Inequalities
  Understand solving equations as a process of reasoning and explain the reasoning

  Represent and solve equations and inequalities graphically

Chapter 1

An Introduction to Functions

Number and Quantity

Quantities
Reason quantitatively and use units to solve problems

Algebra

Seeing Structure in Expressions
Interpret the structure of expressions

Creating Equations
Create equations that describe numbers or relationships

Reasoning with Equations and Inequalities
Represent and solve equations and inequalities graphically

Functions

Interpreting Functions
Understand the concept of a function and use function notation
Interpret functions that arise in applications in terms of the context

Building Functions
Build a function that models a relationship between two quantities
Build new functions from existing functions.

3

Linear Functions

Chapter 3

Algebra

Seeing Structure in Expressions
    Interpret the structure of expressions
Creating Equations
    Create equations that describe numbers or relationships

Functions

Interpreting Functions
    Interpret functions that arise in applications in terms of the co
    Analyze functions using different representations
Building Functions
    Build new functions from existing functions
Linear and Exponential Models
    Construct and compare linear and exponential models and so
    problems.
    Interpret expressions for functions in terms of the situation
    they model

4

Systems of Equations and Inequalities

Number and Quantity

Quantities
Reason quantitatively and use units to solve problems

Algebra

Creating Equations
Create equations that describe numbers or relationships

Reasoning with Equations and Inequalities
Represent and solve equations and inequalities graphically

Exponential and Radical Functions

Chapter 5

Algebra

Seeing Structure in Expressions
Interpret the structure of expressions.

Creating Equations
Create equations that describe numbers or relationships
Represent and solve equations and inequalities graphically

Functions

Interpreting Functions
Interpret functions that arise in applications in terms of the context
Analyze functions using different representations

Building Functions
Build a function that models a relationship between two quan

Linear and Exponential Models
Construct and compare linear and exponential models and solve problems.

Data Analysis

Number and Quantity

Quantities
  Reason quantitatively and use units to solve problems

Statistics and Probability

Interpreting Categorical and Quantitative Data
  Summarize, represent, and interpret data on a single count or measurement variable
  Summarize, represent, and interpret data on two categorical and quantitative variables
  Interpret linear models.

7

Tools of Geometry

Chapter 7

Geometry
Congruence
  Experiment with transformations in the plane.

Geometry
Expressing Geometric Properties with Equations
  Use coordinates to prove simple geometric theorems algeb

Get Ready!

Factors

Find the greatest common factor of each set of numbers.

1. 12, 18   **2.** 25, 35   **3.** 13, 20   **4.** 40, 80, 100

Least Common Multiple

Find the least common multiple of each set of numbers.

5. 5, 15   **6.** 11, 44   **7.** 8, 9   **8.** 10, 15, 25

Using Estimation

Estimate each sum or difference.

9. $956 - 542$ **10.** $1.259 + 5.312 + 1.7$ **11.** $\$14.32 + \$1.65 + \$278.05$

Simplifying Fractions

Write in simplest form.

12. $\frac{12}{15}$ **13.** $\frac{20}{28}$ **14.** $\frac{8}{56}$ **15.** $\frac{48}{52}$

Fractions and Decimals

Write each fraction as a decimal.

16. $\frac{7}{10}$ **17.** $\frac{3}{5}$ **18.** $\frac{13}{20}$ **19.** $\frac{93}{100}$ **20.** $\frac{7}{15}$

Adding and Subtracting Fractions

Find the sum or difference.

21. $\frac{4}{7} + \frac{3}{14}$ **22.** $6\frac{2}{3} + 3\frac{4}{5}$ **23.** $\frac{9}{10} - \frac{4}{5}$ **24.** $8\frac{3}{4} - 4\frac{5}{6}$

 ## Looking Ahead Vocabulary

25. A mailman *distributes* mail to each resident of a neighborhood. What does it mean to *distribute* the 4 in the product $4(10 + 7)$?

26. An *interval* of time is a duration between two moments. What is an *interval* between two numbers a and b?

27. When two things are *identical*, they are the same. What does it mean for an equation to be an *identity*?

CHAPTER 1

Solving Equations and Inequalities

Big Ideas

1 Solving Equations and Inequalities

Essential Question How can you solve equations?

Essential Question How can you solve inequalities?

2 Equivalence

Essential Question Can equations that appear to be different be equivalent?

© Domains

- Quantities
- Creating Equations
- Reasoning with Equations and Inequalities

Interactive Digital Path

 Log in to **pearsonsuccessnet.com** and click on Interactive Digital Path to access the Solve Its and animated Problems.

Chapter Preview

Vocabulary

English/Spanish Vocabulary Audio Online:

English	Spanish
coefficient, *p. 6*	coeficiente
compound inequality *p. 70*	desigualdad compusta
conversion factor, *p. 38*	factor de conversión
formula, *p. 31*	ecuaciones equivalent
identity, *p. 24*	identidad
like terms, *p. 7*	terminus semejantes
literal equation, *p. 29*	ecuación literal
proportion, *p. 52*	proporción
rate, *p. 37*	tasa
ratio, *p. 37*	razón
term, *p. 6*	término
unit rate, *p. 37*	razón de unidades

1-1 The Distributive Property

A.SSE.1.a Interpret parts of an expression . . . Also **A.SSE.1**

Objective   To use the Distributive Property to simplify expressions

Solve It!   Write your solution to the Solve It in the space below.

To solve problems in mathematics, it is often useful to rewrite expressions in simpler forms. The **Distributive Property**, illustrated by the area model below, is one property of real numbers that helps you to simplify expressions.

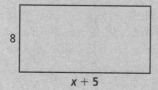

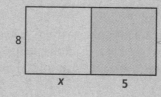

> The model shows that $8(x + 5) = 8(x) + 8(5)$.

Essential Understanding You can use the Distributive Property to simplify the product of a number and a sum or difference.

take note

Property   Distributive Property

Let a, b, and c be real numbers.

Algebra	Examples
$a(b + c) = ab + ac$	$4(20 + 6) = 4(20) + 4(6)$
$(b + c)a = ba + ca$	$(20 + 6)4 = 20(4) + 6(4)$
$a(b - c) = ab - ac$	$7(30 - 2) = 7(30) - 7(2)$
$(b - c)a = ba - ca$	$(30 - 2)7 = 30(7) - 2(7)$

Problem 1 Simplifying Expressions

Got It?   What is the simplified form of each expression?

    a. $5(x + 7)$

    b. $12\left(3 - \frac{1}{6}t\right)$

    c. $(0.4 + 1.1c)3$

    d. $(2y - 1)(-y)$

A Practice   Use the Distributive Property to simplify each expression.

    1. $\frac{1}{4}(4f - 8)$

    2. $(-8z - 10)(-1.5)$

> A fraction bar may act as a grouping symbol. A fraction bar indicates division. Any fraction $\frac{a}{b}$ can also be written as $a \cdot \frac{1}{b}$. You can use this fact and the Distributive Property to rewrite some fractions as sums or differences.

Problem 2 Rewriting Fraction Expressions

Got It?   What sum or difference is equivalent to each expression?

    a. $\frac{4x - 16}{3}$

    b. $\frac{11 + 3x}{6}$

    c. $\frac{15 + 6x}{12}$

    d. $\frac{4 - 2x}{8}$

Practice Write each fraction as a sum or difference.

3. $\dfrac{22 - 2n}{2}$

4. $\dfrac{42w + 14}{7}$

The Multiplication Property of -1 states that $-1 \cdot x = -x$. To simplify an expression such as $-(x + 6)$, you can rewrite the expression as $-1(x + 6)$.

 Problem 3 **Using the Multiplication Property of -1**

Got It? What is the simplified form of each expression?

a. $-(a + 5)$

b. $-(-x + 31)$

 Think
What does the negative sign in front of the parentheses mean?

c. $-(4x - 12)$

d. $-(6m - 9n)$

Practice Simplify each expression.

5. $-(-m + n + 1)$

6. $-(x + 3y - 3)$

You can use the Distributive Property to make calculations easier to do with mental math. Some numbers can be thought of as simple sums or differences.

Problem 4 Using the Distributive Property for Mental Math

Got It? Julia commutes to work on the train 4 times each week. A round-trip ticket costs $7.25. What is her weekly cost for tickets? Use mental math.

Practice 7. One hundred five students see a play. Each ticket costs $45. What is the total amount the students spend for tickets? Use mental math.

8. Suppose the distance you travel to school is 5 mi. What is the total distance for 197 trips from home to school? Use mental math.

Essential Understanding You can simplify an algebraic expression by combining the parts of the expression that are alike.

In an algebraic expression, a **term** is a number, a variable, or the product of a number and one or more variables. A **constant** is a term that has no variable. A **coefficient** is a numerical factor of a term. Rewrite expressions as sums to identify these parts of an expression.

$6a^2$, $-5ab$, $3b$, and -12 are terms.

$$6a^2 - 5ab + 3b - 12 = 6a^2 + (-5ab) + 3b + (-12)$$

coefficients   constant

In the algebraic expression $6a^2 - 5ab + 3b - 12$, the terms have coefficients of 6, -5, and 3. The term -12 is a constant.

Like terms have the same variable factors. To identify like terms, compare the variable factors of the terms, as shown below.

Terms	$4x^2$ and $12x^2$	$6ab$ and $-2a$	xy^2 and x^2y
Variable Factors	x^2 and x^2	ab and a	xy^2 and x^2y
Like Terms?	yes	no	no

An algebraic expression in simplest form has no like terms or parentheses.

Not Simplified	Simplified
$2(3x - 5 + 4x)$	$14x - 10$

You can use the Distributive Property to help combine like terms. Think of the Distributive Property as $ba + ca = (b + c)a$.

Problem 5 Combining Like Terms

Got It? What is the simplified form of each expression in parts (a)–(c)?

   a. $3y - y$

Plan

Which terms can you combine?

   b. $-7mn^4 - 5mn^4$

   c. $7y^3z - 6yz^3 + y^3z$

   d. Reasoning Can you simplify $8x^2 - 2x^4 - 2x + 2 + xy$ further? Explain.

A Practice Simplify each expression by combining like terms.

9. $-7h + 3h^2 - 4h - 3$

10. $10ab + 2ab^2 - 9ab$

Lesson Check

Do you know HOW?

11. What is the simplified form of each expression? Use the Distributive Property.

a. $(j + 2)7$

b. $-8(x - 3)$

c. $-(4 - c)$

d. $-(11 + 2b)$

Rewrite each expression as a sum.

12. $-8x^2 + 3xy - 9x - 3$

13. $2ab - 5ab^2 - 9a^2b$

Tell whether the terms are like terms.

14. $3a$ and $-5a$

15. $2xy^2$ and $-x^2y$

Do you UNDERSTAND?

◎ 16. Vocabulary Does each equation demonstrate the Distributive Property? Explain.

a. $-2(x + 1) = -2x - 2$

b. $(s - 4)8 = 8(s - 4)$

c. $5n - 45 = 5(n - 9)$

d. $8 + (t + 6) = (8 + t) + 6$

◎ 17. Mental Math How can you express 499 to find the product 499×5 using mental math? Explain.

18. Reasoning Is each expression in simplified form? Justify your answer.

a. $4xy^3 + 5x^3y$

b. $-(y - 1)$

c. $5x^2 + 12xy - 3yx$

More Practice and Problem-Solving Exercises

 MATHEMATICAL PRACTICES

B Apply

Write a word phrase for each expression. Then simplify each expression.

19. $3(t - 1)$ **20.** $4(d + 7)$ **21.** $\frac{1}{3}(6x - 1)$

STEM 22. Physiology The recommended heart rate for exercise, in beats per minute, is given by the expression $0.8(200 - y)$ where y is a person's age in years. Rewrite this expression using the Distributive Property. What is the recommended heart rate for a 20-year-old person? For a 50-year-old person? Use mental math.

23. Error Analysis Identify and correct the error shown at the right.

24. Error Analysis A friend uses the Distributive Property to simplify $4(2b - 5)$ and gets $8b - 5$ as the result. Describe and correct the error.

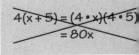

$4(x + 5) = (4 \cdot x)(4 \cdot 5)$
$= 80x$

Geometry Write an expression in simplified form for the area of each rectangle.

25.

11

3x + 2

26.

5 + 2y

5

27.

7

5n − 9

© **28. Think About a Plan** You are replacing your regular shower head with a water-saving shower head. These shower heads use the amount of water per minute shown. If you take an 8-min shower, how many gallons of water will you save?

- Which would you use to represent water saved each minute, an expression involving addition or an expression involving subtraction?
- How can you use the Distributive Property to find the total amount of water saved?

New

2.5 gallons per minute

7 gallons per minute

Simplify each expression.

29. $6yz + 2yz − 8yz$

30. $−2ab + ab + 9ab − 3ab$

31. $−9m^3n + 4m^3n + 5mn$

32. $3(−4cd − 5)$

33. $12x^2y − 8x^2y^2 + 11x^2y − 4x^3y^2 − 9xy^2$

34. $a − \frac{a}{4} + \frac{3}{4}a$

© **35. Reasoning** The Distributive Property also applies to division, as shown.

$$\frac{a + b}{c} = \frac{a}{c} + \frac{b}{c}$$

Use the Distributive Property of Division to rewrite $\frac{9 + 12n}{3}$. Then simplify.

36. Lawn Game You play a game where you throw a pair of connected balls at a structure, as shown at the right. When a pair wraps around a bar, you earn the points shown. You toss 3 pairs, and all of them wrap around a bar. Which expression could represent your total score if a pairs of balls wrap around the blue bar?

10 points

20 points

Ⓐ $30 + 10a$ Ⓑ $20a + 3 − 10a$ Ⓒ $10a + 20(3 − a)$ Ⓓ $30a + 10$

© **37. Open-Ended** Suppose you used the Distributive Property to get the expression $3m − 6n − 15$. With what expression could you have started?

Challenge

© **38. Writing** Your friend uses the order of operations to find the value of $11(39 − 3)$. Would you prefer to use the Distributive Property instead? Explain.

Simplify each expression.

39. $5(2d + 1) + 7(5d + 3)$

40. $6(4t − 3) + 6(4 − 3t)$

41. $9(5 + t) − 7(t + 3)$

42. $4(r + 8) − 5(2r − 1)$

43. $−(m + 9n − 12)$

44. $−6(3 − 3x − 7y) + 2y − x$

1-2 Solving Multi-Step Equations

A.CED.1 Create equations and inequalities in one variable and . . . solve problems . . . Also **A.REI.1, A.REI.3**

Objective   To solve multi-step equations in one variable

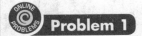

Solve It!   Write your solution to the Solve It in the space below.

In this lesson, you will learn to write and solve multi-step equations.

Essential Understanding To solve multi-step equations, you form a series of simpler equivalent equations. To do this, use the properties of equality, inverse operations, and properties of real numbers. You use the properties until you isolate the variable.

Problem 1   Combining Like Terms

Got It?   What is the solution of each equation? Check each answer.

a. $11m - 8 - 6m = 22$

Think

How can you simplify the left side of each equation?

b. $-2y + 5 + 5y = 14$

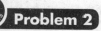 **Practice** Solve each equation. Check your answer.

1. $17 = p - 3 - 3p$

2. $-23 = -2a - 10 + a$

Problem 2 **Solving a Multi-Step Equation**

Got It? Noah and Kate are shopping for new guitar strings in a music store. Noah buys 2 packs of strings. Kate buys 2 packs of strings and a music book. The book costs $16. Their total cost is $72. How much is one pack of strings?

Think

How can a model help you write an equation for this situation?

 Practice Write an equation to model each situation. Then solve the equation.

3. Employment You have a part-time job. You work for 3 h on Friday and 6 h on Saturday. You also receive an allowance of $20 per week. You earn $92 per week. How much do you earn per hour at your part-time job?

4. Travel A family buys airline tickets online. Each ticket costs $167. The family buys travel insurance with each ticket that costs $19 per ticket. The Web site charges a fee of $16 for the entire purchase. The family is charged a total of $1132. How many tickets did the family buy?

Problem 3 **Solving an Equation Using the Distributive Property**

Got It? **a.** What is the solution of $18 = 3(2x - 6)$? Check your answer.

©**b.** **Reasoning** Can you solve the equation in part (a) by using the Division Property of Equality instead of the Distributive Property? Explain.

Ⓐ**Practice** Solve each equation. Check your answer.

5. $n + 5(n - 1) = 7$

6. $-4(r + 6) = -63$

You can use different methods to solve equations that contain fractions.

 Problem 4   **Solving an Equation That Contains Fractions**

Got It?   What is the solution of each equation? Why did you choose the method you used to solve each equation?

a. $\dfrac{2b}{5} + \dfrac{3b}{4} = 3$

b. $\dfrac{1}{9} = \dfrac{5}{6} - \dfrac{m}{3}$

Practice   Solve each equation. Choose the method you prefer to use. Check your answer.

7. $\dfrac{11z}{16} + \dfrac{7z}{8} = \dfrac{5}{16}$

8. $\dfrac{x}{3} - \dfrac{7x}{12} = \dfrac{2}{3}$

You can clear decimals from an equation by multiplying by a power of 10. First, find the greatest number of digits to the right of any decimal point, and then multiply by 10 raised to that power.

 Problem 5 **Solving an Equation That Contains Decimals**

Got It? What is the solution of $0.5x - 2.325 = 3.95$? Check your answer.

Ⓐ **Practice** Solve each equation. Check your answer.

9. $25.24 = 5g + 3.89$

10. $0.25n + 0.1n = 9.8$

Lesson Check

Do you know HOW?

Solve each equation. Check your answer.

11. $7p + 8p - 12 = 59$

12. $-2(3x + 9) = 24$

13. $\frac{2m}{7} + \frac{3m}{14} = 1$

14. $1.2 = 2.4 - 0.6x$

15. Gardening There is a 12-ft fence on one side of a rectangular garden. The gardener has 44 ft of fencing to enclose the other three sides. What is the length of the garden's longer dimension?

Do you UNDERSTAND?

Explain how you would solve each equation.

16. $1.3 + 0.5x = -3.41$

17. $7(3x - 4) = 49$

18. $-\frac{2}{9}x - 4 = \frac{7}{18}$

Ⓒ **19. Reasoning** Ben solves the equation $-24 = 5(g + 3)$ by first dividing each side by 5. Amelia solves the equation by using the Distributive Property. Whose method do you prefer? Explain.

More Practice and Problem-Solving Exercises

B Apply

Solve each equation.

20. $6 + \frac{v}{-8} = \frac{4}{7}$

21. $\frac{2}{3}(c - 18) = 7$

22. $3d + d - 7 = \frac{25}{4}$

23. $0.25(d - 12) = 4$

24. $8n - (2n - 3) = 12$

25. $\frac{2}{3} + n + 6 = \frac{3}{4}$

26. $0.5d - 3d + 5 = 0$

27. $-(w + 5) = -14$

28. $\frac{a}{20} + \frac{4}{15} = \frac{9}{15}$

© 29. Think About a Plan Jillian and Tyson are shopping for knitting supplies. Jillian wants 3 balls of yarn and 1 set of knitting needles. Tyson wants 1 ball of yarn and 2 sets of knitting needles. Each ball of yarn costs $6.25. If their total cost is $34.60, what is the cost of 1 set of knitting needles?

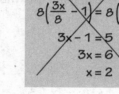

- How can the model at the right help you solve the problem?
- How does the model tell you which operations to use in the equation?

30. Online Video Games Angie and Kenny play online video games. Angie buys 1 software package and 3 months of game play. Kenny buys 1 software package and 2 months of game play. Each software package costs $20. If their total cost is $115, what is the cost of one month of game play?

© 31. Error Analysis Describe and correct the error in solving the equation at the right.

© 32. Reasoning Suppose you want to solve $-4m + 5 + 6m = -3$. What would you do as your first step? Explain.

© 33. Writing Describe two ways in which you can solve $-\frac{1}{2}(5x - 9) = 17$.

$$\frac{3x}{8} - 1 = \frac{5}{8}$$
$$8\left(\frac{3x}{8} - 1\right) = 8\left(\frac{5}{8}\right)$$
$$3x - 1 = 5$$
$$3x = 6$$
$$x = 2$$

34. Bowling Three friends go bowling. The cost per person per game is $5.30. The cost to rent shoes is $2.50 per person. Their total cost is $55.20. How many games did they play?

35. Moving Expenses A college student is moving into a campus dormitory. The student rents a moving truck for $19.95 plus $.99 per mile. Before returning the truck, the student fills the tank with gasoline, which costs $65.32. The total cost is $144.67. How many miles did the student drive the truck?

Geometry Find the value of *x*. (*Hint*: The sum of the angle measures of a quadrilateral is 360°.)

36.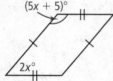

37.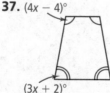

38.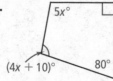

39. Dining Out You are ordering a meal and have $15 to spend. The restaurant charges 6% sales tax. You plan to leave a 15% tip. The equation $c = x + 0.06x + 0.15x$ gives the total cost c of your meal, where x is the cost before tax and tip. What is the maximum amount you can spend before tax and tip?

40. Savings You have $85 in your bank account. Each week you plan to deposit $8 from your allowance and $15 from your paycheck. The equation $b = 85 + (15 + 8)w$ gives the amount b in your bank account after w weeks. How many weeks from now will you have $175 in your bank account?

ⒸChallenge

41. Find three consecutive integers with a sum of 45. Show your work.

42. Cooking A cook buys two identical bags of rice and uses some of the rice in each bag so that one bag is half full and the other is one-third full. The cook combines them into one bag, which then contains $3\frac{1}{3}$ cups of rice. How much rice was in a full bag?

43. Painting Tim can paint a house in 6 days. Tara can paint the same house in 3 days.
  a. What fraction of the house can Tim paint in one day? What fraction of the house can Tara paint in one day?
  b. What fraction of the house can Tim paint in d days? What fraction of the house can Tara paint in d days?
  c. What fraction of the house can Tim and Tara together paint in one day? What fraction of the house can Tim and Tara together paint in d days?
  d. Write and solve an equation to find the number of days it will take Tim and Tara to paint the whole house working together.

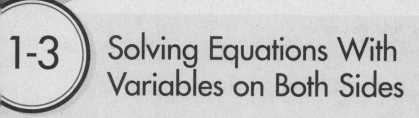

A.CED.1 Create equations and inequalities in one variable and . . . solve problems . . . Also **A.REI.1, A.REI.3**

Objectives   To solve equations with variables on both sides
To identify equations that are identities or have no solution

Solve It!   Write your solution to the Solve It in the space below.

The problem in the Solve It can be modeled by an equation that has variables on both sides.

Essential Understanding   To solve equations with variables on both sides, you can use the properties of equality and inverse operations to write a series of simpler equivalent equations.

Problem 1   Solving an Equation With Variables on Both Sides

Got It?   **a.** What is the solution of $7k + 2 = 4k - 10$?

b. Reasoning   Solve the equation in Problem 1 by subtracting $5x$ from each side instead of $2x$. Compare and contrast your solution with the solution in Problem 1.

Practice Solve each equation. Check your answer.

1. $-3c - 12 = -5 + c$

2. $-n - 23 = 5 + n$

Ⓞ **Problem 2** **Using an Equation With Variables on Both Sides**

Got It? An office manager spent $650 on a new energy-saving copier that will reduce the monthly electric bill for the office from $112 to $88. In how many months will the copier pay for itself?

Ⓐ **Practice** Write and solve an equation for each situation. Check your solution.

STEM **3. Architecture** An architect is designing a rectangular greenhouse. Along one wall is a 7-ft storage area and 5 sections for different kinds of plants. On the opposite wall is a 4-ft storage area and 6 sections for plants. All of the sections for plants are of equal length. What is the length of each wall?

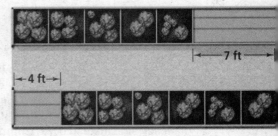

4. Business A hairdresser is deciding where to open her own studio. If the hairdresser chooses Location A, she will pay $1200 per month in rent and will charge $45 per haircut. If she chooses Location B, she will pay $1800 per month in rent and will charge $60 per haircut. How many haircuts would she have to give in one month to make the same profit at either location?

Problem 3   Solving an Equation With Grouping Symbols

Plan

How do you get started?

Got It?   What is the solution of each equation?

a. $4(2y + 1) = 2(y - 13)$

b. $7(4 - a) = 3(a - 4)$

A Practice Solve each equation. Check your answer.

5. $2r - (5 - r) = 13 + 2r$

6. $5g + 4(-5 + 3g) = 1 - g$

An equation that is true for every possible value of the variable is an **identity**. For example, $x + 1 = x + 1$ is an identity. An equation has no solution if there is no value of the variable that makes the equation true. The equation $x + 1 = x + 2$ has no solution.

Problem 4 **Identities and Equations With No Solution**

Think

How can you tell how many solutions an equation has?

Got It? What is the solution of each equation?

a. $3(4b - 2) = -6 + 12b$

b. $2x + 7 = -1(3 - 2x)$

Practice Determine whether each equation is an *identity* or whether it has *no solution*.

7. $-6a + 3 = -3(2a - 3)$

8. $4 - d = -(d - 4)$

When you solve an equation, you use reasoning to select properties of equality that produce simpler equivalent equations until you find a solution. The steps below provide a general guideline for solving equations.

note

Concept Summary   Solving Equations

Step 1   Use the Distributive Property to remove any grouping symbols. Use properties of equality to clear decimals and fractions.

Step 2   Combine like terms on each side of the equation.

Step 3   Use the properties of equality to get the variable terms on one side of the equation and the constants on the other.

Step 4   Use the properties of equality to solve for the variable.

Step 5   Check your solution in the original equation.

Lesson Check

Do you know HOW?

Solve each equation. Check your answer.

9. $3x + 4 = 5x - 10$

10. $5(y - 4) = 7(2y + 1)$

11. $2a + 3 = \frac{1}{2}(6 + 4a)$

12. $4x - 5 = 2(2x + 1)$

13. Printing Pristine Printing will print business cards for $.10 each plus a setup charge of $15. The Printing Place offers business cards for $.15 each with a setup charge of $10. What number of business cards costs the same from either printer?

Do you UNDERSTAND?

Vocabulary Match each equation with the appropriate number of solutions.

14. $3y - 5 = y + 2y - 9$ **A.** infinitely many

15. $2y + 4 = 2(y + 2)$ **B.** one solution

16. $2y - 4 = 3y - 5$ **C.** no solution

17. Writing A student solved an equation and found that the variable was eliminated in the process of solving the equation. How would the student know whether the equation is an identity or an equation with no solution?

More Practice and Problem-Solving Exercises

B Apply

Solve each equation. If the equation is an identity, write *identity*. If it has no solution, write *no solution*.

18. $3.2 - 4d = 2.3d + 3$

19. $3d + 4 = 2 + 3d - \frac{1}{2}$

20. $2.25(4x - 4) = -2 + 10x + 12$

21. $3a + 1 = -3.6(a - 1)$

22. $\frac{1}{2}h + \frac{1}{3}(h - 6) = \frac{5}{6}h + 2$

23. $0.5b + 4 = 2(b + 2)$

24. $-2(-c - 12) = -2c - 12$

25. $3(m + 1.5) = 1.5(2m + 3)$

26. Travel Suppose a family drives at an average rate of 60 mi/h on the way to visit relatives and then at an average rate of 40 mi/h on the way back. The return trip takes 1 h longer than the trip there.

    a. Let d be the distance in miles the family traveled to visit their relatives. How many hours did it take to drive there?

    b. In terms of d, how many hours did it take to make the return trip?

    c. Write and solve an equation to determine the distance the family drove to see their relatives. What was the average rate for the entire trip?

© 27. Think About a Plan Each morning, a deli worker has to make several pies and peel a bucket of potatoes. On Monday, it took the worker 2 h to make the pies and an average of 1.5 min to peel each potato. On Tuesday, the worker finished the work in the same amount of time, but it took 2.5 h to make the pies and an average of 1 min to peel each potato. About how many potatoes are in a bucket?

    • What quantities do you know and how are they related to each other?

    • How can you use the known and unknown quantities to write an equation for this situation?

© 28. Error Analysis Describe and correct the error in finding the solution of the equation $2x = 6x$.

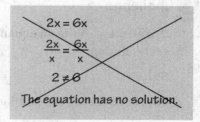

29. Skiing A skier is trying to decide whether or not to buy a season ski pass. A daily pass costs $67. A season ski pass costs $350. The skier would have to rent skis with either pass for $25 per day. How many days would the skier have to go skiing in order to make the season pass less expensive than daily passes?

30. Health Clubs One health club charges a $50 sign-up fee and $65 per month. Another club charges a $90 sign-up fee and $45 per month. For what number of months is the cost of the clubs equal?

31. Geometry The perimeters of the triangles shown are equal. Find the side lengths of each triangle.

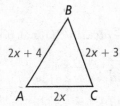 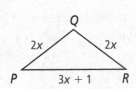

32. Business A small juice company spends $1200 per day on business expenses plus $1.10 per bottle of juice they make. They charge $2.50 for each bottle of juice they produce. How many bottles of juice must the company sell in one day in order to equal its daily costs?

33. Spreadsheet You set up a spreadsheet to solve $7(x + 1) = 3(x - 1)$.

   a. Does your spreadsheet show the solution of the equation?

   b. Between which two values of x is the solution of the equation? How do you know?

   c. For what spreadsheet values of x is $7(x + 1)$ less than $3(x - 1)$?

	A	B	C
1	x	$7(x + 1)$	$3(x - 1)$
2	-5	-28	-18
3	-3	-14	-12
4	-1	0	-6
5	1	14	0
6	3	28	6

© 34. Reasoning Determine whether each statement is *always*, *sometimes*, or *never* true.

   a. An equation of the form $ax + 1 = ax$ has no solution.

   b. An equation in one variable has at least one solution.

   c. An equation of the form $\frac{x}{a} = \frac{x}{b}$ has infinitely many solutions.

 **Challenge**

Open-Ended Write an equation with a variable on both sides such that you get each solution.

35. $x = 5$ **36.** $x = 0$ **37.** x can be any number.

38. No values of x are solutions.   **39.** x is a negative number.   **40.** x is a fraction.

41. Suppose you have three consecutive integers. The greatest of the three integers is twice as great as the sum of the first two. What are the integers?

1-4 Literal Equations and Formulas

A.CED.4 Rearrange formulas to highlight a quantity of interest . . . Also **N.Q.1, A.CED.1, A.REI.3**

Objective To rewrite and use literal equations and formulas

Solve It! Write your solution to the Solve It in the space below.

> In this lesson, you will learn to solve problems using equations in more than one variable. A **literal equation** is an equation that involves two or more variables.
>
> **Essential Understanding** When you work with literal equations, you can use the methods you have learned in this chapter to isolate any particular variable.

Problem 1 Rewriting a Literal Equation

Got It?

a. Solve the equation $4 = 2m - 5n$ for m. What are the values of m when $n = -2, 0,$ and 2?

b. **Reasoning** Solve Problem 1 by substituting $x = 3$ and $x = 6$ into the equation $10x + 5y = 80$ and then solving for y in each case. Do you prefer this method or the method shown in Problem 1? Explain.

Practice Solve each equation for *y*. Then find the value of *y* for each value of *x*.

1. $x - 4y = -4$; $x = -2, 4, 6$

2. $6x = 7 - 4y$; $x = -2, -1, 0$

When you rewrite literal equations, you may have to divide by a variable or variable expression. When you do so in this lesson, assume that the variable or variable expression is not equal to zero because division by zero is not defined.

Problem 2 **Rewriting a Literal Equation With Only Variables**

Got It? What equation do you get when you solve $-t = r + px$ for *x*?

> **Think**
>
> How can you solve a literal equation for a variable?

Practice Solve each equation for *x*.

3. $4(x - b) = x$

4. $A = Bxt + c$

A **formula** is an equation that states a relationship among quantities. Formulas are special types of literal equations. Some common formulas are given below. Notice that some of the formulas use the same variables, but the definitions of the variables are different.

Formula Name	Formula	Definitions of Variables
Perimeter of a rectangle	$P = 2\ell + 2w$	P = perimeter, ℓ = length, w = width
Circumference of a circle	$C = 2\pi r$	C = circumference, r = radius
Area of a rectangle	$A = \ell w$	A = area, ℓ = length, w = width
Area of a triangle	$A = \frac{1}{2}bh$	A = area, b = base, h = height
Area of a circle	$A = \pi r^2$	A = area, r = radius
Distance traveled	$d = rt$	d = distance, r = rate, t = time
Temperature	$C = \frac{5}{9}(F - 32)$	C = degrees Celsius, F = degrees Fahrenheit

Problem 3 **Rewriting a Geometric Formula**

Think

How do you know which formula to use?

Got It? What is the height of a triangle that has an area of 24 in.²
and a base with a length of 8 in.?

Practice Solve the problem. Round to the nearest tenth, if necessary.

5. A rectangle has perimeter 84 cm and length 35 cm. What is its width?

6. Parks A public park is in the shape of a triangle. The side of the park that forms the base of the triangle is 200 yd long, and the area of the park is 7500 yd². What is the length of the side of the park that forms the height of the triangle?

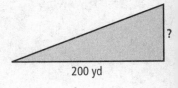

200 yd

ONLINE PROBLEMS **Problem 4** **Rewriting a Formula**

Got It? Pacific gray whales migrate annually from the waters near Alaska to the waters near Baja California, Mexico, and back. The whales travel a distance of about 5000 mi each way at an average rate of 91 mi per day. About how many days does it take the whales to migrate one way?

Ⓐ Practice Solve each problem. Round to the nearest tenth, if necessary.

7. Baseball You can use the formula $a = \frac{h}{n}$ to find the batting average a of a batter who has h hits in n times at bat. Solve the formula for h. If a batter has a batting average of .290 and has been at bat 300 times, how many hits does the batter have?

STEM **8. Construction** Bricklayers use the formula $n = 7\ell h$ to estimate the number n of bricks needed to build a wall of length ℓ and height h, where ℓ and h are in feet. Solve the formula for h. Estimate the height of a wall 28 ft long that requires 1568 bricks.

Lesson Check

Do you know HOW?

Solve each equation for the given variable.

9. $-2x + 5y = 12$ for y

10. $a - 2b = -10$ for b

11. $mx + 2nx = p$ for x

12. $C = \frac{5}{9}(F - 32)$ for F

13. Gardening Jonah is planting a rectangular garden. The perimeter of the garden is 120 yd, and the width is 20 yd. What is the length of the garden?

Do you UNDERSTAND?

Vocabulary Classify each equation below as a formula, a literal equation, or both.

14. $c = 2d$

15. $y = 2x - 1$

16. $A = \frac{1}{2}bh$

17. $P = 2\ell + 2w$

18. Compare and Contrast How is the process of rewriting literal equations similar to the process of solving equations in one variable? How is it different?

More Practice and Problem-Solving Exercises

B Apply

Solve each equation for the given variable.

19. $2m - nx = x + 4$ for x

20. $\frac{x}{a} - 1 = \frac{y}{b}$ for x

21. $ax + 2xy = 14$ for y

22. $V = \frac{1}{3}\pi r^2 h$ for h

23. $A = \left(\frac{f+g}{2}\right)h$ for g

24. $2(x + a) = 4b$ for a

© **25. Think About a Plan** The interior angles of a polygon are the angles formed inside a polygon by two adjacent sides. The sum S of the measures of the interior angles of a polygon with n sides can be found using the formula $S = 180(n - 2)$. The sum of a polygon's interior angle measures is $1260°$. How many sides does the polygon have?
- What information are you given in the problem?
- What variable do you need to solve for in the formula?

TEM **26. Weather** Polar stratospheric clouds are colorful clouds that form when temperatures fall below $-78°C$. What is this temperature in degrees Fahrenheit?

TEM **27. Science** The energy E of a moving object is called its *kinetic energy*. It is calculated using the formula $E = \frac{1}{2}mv^2$, where m is the object's mass in kilograms and v is its speed in meters per second. The units of kinetic energy are $\frac{kilograms \cdot meters^2}{second^2}$, abbreviated as $kg \cdot m^2/s^2$.
a. Solve the given formula for m.
b. What is the mass of an object moving at 10 m/s with a kinetic energy of 2500 kg $\cdot$ m^2/s^2?

Polar stratospheric clouds

© **28. Error Analysis** Describe and correct the error made in solving the literal equation at the right for n.

© **29. Geometry** The formula for the volume of a cylinder is $V = \pi r^2 h$, where r is the cylinder's radius and h is its height. Solve the equation for h. What is the height of a cylinder with volume 502.4 cm³ and radius 4 cm? Use 3.14 for π.

$$2m = -6n + 3$$
$$2m + 3 = -6n$$
$$\frac{2m + 3}{-6} = n$$

30. Density The density of an object is calculated using the formula $D = \frac{m}{V}$, where m is the object's mass and V is its volume. Gold has a density of 19.3 g/cm³. What is the volume of an amount of gold that has a mass of 96.5 g?

© **31. Open-Ended** Write an equation in three variables. Solve the equation for each variable. Show all your steps.

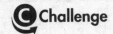

32. Surface Area A rectangular prism with height h and with square bases with side length s is shown.

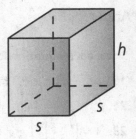

a. Write a formula for the surface area A of the prism.

b. Rewrite the formula to find h in terms of A and s. If s is 10 cm and A is 760 cm², what is the height of the prism?

Ⓒ c. **Writing** Suppose h is equal to s. Write a formula for A in terms of s only.

33. Midpoints Suppose a segment on a number line has endpoints with coordinates a and b. The coordinate of the segment's midpoint m is given by the formula $m = \frac{a+b}{2}$.

a. Find the midpoint of a segment with endpoints at 9.3 and 2.1.

b. Rewrite the given formula to find b in terms of a and m.

c. The midpoint of a segment is at 3.5. One endpoint is at 8.9. Find the other endpoint.

1-5 Ratios, Rates, and Conversions

N.Q.1 Use units as a way to understand problems and to guide the solution of . . . problems; choose and interpret units consistently . . . ; choose and interpret the scale and the origin in graphs and data displays. Also N.Q.2

Objectives   To find ratios and rates
                  To convert units and rates

Solve It!   Write your solution to the Solve It in the space below.

A **ratio** compares two numbers by division. The ratio of two numbers a and b, where $b \neq 0$, can be written in three ways: $\frac{a}{b}$, $a : b$, and a to b. For every a units of one quantity, you have b units of another quantity.

You can also think of a ratio as a multiplicative relationship. For example, if the ratio of the number of boys to the number of girls in a class is $2 : 1$, then the number of boys is *two times* the number of girls.

A ratio that compares quantities measured in different units is called a **rate.** A rate with a denominator of 1 unit is a **unit rate.** In the Solve It, you can express each athlete's speed as the number of meters traveled per 1 second of time. This is an example of a unit rate.

Essential Understanding You can write ratios and find unit rates to compare quantities. You can also convert units and rates to solve problems.

Problem 1   Comparing Unit Rates

Got It?   In Problem 1, if Store B lowers its price to $42 for 4 shirts, does the solution change? Explain.

1. Running Trisha ran 10 km in 2.5 h. Jason ran 7.5 km in 2 h. Olga ran 9.5 km in 2.25 h. Who had the fastest average speed?

2. Population Bellingham, Washington, had an area of 25.4 mi² and a population of 74,547 during one year. Bakersfield, California, had an area of 113.1 mi² and a population of 295,536 during the same year. Which city had a greater number of people per square mile?

> To convert from one unit to another, such as feet to inches, you multiply the original unit by a *conversion factor* that produces the desired unit. A **conversion factor** is a ratio of two equivalent measures in different units. A conversion factor is always equal to 1, such as $\frac{1\,\text{ft}}{12\,\text{in.}}$.

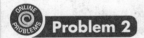 **Problem 2** **Converting Units**

Got It? What is 1250 cm converted to meters?

Plan

How do you choose the conversion factor?

 Practice Convert the given amount to the given unit.

    3. 63 yd; feet   **4.** 168 h; days

In Problem 2, notice that the units for each quantity are included in the calculations to help determine the units for the answers. This process is called **unit analysis**, or *dimensional analysis*.

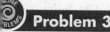

Problem 3   Converting Units Between Systems

Plan

How can you convert units?

Got It?   **a.** A building is 1450 ft tall. How many meters tall is the building? Use the fact that 1 m ≈ 3.28 ft.

b. Monetary exchange rates change from day to day. On a particular day, the exchange rate for dollars to euros was about 1 dollar = 0.63 euro. About how many euros could you get for $325 on that day?

Ⓐ Practice   Convert the given amount to the given unit.

5. 5 kg; pounds

6. 2 ft; centimeters

You can also convert rates. For example, you can convert a speed in miles per hour to feet per second. Because rates compare measures in two different units, you must multiply by two conversion factors to change both of the units.

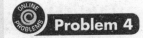 **Problem 4** **Converting Rates**

Got It?
a. An athlete ran a sprint of 100 ft in 3.1 s. At what speed was the athlete running in miles per hour? Round to the nearest mile per hour.

b. **Reasoning** In Problem 4, one student multiplied by the conversion factors $\frac{1\,\text{mi}}{1760\,\text{yd}}$, $\frac{60\,\text{s}}{1\,\text{min}}$, and $\frac{60\,\text{min}}{1\,\text{h}}$ to find the speed. Can this method work? Why or why not?

 Practice
7. **Maintenance** The janitor at a school discovered a slow leak in a pipe. The janitor found that it was leaking at a rate of 4 fl oz per minute. How fast was the pipe leaking in gallons per hour?

8. Shopping Mr. Swanson bought a package of 10 disposable razors for $6.30. He found that each razor lasted for 1 week. What was the cost per day?

Lesson Check

Do you know HOW?

9. Which is the better buy, 6 bagels for $3.29 or 8 bagels for $4.15?

10. What is 7 lb 4 oz converted to ounces?

11. Which is longer, 12 m or 13 yd?

12. A car is traveling at 55 mi/h. What is the car's speed in feet per second?

Do you UNDERSTAND?

ⓒ **Vocabulary** Tell whether each rate is a unit rate.

13. 20 mi every 3 h

14. 2 dollars per day

ⓒ **15. Reasoning** Does multiplying by a conversion factor change the amount of what is being measured? How do you know?

ⓒ **16. Reasoning** If you convert pounds to ounces, will the number of ounces be greater or less than the number of pounds? Explain.

More Practice and Problem-Solving Exercises

 MATHEMATICAL PRACTICES

Ⓑ **Apply**

Copy and complete each statement.

17. 7 ft 3 in. = ___ in.

18. 2.2 kg = ___ lb

19. 2.5 h = ___ min

20. 2 qt/min = ___ gal/s

21. 75 cents/h = ___ dollars/day

22. 60 ft/s = ___ km/h

ⓒ **Choose a Method** Choose paper and pencil, mental math, or a calculator to tell which measurement is greater.

23. 640 ft; 0.5 mi

24. 63 in.; 125 cm

25. 75 g; 5 oz

ⓒ **26. Think About a Plan** A college student is considering a subscription to a social-networking Internet site that advertises its cost as "only 87 cents per day." What is the cost of membership in dollars per year?
  • How many conversion factors will you need to use to solve the problem?
  • How do you choose the appropriate conversion factors?

27. Recipes Recipe A makes 5 dinner rolls using 1 c of flour. Recipe B makes 24 rolls using $7\frac{1}{2}$ c of flour. Recipe C makes 45 rolls using 10 c of flour. Which recipe requires the most flour per roll?

28. Error Analysis Find the mistake in the conversion at the right. Explain the mistake and convert the units correctly.

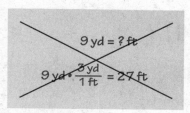

9 yd = ? ft

$9 \text{ yd} \cdot \dfrac{3 \text{ yd}}{1 \text{ ft}} = 27 \text{ ft}$

29. Writing Suppose you want to convert kilometers to miles. Which unit should be in the numerator of the conversion factor? Which unit should be in the denominator? Explain how you know.

30. Reasoning Without performing the conversion, determine whether the number of new units will be greater or less than the number of original units.
  a. 3 min 20 s converted to seconds
  b. 23 cm converted to inches
  c. kilometers per hour converted to miles per hour

31. Exchange Rates The table below shows some exchange rates on a particular day. If a sweater sells for $39.95 in U.S. dollars, what should its price be in rupees and pounds?

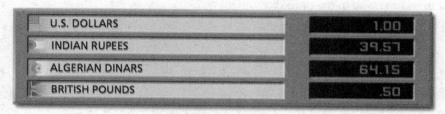

U.S. DOLLARS	1.00
INDIAN RUPEES	39.57
ALGERIAN DINARS	64.15
BRITISH POUNDS	.50

32. Estimation Five mi is approximately equal to 8 km. Use mental math to estimate the distance in kilometers to a town that is 30 mi away.

33. Reasoning A carpenter is building an entertainment center. She is calculating the size of the space to leave for the television. She wants to leave about a foot of space on either side of the television. Would measuring the size of the television exactly or estimating the size to the nearest inch be more appropriate? Explain.

34. Reasoning A traveler changed $300 to euros for a trip to Germany, but the trip was canceled. Three months later, the traveler changed the euros back to dollars. Would you expect that the traveler got exactly $300 back? Explain.

Challenge

35. Measurement Dietrich draws a line on the blackboard whose length is given by the expression 1 mm + 1 cm + 1 in. + 1 ft + 1 yd + 1 m. What is the length of the line in millimeters?

36. Square Measurements There are 2.54 cm in 1 in.
  a. How many square centimeters are there in 1 in.^{2}? Give your answer to the nearest hundredth of a square centimeter.
  b. How many square inches are there in 129 cm^2?

Unit Analysis

N.Q.1 Use units as a way to understand problems and to guide the solution of . . . problems; choose and interpret units consistently . . . ; choose and interpret the scale and the origin in graphs and data displays. Also **N.Q.2**

In Lesson 1-5, you learned that you can use unit analysis when converting units. You can also use unit analysis to help guide you to the solution of a problem.

Activity 1

The speed of light is about 3.0×10^{10} cm/s. If a rocket car of the future can travel at the speed of light, what is this rate in miles per hour?

Step 1 Make sense of the given information.

1. What units are given in the problem statement?

2. What units of measure should you have in your answer?

Step 2 Formulate a plan to solve the problem.

3. Which units need to be converted to solve the problem?

4. How do you know which conversion factors to use to solve the problem?

5. Can you use different conversion factors to solve the problem? Explain.

Step 3 Solve the problem.

6. Use unit analysis to write an expression by using the conversion factors you chose in Step 2.

7. Simplify the expression.

Step 4 Check your solution.

8. Are the units of your solution what you expected? Explain.

9. Does your answer make sense? Explain.

You can also use unit analysis to determine the reasonableness of a solution or a claim.

Activity 2

Suppose you are a gold miner in California in 1849. You have your tools in one hand. Can you use your free hand to carry a 4-liter bucket full of gold dust? The density of gold is 19.3 g/cm^3. Use unit analysis to determine whether the bucket is too heavy to carry. (*Hint:* 1 lb $\approx$ 454 g and 1000 cm^3 = 1 L.)

Step 1 Make sense of the given information.

10. What units are given in the problem statement?

11. Describe what you need to find in order to determine whether the bucket is too heavy to carry.

12. Will the information you need to find have units of measure? If so, what do you think those units will be?

Step 2 Formulate a plan to solve the problem.

13. Which units need to be converted to solve the problem?

14. How do you know which conversion factors to use to solve the problem?

Step 3 Solve the problem.

15. Use unit analysis to find what you described in Step 1.

16. Can you carry a 4-liter bucket of gold dust using one hand? Explain.

Step 4 Check your solution.

17. Are the units of your solution what you expected? Explain.

18. Does your answer make sense? Explain.

Exercises

19. The units mi/h and cm/s are units of distance/time. What do these units measure?

20. How can you use unit analysis to help you solve a problem?

Use unit analysis to help you solve each exercise.

21. A popular racetrack is 2.5 miles long. A race is completed in 150 laps. One year, the winner's average speed was 161 miles per hour. During cautionary lap runs, the speed was only about 80 miles per hour. If the race had 30 cautionary laps, about how long did it take the winner to complete the race?

Ⓒ **22. Error Analysis** Your gas tank holds 13.5 gallons of gas. Your fuel gauge shows that your tank is one-quarter full. Your car gets an average of 25 miles per gallon. The GPS shows that you are 85 miles from your destination. Your brother says you will make it. Is he correct? Use unit analysis to justify your response.

STEM **23. Chemistry** A metal bar in the shape of a rectangular prism with dimensions 6 cm × 8 cm × 2 cm has a mass of 53 g. The density of the metal is expressed in units of g/cm^3. Use what you have learned about unit analysis to find the density of the metal.

24. According to the directions, a 12-ounce can of lemonade concentrate makes 64 ounces of lemonade. If each serving is 8 ounces, how many 12-ounce cans of concentrate are needed to make 120 servings?

Accuracy and Measurement

Accuracy is the degree of how close a measured value is to the true value of the measurement. When making measurements, you have to be careful to take into consideration the level of accuracy of your measurements, given the tool you are using. A measurement is more accurate when it is closer to the true value of the attribute (length, weight, capacity, temperature) being measured.

Activity

You want to know the weight of three bags of sand. You weigh one bag of sand on a scale that reports weight to the nearest pound. The scale reports that the bag weighs 20 pounds.

1. What are the upper and lower bounds of the true weight of the bag?

2. What are the possible values for the true weight of the bag?

When you weigh the other two bags, the scale reads 19 pounds for one bag and 22 pounds for the other bag.

3. What is the total weight of the three bags according to the scale?

4. What are the upper and lower bounds for the total weight of the bags? What are the possible values for the true weight of the bags?

Another scale reports weights to the nearest tenth of a pound. The scale reads 20.2, 19.1, and 22.3 pounds for the same bags when weighed separately.

5. According to this scale, what are the possible values for the combined weight of the three bags?

6. Which scale is more accurate? Explain.

Exercises

You want to know the perimeter of a painting that appears to be in the shape of a rectangle. You measure the lengths of the sides with a ruler that can measure lengths to the nearest quarter-inch. The measurements are 18 in., 24 in., 24 in., and 18 in.

7. What are the upper and lower bounds for the true lengths of each side of the painting? What are the possible values for the true lengths of each side?

8. What is the perimeter of the painting according to the measured values?

9. What are the upper and lower bounds for the true perimeter of the painting? What are the possible values for the true perimeter?

You measure the lengths again with another ruler that can measure to the nearest eighth of an inch. This time you record the measurements as $18\frac{1}{8}$ in., $23\frac{7}{8}$ in., 24 in., and $18\frac{1}{8}$ in.

10. According to this ruler, what are the possible values for the true perimeter of the painting?

11. Explain why using the ruler that can measure lengths to the nearest eighth of an inch gives a more accurate measurement of the perimeter than using the ruler that can measure only to the nearest quarter-inch.

1-6 Solving Proportions

A.REI.3 Solve linear equations and inequalities in one variable . . . Also **N.Q.1, A.CED.1**

Objective To solve and apply proportions

Solve It! Write your solution to the Solve It in the space below.

In the Solve It, the number of red beads and the number of blue beads are quantities that have a proportional relationship. This means that the ratio of the quantities is constant even though the quantities themselves can change. For example, as you are making the necklace you will have 2 red beads and 3 blue beads, then 4 red beads and 6 blue beads, then 6 red beads and 9 blue beads, and so on. At each stage, the ratio of red beads to blue beads remains constant, 2 : 3.

A proportional relationship can produce an infinite number of equivalent ratios. Any two of these can be used to write a proportion. A **proportion** is an equation that states that two ratios are equal. For example, $\frac{a}{b} = \frac{c}{d}$, where $b \neq 0$ and $d \neq 0$, is a proportion. You read this as "a is to b as c is to d."

Essential Understanding If two ratios are equal and a quantity in one of the ratios is unknown, you can write and solve a proportion to find the unknown quantity.

 **Problem 1** **Solving a Proportion Using the Multiplication Property**

Got It? What is the solution of the proportion $\frac{x}{7} = \frac{4}{5}$?

Ⓐ Practice Solve each proportion using the Multiplication Property of Equality.

1. $\dfrac{m}{7} = \dfrac{3}{5}$

2. $\dfrac{3}{16} = \dfrac{x}{12}$

In the proportion $\dfrac{a}{b} = \dfrac{c}{d}$, the products ad and bc are called **cross products**. You can use the following property of cross products to solve proportions.

take note

Property Cross Products Property of a Proportion

Words   The cross products of a proportion are equal.

Algebra   If $\dfrac{a}{b} = \dfrac{c}{d}$, where $b \neq 0$ and $d \neq 0$, then $ad = bc$.

Example $\dfrac{3}{4} = \dfrac{9}{12}$, so $3(12) = 4(9)$, or $36 = 36$.

Here's Why It Works You can use the Multiplication Property of Equality to prove the Cross Products Property.

$$\dfrac{a}{b} = \dfrac{c}{d} \qquad \text{Assume this equation is true.}$$

$$bd \cdot \dfrac{a}{b} = bd \cdot \dfrac{c}{d} \qquad \text{Multiplication Property of Equality}$$

$$\cancel{b}d \cdot \dfrac{a}{\cancel{b}} = b\cancel{d} \cdot \dfrac{c}{\cancel{d}} \qquad \text{Divide the common factors.}$$

$$da = bc \qquad \text{Simplify.}$$

$$ad = bc \qquad \text{Commutative Property of Multiplication}$$

For this proportion, a and d are called the *extremes* of the proportion and b and c are called the *means*. Notice that in the Cross Products Property the product of the means equals the product of the extremes.

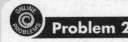 **Problem 2** **Solving a Proportion Using the Cross Products Property**

Got It? **a.** What is the solution of the proportion $\frac{y}{3} = \frac{3}{5}$?

 b. Reasoning Would you rather use the Cross Products Property or the Multiplication Property of Equality to solve $\frac{3}{5} = \frac{13}{b}$? Explain.

 Practice Solve each proportion using the Cross Products Property.

3. $\frac{-3}{4} = \frac{m}{22}$

4. $\frac{2}{-5} = \frac{6}{t}$

Problem 3 **Solving a Multi-Step Proportion**

Got It? What is the solution of the proportion $\frac{n}{5} = \frac{2n + 4}{6}$?

Think
What property can you use to rewrite the equation?

Ⓐ Practice Solve each proportion using any method.

5. $\dfrac{q+2}{5} = \dfrac{2q-11}{7}$

6. $\dfrac{c+1}{c-2} = \dfrac{4}{7}$

When you model a real-world situation with a proportion, you must write the proportion carefully. You can write the proportion so that the numerators have the same units and the denominators have the same units.

Correct: $\dfrac{100\,\text{mi}}{2\,\text{h}} = \dfrac{x\,\text{mi}}{5\,\text{h}}$ **Incorrect:** $\dfrac{100\,\text{mi}}{2\,\text{h}} = \dfrac{5\,\text{h}}{x\,\text{mi}}$

Problem 4 Using a Proportion to Solve a Problem

Think
How can you set up a proportion to solve this problem?

Got It? An 8-oz can of orange juice contains about 97 mg of vitamin C. About how many milligrams of vitamin C are there in a 12-oz can of orange juice?

7. Gardening A gardener is transplanting flowers into a flower bed. She has been working for an hour and has transplanted 14 flowers. She has 35 more flowers to transplant. If she works at the same rate, how many more hours will it take her?

8. Florists A florist is making centerpieces. He uses 2 dozen roses for every 5 centerpieces. How many dozens of roses will he need to make 20 centerpieces?

Lesson Check

Do you know HOW?

Solve each proportion.

9. $\frac{b}{6} = \frac{4}{5}$

10. $\frac{5}{9} = \frac{15}{x}$

11. $\frac{w+3}{4} = \frac{w}{2}$

12. $\frac{3}{x+1} = \frac{1}{2}$

13. **Music** A band went to a recording studio and recorded 4 songs in 3 h. How long would it take the band to record 9 songs if they record at the same rate?

Do you UNDERSTAND?

Ⓒ **Vocabulary** Use the proportion $\frac{m}{n} = \frac{p}{q}$. Identify the following.

14. the extremes

15. the means

16. the cross products

Ⓒ 17. **Reasoning** When solving $\frac{x}{5} = \frac{3}{4}$, Lisa's first step was to write $4x = 5(3)$. Jen's first step was to write $20\left(\frac{x}{5}\right) = 20\left(\frac{3}{4}\right)$. Will both methods work? Explain.

More Practice and Problem-Solving Exercises

B Apply

18. **Statistics** Approximately 3 people out of every 30 are left-handed. About how many left-handed people would you expect in a group of 140 people?

19. **Think About a Plan** Maya runs 100 m in 13.4 s. Amy can run 100 m in 14.1 s. If Amy were to finish a 100-m race at the same time as Maya, how much of a head start, in meters, would Amy need?
    • What information do you know? What information is unknown?
    • What proportion can you write that will help you solve the problem?

20. **Electricity** The electric bill for Ferguson's Furniture is shown at the right. The cost of electricity per kilowatt-hour and the total charges for one month are given. How many kilowatt-hours of electricity did Ferguson's Furniture use in that month?

21. **Video Downloads** A particular computer takes 15 min to download a 45-min TV show. How long will it take the computer to download a 2-h movie?

$\stackrel{\textstyle \blacksquare}{\textstyle \equiv}$ **⑤ Centerville Electric**	
Account Name: Ferguson's Furniture	
Account Number: 34-14567-89	
Cost per kilowatt-hour	$.07
Total charges	$143.32
Previous balance	$.00
Total Amount Due	$143.32

22. **Schedules** You want to meet your friend at a park 4 mi away from your house. You are going to bike to the park at an average rate of 10 mi/h. Your friend lives 1.2 mi away from the park and walks at an average rate of 3 mi/h. How many minutes ahead of you should your friend start out so that you meet at the park at the same time?

Solve each proportion. Tell whether you used the Multiplication Property of Equality or the Cross Products Property for your first step. Explain your choice.

23. $\frac{p}{4} = \frac{7}{8}$

24. $\frac{m}{4.5} = \frac{2}{5}$

25. $\frac{3}{10} = \frac{b}{7}$

26. $\frac{r}{2.1} = \frac{3.6}{2.8}$

27. $\frac{9}{14} = \frac{3}{n}$

28. $\frac{1.5}{y} = \frac{2.5}{7}$

29. $\frac{b + 13}{2} = \frac{-5b}{3}$

30. $\frac{3b}{b - 4} = \frac{3}{7}$

31. $\frac{x + 2}{2x - 6} = \frac{3}{8}$

32. **Error Analysis** Describe and correct the error in solving the proportion at the right.

33. **Bakery** A bakery sells packages of 10 bagels for $3.69. If the bakery starts selling the bagels in packages of 12, how much would you expect a package of 12 to cost?

    Ⓐ $3.08

    Ⓒ $4.43

    Ⓑ $4.32

    Ⓓ $4.69

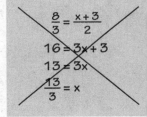

34. Open-Ended Write a proportion that contains a variable. Name the extremes, the means, and the cross products. Solve the proportion. Tell whether you used the Multiplication Property of Equality or the Cross Products Property to solve the proportion. Explain your choice.

TEM 35. Biology Many trees have concentric rings that can be counted to determine the tree's age. Each ring represents one year's growth. A maple tree with a diameter of 12 in. has 32 rings. If the tree continues to grow at about the same rate, how many rings will the tree have when its diameter is 20 in.?

Challenge

Solve each proportion.

36. $\dfrac{4y - 3}{y^2 + 1} = \dfrac{4}{y}$

37. $\dfrac{w^2 + 3}{2w + 2} = \dfrac{w}{2}$

38. $\dfrac{5x}{x^3 + 5} = \dfrac{5}{x^2 - 7}$

39. Parade Floats A group of high school students is making a parade float by stuffing pieces of tissue paper into a wire frame. They use 150 tissues to fill an area 3 ft long and 2 ft wide. The total area they want to fill is 8 ft long and 7 ft wide. What is the total number of tissues they will need?

40. Insects It takes an insect 15 s to crawl 1 ft. How many hours would it take the insect to crawl 1 mi if the insect crawls at the same rate?

Solving Multi-Step Inequalities

A.REI.3 Solve linear equations and inequalities in one variable . . . Also A.CED.1

Objective To solve multi-step inequalities

Solve It! Write your solution to the Solve It in the space below.

You can model the situation in the Solve It with the inequality $337.50 + 7.50x \geq 500$. In this lesson, you will learn how to write and solve multi-step inequalities like this one.

Essential Understanding You solve a multi-step inequality in the same way you solve a one-step inequality. You use the properties of inequality to transform the original inequality into a series of simpler, equivalent inequalities.

Problem 1 **Using More Than One Step**

Got It? What are the solutions of the inequality? Check your solutions.

a. $-6a - 7 \leq 17$

b. $-4 < 5 - 3n$

Plan

How can you check the solutions of each inequality?

c. $50 > 0.8x + 30$

Practice   Solve each inequality. Check your solutions.

1. $-5y - 2 < 8$

2. $6 \le 12 + 4j$

You can adapt familiar formulas to write inequalities. You use the real-world situation to determine which inequality symbol to use.

Problem 2   **Writing and Solving a Multi-Step Inequality**

Got It?   You want to make a rectangular banner that is 18 ft long with a trim that goes around the entire border of the banner. You have no more than 48 ft of trim for the banner. What are the possible widths of the banner?

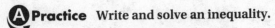

A Practice Write and solve an inequality.

3. Family Trip On a trip from Buffalo, New York, to St. Augustine, Florida, a family wants to travel at least 250 mi in the first 5 h of driving. What should their average speed be in order to meet this goal?

4. Geometry An isosceles triangle has at least two congruent sides. The perimeter of a certain isosceles triangle is at most 12 in. The length of each of the two congruent sides is 5 in. What are the possible lengths of the remaining side?

Problem 3 **Using the Distributive Property**

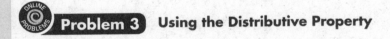

Got It? What are the solutions of $15 \leq 5 - 2(4m + 7)$? Check your solutions.

Practice Solve each inequality.

    5. $-3(j + 3) + 9j < -15$

    6. $-4 \leq 4(6y - 12) - 2y$

Some inequalities have variables on both sides of the inequality symbol. You need to gather the variable terms on one side of the inequality and the constant terms on the other side.

Problem 4   **Solving an Inequality With Variables on Both Sides**

Got It?   **a.** What are the solutions of $3b + 12 > 27 - 2b$? Check your solutions.

    ©**b. Reasoning** The first step in solving Problem 4 was to subtract $3n$ from each side of the inequality. What else could have been the first step in solving the inequality? Explain.

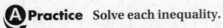 **Practice** Solve each inequality.

7. $3m - 4 \le 6m + 11$

8. $4t + 17 > 7 + 5t$

Sometimes solving an inequality gives a statement that is *always* true, such as $4 > 1$. In that case, the solutions are all real numbers. If the statement is *never* true, as is $9 \le -5$, then the inequality has no solution.

 Problem 5 Inequalities With Special Solutions

Got It? What are the solutions of each inequality?

a. $9 + 5n \le 5n - 1$

Think

Without solving, how can you tell that this inequality has no solution?

b. $8 + 6x \ge 7x + 2 - x$

Solve each inequality, if possible. If the inequality has no solution, write *no solution*. If the solutions are all real numbers, write *all real numbers*.

9. $-5r + 6 \le -5(r - 2)$

10. $9 + 2x < 7 + 2(x - 3)$

Lesson Check

Do you know HOW?

In Exercises 11–14, solve each inequality, if possible. If the inequality has no solution, write *no solution*. If the solutions are all real numbers, write *all real numbers*.

11. $7 + 6a > 19$

12. $2(t + 2) - 3t \ge -1$

13. $6z - 15 < 4z + 11$

14. $18x - 5 \le 3(6x - 2)$

15. The perimeter of a rectangle is at most 24 cm. Two opposite sides are both 4 cm long. What are the possible lengths of the other two sides?

Do you UNDERSTAND?

 MATHEMATICAL PRACTICES

©️ **16. Reasoning** How can you tell that the inequality $3t + 1 > 3t + 2$ has no solution just by looking at the terms in the inequality?

© **17. Reasoning** Can you solve the inequality $2(x - 3) \le 10$ *without* using the Distributive Property? Explain.

© **18. Error Analysis** Your friend says that the solutions of the inequality $-2(3 - x) > 2x - 6$ are all real numbers. Do you agree with your friend? Explain. What if the inequality symbol were $\ge$?

More Practice and Problem-Solving Exercises

B Apply

Solve each inequality, if possible. If the inequality has no solution, write *no solution*. If the solutions are all real numbers, write *all real numbers*.

19. $-3(x - 3) \ge 5 - 4x$ **20.** $3s + 6 \le -5(s + 2)$ **21.** $3(2 + t) \ge 15 - 2t$

22. $\frac{4}{3}s - 3 < s + \frac{2}{3} - \frac{1}{3}s$ **23.** $4 - 2n \le 5 - n + 1$ **24.** $-2(0.5 - 4t) \ge -3(4 - 3.5t)$

25. $4(a - 2) - 6a \le -9$ **26.** $4(3n - 1) \ge 2(n + 3)$ **27.** $17 - (4k - 2) \ge 2(k + 3)$

© **28. Think About a Plan** Your cell phone plan costs $39.99 per month plus $.15 for each text message you send or receive. You have at most $45 to spend on your cell phone bill. What is the maximum number of text messages that you can send or receive next month?

- What information do you know? What information do you need?
- What inequality can you use to find the maximum number of text messages that you can send or receive?
- What are the solutions of the inequality? Are they reasonable?

29. Rental Rates The student council wants to rent a ballroom for the junior prom. The ballroom's rental rate is $1500 for 3 h and $125 for each additional half hour. Suppose the student council raises $2125. What is the maximum number of hours for which they can rent the ballroom?

30. Writing Suppose a friend is having difficulty solving $3.75(q - 5) > 4(q + 3)$. Explain how to solve the inequality, showing all the necessary steps and identifying the properties you would use.

STEM **31. Biology** The average normal body temperature for humans is 98.6°F. An abnormal increase in body temperature is classified as hyperthermia, or fever. Which inequality represents the body temperature in degrees Celsius of a person with hyperthermia? (*Hint*: To convert from degrees Celsius C to degrees Fahrenheit F, use the formula $F = \frac{9}{5}C + 32$.)

- (A) $\frac{9}{5}C + 32 \geq 98.6$
- (B) $\frac{9}{5}C + 32 \leq 98.6$
- (C) $\frac{9}{5}C + 32 < 98.6$
- (D) $\frac{9}{5}C + 32 > 98.6$

32. Open-Ended Write two different inequalities that you can solve by subtracting 3 from each side and then dividing each side by -5. Solve each inequality.

33. a. Solve $6v + 5 \leq 9v - 7$ by gathering the variable terms on the left side and the constant terms on the right side of the inequality.
   b. Solve $6v + 5 \leq 9v - 7$ by gathering the constant terms on the left side and the variable terms on the right side of the inequality.
   c. Compare the results of parts (a) and (b).
   d. Which method do you prefer? Explain.

34. Mental Math Determine whether each inequality is *always true* or *never true*.
   a. $5s + 7 \geq 7 + 5s$
   b. $4t + 6 > 4t - 3$
   c. $5(m + 2) < 5m - 4$

35. Commission A sales associate in a shoe store earns \$325 per week, plus a commission equal to 4% of her sales. This week her goal is to earn at least \$475. At least how many dollars' worth of shoes must she sell in order to reach her goal?

36. A student uses the table below to help solve $7y + 2 < 6(4 - y)$.

y	$7y + 2$	$<$	$6(4 - y)$
0.5	$7(0.5) + 2 = 5.5$	True	$6(4 - 0.5) = 21$
1	$7(1) + 2 = 9$	True	$6(4 - 1) = 18$
1.5	$7(1.5) + 2 = 12.5$	True	$6(4 - 1.5) = 15$
2	$7(2) + 2 = 16$	False	$6(4 - 2) = 12$

Ⓒ **a. Reasoning** Based on the table, would you expect the solution of $7y + 2 < 6(4 - y)$ to be of the form $y < c$ or $y > c$, where c is a real number? Explain.

 b. Estimate Based on the table, estimate the value of c.

 c. Solve the inequality. Compare the actual solution to your estimated solution.

Ⓒ **Error Analysis** Describe and correct the error in each solution.

37.

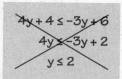

$4y + 4 \le -3y + 6$
$4y \le -3y + 2$
$y \le 2$

38.

$5(p + 3) > 4p + 2$
$5p + 3 > 4p + 2$
$5p > 4p - 1$
$p > -1$

Ⓒ **Challenge**

39. Geometry The base of a triangle is 12 in. Its height is $(x + 6)$ in. Its area is no more than 72 in.² What are the possible integer values of x?

40. Part-Time Jobs You can earn money by tutoring for $8 per hour and by walking dogs for $7.50 per hour. You have 15 h available to work. What is the greatest number of hours you can spend walking dogs and still make at least $115?

41. Freight Handling The elevator of a building can safely carry no more than 4000 lb. A worker moves supplies in 50-lb boxes from the loading dock to the fourth floor of the building. The worker weighs 210 lb. The cart he uses weighs 95 lb.
 a. What is the greatest number of boxes he can move in one trip?
 b. The worker needs to deliver 275 boxes. How many trips must he make?

1-8 Compound Inequalities

A.REI.3 Solve linear equations and inequalities in one variable . . . Also **A.CED.1**

Objectives To solve and graph inequalities containing the word *and*
To solve and graph inequalities containing the word *or*

 Solve It! Write your solution to the Solve It in the space below.

The Solve It involves a value that is between two numbers. You can use a compound inequality to represent this relationship. A **compound inequality** consists of two distinct inequalities joined by the word *and* or the word *or*.

Essential Understanding You find the solutions of a compound inequality either by identifying where the solution sets of the distinct inequalities overlap or by combining the solution sets to form a larger solution set.

The graph of a compound inequality with the word *and* contains the *overlap* of the graphs of the two inequalities that form the compound inequality.

The graph of a compound inequality with the word *or* contains *each* graph of the two inequalities that form the compound inequality.

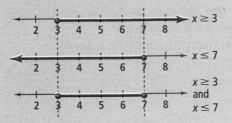

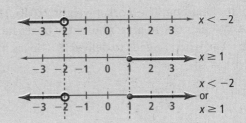

You can rewrite a compound inequality involving *and* as a single inequality. For instance, in the inequality above, you can write $x \geq 3$ and $x \leq 7$ as $3 \leq x \leq 7$. You read this as "*x* is greater than or equal to 3 and less than or equal to 7." Another way to read it is "*x* is between 3 and 7, inclusive." In this example, *inclusive* means the solutions of the inequality include both 3 and 7.

Got It! For parts (a) and (b) below, write a compound inequality that represents each phrase. Graph the solutions.

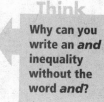

Think

Why can you write an *and* inequality without the word *and*?

 a. all real numbers that are greater than or equal to −4 and less than 6

 b. all real numbers that are less than or equal to $2\frac{1}{2}$ or greater than 6

 © **c. Reasoning** What is the difference between "*x* is between −5 and 7" and "*x* is between −5 and 7, inclusive"?

 Practice Write a compound inequality that represents each phrase. Graph the solutions.

 1. all real numbers that are between −5 and 7

2. The circumference of a women's basketball must be between 28.5 in. and 29 in., inclusive.

A solution of a compound inequality involving *and* is any number that makes *both* inequalities true. One way you can solve a compound inequality is by separating it into two inequalities.

Problem 2 Solving a Compound Inequality Involving *And*

Got It? What are the solutions of $-2 < 3y - 4 < 14$? Graph the solutions.

Practice Solve each compound inequality. Graph your solutions.

3. $-4 < k + 3 < 8$

4. $5 \leq y + 2 \leq 11$

You can also solve an inequality like $-3 \leq m - 4 < -1$ by working on all three parts of the inequality at the same time. You work to isolate the variable between the inequality symbols. This method is used in Problem 3.

Writing and Solving a Compound Inequality

© **Got It? Reasoning** Suppose you scored 78, 78, and 79 on the first three tests. Is it possible for you to earn a B in the course? Assume that 100 is the maximum grade you can earn in the course and on the test. Explain.

Ⓐ **Practice** Solve each compound inequality. Graph your solutions.

5. $\frac{1}{4} < \frac{2x - 7}{2} < 5$

6. $-3 \leq \frac{6 - q}{9} \leq 3$

A solution of a compound inequality involving *or* is any number that makes *either* inequality true. To solve a compound inequality involving *or*, you must solve separately the two inequalities that form the compound inequality.

Problem 4   Solving a Compound Inequality Involving *Or*

Got It?   What are the solutions of $-2y + 7 < 1$ or $4y + 3 \leq -5$? Graph the solutions.

Think

What does the graph of an inequality involving *or* look like?

Ⓐ Practice Solve each compound inequality. Graph your solutions.

7. $5y + 7 \leq -3$ or $3y - 2 \geq 13$

8. $5z - 3 > 7$ or $4z - 6 < -10$

You can use an inequality such as $x \leq -3$ to describe a portion of the number line called an *interval*. You can also use *interval notation* to describe an interval on the number line. **Interval notation** includes the use of three special symbols. These symbols include

parentheses: Use (or) when a < or > symbol indicates that the interval's endpoints are *not* included.

brackets: Use [or] when a ≤ or ≥ symbol indicates that the interval's endpoints *are* included.

infinity: Use ∞ when the interval continues forever in a *positive* direction. Use −∞ when the interval continues forever in a *negative* direction.

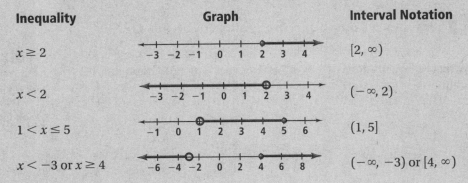

Inequality	Graph	Interval Notation
$x \geq 2$		$[2, \infty)$
$x < 2$		$(-\infty, 2)$
$1 < x \leq 5$		$(1, 5]$
$x < -3$ or $x \geq 4$		$(-\infty, -3)$ or $[4, \infty)$

Got It?   **a.** What is the graph of $(-2, 7]$? How do you write $(-2, 7]$ as an inequality?

b. What is the graph of $y > 7$? How do you write $y > 7$ in interval notation?

Practice   **9.** Write the interval $(-\infty, -1]$ or $(3, \infty)$ as an inequality. Then graph the solution.

10. Write the inequality $x < -2$ or $x \geq 1$ in interval notation. The graph the interval.

11. What compound inequality represents the phrase "all real numbers that are greater than or equal to 0 and less than 8"? Graph the solutions.

12. What are the solutions of $-4 \leq r - 5 < -1$? Graph the solutions.

13. Your test scores in science are 83 and 87. What possible scores can you earn on your next test to have a test average between 85 and 90, inclusive?

14. Write the interval represented on the number line below as an inequality and in interval notation.

Do you UNDERSTAND?

Ⓖ **15. Vocabulary** Which of the following are compound inequalities?

    Ⓐ $x > 4$ or $x < -4$

    Ⓑ $x \geq 6$

    Ⓒ $8 \leq 5x < 30$

    Ⓓ $7x > 42$ or $-5x \leq 10$

Ⓖ **16. Error Analysis** A student writes the inequality $x \geq 17$ in interval notation as $[17, \infty]$. Explain why this is incorrect.

Ⓖ **17. Reasoning** What are the solutions of $3x - 7 \leq 14$ or $4x - 8 > 20$? Write your solutions as a compound inequality and in interval notation.

Ⓖ **18. Writing** Compare the graph of a compound inequality involving *and* with the graph of a compound inequality involving *or*.

More Practice and Problem-Solving Exercises

B Apply

Solve each inequality. Write each set in interval notation.

19. $7 < x + 6 \le 12$

20. $-9 < 3m + 6 \le 18$

21. $f + 14 < 9$ or $-9f \le -45$

22. $12h - 3 \ge 15h$ or $5 > -0.2h + 10$

Write a compound inequality that each graph could represent.

23.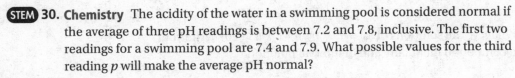

24.

25.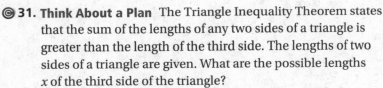

Solve each compound inequality. Justify each step.

26. $4r - 3 > 11$ or $4r - 3 \le -11$

27. $2 \le 0.75v \le 4.5$

28. $\frac{4y + 2}{5} - 5 > 3$ or $\frac{4 - 3y}{6} > 4$

29. $-\frac{4}{3} \le \frac{1}{7}w - \frac{3}{4} < 1$

STEM **30. Chemistry** The acidity of the water in a swimming pool is considered normal if the average of three pH readings is between 7.2 and 7.8, inclusive. The first two readings for a swimming pool are 7.4 and 7.9. What possible values for the third reading p will make the average pH normal?

31. Think About a Plan The Triangle Inequality Theorem states that the sum of the lengths of any two sides of a triangle is greater than the length of the third side. The lengths of two sides of a triangle are given. What are the possible lengths x of the third side of the triangle?

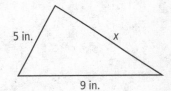

- Is there an upper limit on the value of x? Is there a lower limit?
- How can you use your answers to the previous question to write one or more inequalities involving x?

Use your answers to Exercise 31 to answer Exercises 32–35. The lengths of two sides of a triangle are given. Find the possible lengths of the third side.

32. 3.75 in., 7 in.   **33.** 15 ft, 21 ft   **34.** 14 mm, 35 mm   **35.** 6 m, 17 m

STEM **36. Physics** The force exerted on a spring is proportional to the distance the spring is stretched from its relaxed position. Suppose you stretch a spring a distance of d inches by applying a force of F pounds. For your spring, $\frac{d}{F} = 0.8$. You apply forces between 25 lb and 40 lb, inclusive. What inequality describes the distances the spring is stretched?

© **37. Reasoning** Describe the solutions of $4x - 9 < 7$ or $3x - 10 > 2$.

38. Nutrition A sedentary 15-year-old male should consume no more than 2200 Calories per day. A moderately active 15-year-old male should consume between 2400 and 2800 Calories per day. An active 15-year-old male should consume between 2800 and 3200 Calories per day. Model these ranges on a number line. Represent each range of Calories using interval notation.

© **Challenge**

39. Heart Rates Recommended heart rates during exercise vary with age and physical condition. For a healthy person doing moderate to intense exercise, such as hiking, the inequality $0.5(220 - a) \le R \le 0.9(220 - a)$ gives a target range for the heart rate R (in beats per minute), based on age a (in years).
   a. What is the target range for heart rates for a person 15 years old?
   b. How old is a person whose target range is between 99 and 178.2 beats per minute?

STEM **40. Chemistry** Matter is in a liquid state when its temperature is between its melting point and its boiling point. The melting point of the element mercury is $-38.87°C$, and its boiling point is $356.58°C$. What is the range of temperatures in degrees Fahrenheit for which mercury is *not* in a liquid state? (*Hint:* $C = \frac{5}{9}(F - 32)$) Express the range as an inequality and in interval notation.

1-9 Absolute Value Equations and Inequalities

A.CED.1 Create equations and inequalities in one variable and . . . solve problems . . . Also **A.SSE.1, A.SSE.1.b**

Objective To solve equations and inequalities involving absolute value

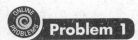

Solve It! Write your solution to the Solve It in the space below.

In the Solve It, Serena's distance from Darius decreases and then increases. You can use absolute value to model such changes. The absolute value of a number is its distance from 0 on a number line. Absolute value is always nonnegative since distance is always nonnegative.

Essential Understanding You can solve absolute value equations and inequalities by first isolating the absolute value expression, if necessary. Then write an equivalent pair of linear equations or inequalities.

Problem 1 Solving an Absolute Value Equation

Got It? What are the solutions of $|n| - 5 = -2$? Graph and check the solutions.

Think
How many solutions does the equation have?

Practice Solve each equation. Graph and check your solutions.

1. $|n| + 3 = 7$

2. $-3|m| = -9$

Some equations, such as $|2x - 5| = 13$, have variable expressions within absolute value symbols. The equation $|2x - 5| = 13$ means that the distance on a number line from $2x - 5$ to 0 is 13 units. There are two points that are 13 units from 0: 13 and -13. So to find the values of x, solve the equations $2x - 5 = 13$ and $2x - 5 = -13$. You can generalize this process as follows.

take note

Key Concept Solving Absolute Value Equations

To solve an equation in the form $|A| = b$, where A represents a variable expression and $b > 0$, solve $A = b$ and $A = -b$.

Problem 2 Solving an Absolute Value Equation

Got It? Another friend's distance d from you (in feet) after t seconds is given by $d = |80 - 5t|$. What does the 80 in the equation represent? What does the 5 in the equation represent? At what times is she 60 ft from you?

Practice Solve each equation.

3. $|r - 8| = 5$

4. $2 = |g + 3|$

> Recall that absolute value represents distance from 0 on a number line. Distance is always nonnegative. So any equation that states that the absolute value of an expression is negative has no solutions.

Problem 3 **Solving an Absolute Value Equation With No Solution**

Plan

Got It? What are the solutions of $|3x - 6| - 5 = -7$?

How can you make the equation look like one you've solved before?

Practice Solve each equation. If there is no solution, write *no solution.*

5. $-2|7d| = 14$

6. $3|v - 3| = 9$

You can write absolute value inequalities as compound inequalities. The graphs below show two absolute value inequalities.

$|n-1| < 2$ 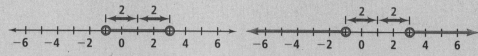 $|n-1| > 2$

$|n-1| < 2$ represents all numbers with a distance from 1 that is less than 2 units. So $|n-1| < 2$ means $-2 < n - 1 < 2$.

$|n-1| > 2$ represents all numbers with a distance from 1 that is greater than 2 units. So $|n-1| > 2$ means $n - 1 < -2$ or $n - 1 > 2$.

Key Concept Solving Absolute Value Inequalities

To solve an inequality in the form $|A| < b$, where A is a variable expression and $b > 0$, solve the compound inequality $-b < A < b$.

To solve an inequality in the form $|A| > b$, where A is a variable expression and $b > 0$, solve the compound inequality $A < -b$ or $A > b$.

Similar rules are true for $|A| \le b$ or $|A| \ge b$.

Problem 4 Solving an Absolute Value Inequality Involving ≥

Got It? What are the solutions of $|2x + 4| \ge 5$? Graph the solutions.

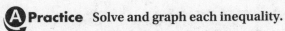

Practice Solve and graph each inequality.

7. $|y + 8| \geq 3$

8. $|5m - 9| \geq 24$

Problem 5   **Solving an Absolute Value Inequality Involving ≤**

Got It?   **a.** A food manufacturer makes 32-oz boxes of pasta. Not every box weighs exactly 32 oz. The allowable difference from the ideal weight is at most 0.05 oz. Write and solve an absolute value inequality to find the range of allowable weights.

b. Reasoning In Problem 5, could you have solved the inequality $|w - 213| \leq 5$ by first adding 213 to each side? Explain your reasoning.

9. Solve and graph the inequality $|2f + 9| \leq 13$.

10. Quality Control The ideal length of one type of model airplane is 90 cm. The actual length may vary from ideal by at most 0.05 cm. What are the acceptable lengths for the model airplane?

Lesson Check

Do you know HOW?

Solve and graph each equation or inequality.

11. $|x| = 5$

12. $|n| - 3 = 4$

13. $|2t| = 6$

14. $|h - 3| < 5$

15. $|x + 2| \geq 1$

Do you UNDERSTAND?

© **16. Reasoning** How many solutions do you expect to get when you solve an absolute value equation? Explain.

Ⓒ **17. Writing** Explain why the absolute value equation $|3x| + 8 = 5$ has no solution.

Ⓒ **18. Compare and Contrast** Explain the similarities and differences in solving the equation $|x - 1| = 2$ with solving the inequalities $|x - 1| \leq 2$ and $|x - 1| \geq 2$.

More Practice and Problem-Solving Exercises

Ⓑ Apply

Solve each equation or inequality. If there is no solution, write *no solution*.

19. $|2d| + 3 = 21$ **20.** $1.2|5p| = 3.6$ **21.** $\left|d + \frac{1}{2}\right| + \frac{3}{4} = 0$ **22.** $|f| - \frac{2}{3} = \frac{5}{6}$

23. $3|5y - 7| - 6 = 24$ **24.** $|t| + 2.7 = 4.5$ **25.** $-2|c - 4| = -8.4$ **26.** $\frac{|y|}{-3} = 5$

27. $|n| - \frac{5}{4} < 5$ **28.** $\frac{7}{8} < |c + 7|$ **29.** $4 - 3|m + 2| > -14$ **30.** $|-3d| \geq 6.3$

Ⓒ **31. Think About a Plan** The monthly average temperature T for San Francisco, California, is usually within 7.5°F of 56.5°F, inclusive. What is the monthly average temperature in San Francisco?

- Should you model this situation with an equation or an inequality?
- How can you use the given information to write the equation or inequality?

STEM 32. **Biology** A horse's body temperature T is considered to be normal if it is within at least 0.9°F of 99.9°F. Find the range of normal body temperatures for a horse.

33. **Biking** Your friend rides his bike toward you and then passes by you at a constant speed. His distance d (in feet) from you t seconds after he started riding his bike is given by $d = |200 - 18t|$. What does the 200 in the equation represent? What does the 18 in the equation represent? At what time(s) is he 120 ft from you?

© **Error Analysis** Find and correct the mistake in solving each equation or inequality.

34.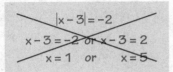

35.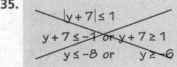

© 36. **Open-Ended** Write an absolute value equation that has 2 and 6 as solutions.

© 37. **Reasoning** Explain why you can rewrite $|x + 5| > 1$ as a compound inequality involving *or*.

38. **Polling** According to a poll for an upcoming school board election, 40% of voters are likely to vote for the incumbent. The poll shows a margin of error of ± 3 percentage points. Write and solve an absolute value equation to find the least and the greatest percents of voters v likely to vote for the incumbent.

39. **Banking** The official weight of a nickel is 5 g, but the actual weight can vary from this amount by up to 0.194 g. Suppose a bank weighs a roll of 40 nickels. The wrapper weighs 1.5 g.
   a. What is the range of possible weights for the roll of nickels?
   © b. **Reasoning** If all of the nickels in the roll each weigh the official amount, then the roll's weight is $40(5) + 1.5 = 201.5$ g. Is it possible for a roll to weigh 201.5 g and contain nickels that do not weigh the official amount? Explain.

STEM 40. **Oil Production** An oil refinery aims to process 900,000 barrels of oil per day. The daily production varies by up to 50,000 barrels from this goal, inclusive. What are the minimum and maximum numbers of barrels of oil processed each day?

Write an absolute value inequality that represents each set of numbers.

41. all real numbers less than 4 units from 0
42. all real numbers at most 7 units from 0

43. all real numbers more than 2 units from 6
44. all real numbers at least 2 units from -1

STEM 45. **Manufacturing** The ideal diameter of a piston for one type of car engine is 90.000 mm. The actual diameter can vary from the ideal by at most 0.008 mm. What is the range of acceptable diameters for the piston?

46. **Farm Maintenance** For safety, the recommended height of a horse fence is 5 ft. Because of uneven ground surfaces, the actual height of the fence can vary from this recommendation by up to 3 in. Write and solve an absolute value equation to find the maximum and minimum heights of the fence.

Challenge

Solve each equation. Check your solutions.

47. $|x + 4| = 3x$

48. $|4t - 5| = 2t + 1$

49. $\frac{4}{3}|2y + 3| = 4y$

Determine whether each statement is *always*, *sometimes*, or *never* true for real numbers *a* and *b*.

50. $|ab| = |a| \cdot |b|$

51. $\left|\frac{a}{b}\right| = \frac{|a|}{|b|}, b \neq 0$

52. $|a + b| = |a| + |b|$

1-1 The Distributive Property

Quick Review

Terms with exactly the same variable factors are **like terms.** You can combine like terms and use the Distributive Property to simplify expressions.

Distributive Property $\quad a(b + c) = ab + ac$

$$a(b - c) = ab - ac$$

Example

Simplify $7t + (3 - 4t)$.

$$
\begin{aligned}
7t + (3 - 4t) &= 7t + (-4t + 3) && \text{Commutative Property} \\
&= (7t + (-4t)) + 3 && \text{Associative Property} \\
&= (7 + (-4))t + 3 && \text{Distributive Property} \\
&= 3t + 3 && \text{Simplify.}
\end{aligned}
$$

Exercises

Simplify each expression.

1. $5(2x - 3)$

2. $-2(7 - a)$

3. $(-j + 8)\frac{1}{2}$

4. $3v^2 - 2v^2$

5. $2(3y - 3)$

6. $(6y - 1)\frac{1}{4}$

7. $(24 - 24y)\frac{1}{4}$

8. $6y - 3 - 5y$

9. $\frac{1}{3}y + 6 - \frac{2}{3}y$

10. $-ab^2 - ab^2$

11. **Music** All 95 members of the jazz club pay $30 each to go see a jazz performance. What is the total cost of tickets? Use mental math.

12. **Reasoning** Are $8x^2y$ and $-5yx^2$ like terms? Explain.

1-2 Solving Multi-Step Equations

Quick Review

To solve some equations, you may need to combine like terms or use the Distributive Property to clear fractions or decimals.

Example

What is the solution of $12 = 2x + \frac{4}{3} - \frac{2x}{3}$?

$$
\begin{aligned}
3 \cdot 12 &= 3\left(2x + \frac{4}{3} - \frac{2x}{3}\right) && \text{Multiply by 3.} \\
36 &= 6x + 4 - 2x && \text{Simplify.} \\
36 &= 4x + 4 && \text{Combine like terms.} \\
36 - 4 &= 4x + 4 - 4 && \text{Subtract 4.} \\
32 &= 4x && \text{Combine like terms.} \\
\frac{32}{4} &= \frac{4x}{4} && \text{Divide each side by 4.} \\
8 &= x && \text{Simplify.}
\end{aligned}
$$

Exercises

Solve each equation. Check your answer.

13. $7(s - 5) = 42$

14. $3a + 2 - 5a = -14$

15. $-4b - 5 + 2b = 10$

16. $3.4t + 0.08 = 11$

17. $10 = \frac{c}{3} - 4 + \frac{c}{6}$

18. $\frac{2x}{7} + \frac{4}{5} = 5$

Write an equation to model each situation. Then solve the equation.

19. **Earnings** You work for 4 h on Saturday and 8 on Sunday. You also receive a $50 bonus. You earn $164. How much did you earn per hour?

20. **Entertainment** Online concert tickets cost $3 each, plus a service charge of $8.50 per ticket. The Web site also charges a transaction fee of $14.99 for the purchase. You paid $242.49. How many tickets did you buy?

1-3 Solving Equations With Variables on Both Sides

Quick Review

When an equation has variables on both sides, you can use properties of equality to isolate the variable on one side. An equation has no solution if no value of the variable makes it true. An equation is an **identity** if every value of the variable makes it true.

Example

What is the solution of $3x - 7 = 5x + 19$?

$3x - 7 - 3x = 5x + 19 - 3x$	Subtract $3x$.
$-7 = 2x + 19$	Simplify.
$-7 - 19 = 2x + 19 - 19$	Subtract 19.
$-26 = 2x$	Simplify.
$\frac{-26}{2} = \frac{2x}{2}$	Divide each side by 2.
$-13 = x$	Simplify.

Exercises

Solve each equation. If the equation is an identity, write *identity*. If it has no solution, write *no solution*.

21. $\frac{2}{3}x + 4 = \frac{3}{5}x - 2$ **22.** $6 - 0.25f = f - 3$

23. $3(h - 4) = -\frac{1}{2}(24 - 6h)$ **24.** $5n = 20(4 + 0.25n)$

25. Architecture Two buildings have the same total height. One building has 8 floors each with height h. The other building has a ground floor of 16 ft and 6 other floors each with height h. Write and solve an equation to find the height h of these floors.

26. Travel A train makes a trip at 65 mi/h. A plane traveling 130 mi/h makes the same trip in 3 fewer hours. Write and solve an equation to find the distance of the trip.

1-4 Literal Equations and Formulas

Quick Review

A **literal equation** is an equation that involves two or more variables. A **formula** is an equation that states a relationship among quantities. You can use properties of equality to solve a literal equation for one variable in terms of the others.

Example

What is the width of a rectangle with area 91 ft² and length 7 ft?

$A = \ell w$	Write the appropriate formula.
$\frac{A}{\ell} = w$	Divide each side by ℓ.
$\frac{91}{7} = w$	Substitute 91 for A and 7 for ℓ.
$13 = w$	Simplify.

The width of the rectangle is 13 ft.

Exercises

Solve each equation for x.

27. $ax + bx = -c$ **28.** $\frac{x + r}{t} + 1 = 0$

29. $m - 3x = 2x + p$ **30.** $\frac{x}{p} + \frac{x}{q} = s$

Solve each problem. Round to the nearest tenth, if necessary. Use 3.14 for π.

31. What is the width of a rectangle with length 5.5 cm and area 220 cm²?

32. What is the radius of a circle with circumference 94.2 mm?

33. A triangle has height 15 in. and area 120 in.². What is the length of its base?

1-5 and 1-6 Ratios, Rates, and Conversions and Solving Proportion:

Quick Review

A ratio between numbers measured in different units is called a **rate**. A **conversion factor** is a ratio of two equivalent measures in different units such as $\frac{1\,h}{60\,min}$, and is always equal to 1. To convert from one unit to another, multiply the original unit by a conversion factor that has the original units in the denominator and the desired units in the numerator.

The **cross products** of a proportion are equal. If $\frac{a}{b} = \frac{c}{d}$, where $b \neq 0$ and $d \neq 0$, then $ad = bc$.

Example

A painting is 17.5 in. wide. What is its width in centimeters? Recall that 1 in. = 2.54 cm.

$$17.5\,\cancel{in.} \cdot \frac{2.54\,cm}{1\,\cancel{in.}} = 44.45\,cm$$

The painting is 44.45 cm wide.

Exercises

Convert the given amount to the given unit.

34. $6\frac{1}{2}$ ft; in. **35.** 4 lb 7 oz; oz

36. 135 s; min **37.** 2.25 mi; yd

38. Production A bread slicer runs 20 h per day for 30 days and slices 144,000 loaves of bread. How many loaves per hour are sliced?

Solve each proportion.

39. $\frac{3}{7} = \frac{9}{x}$ **40.** $\frac{-8}{10} = \frac{y}{5}$

41. $\frac{6}{15} = \frac{a}{4}$ **42.** $\frac{3}{-7} = \frac{-9}{t}$

43. $\frac{b+3}{7} = \frac{b-3}{6}$ **44.** $\frac{5}{2c-3} = \frac{3}{7c+4}$

1-7 Solving Multi-Step Inequalities

Quick Review

When you solve inequalities, sometimes you need to use more than one step. You need to gather the variable terms on one side of the inequality and the constant terms on the other side.

Example

What are the solutions of $3x + 5 > -1$?

$3x + 5 > -1$

$3x > -6$ Subtract 5 from each side.

$x > -2$ Divide each side by 3.

Exercises

Solve each inequality.

45. $4k - 1 \geq -3$

46. $6(c - 1) < -18$

47. $3t > 5t + 12$

48. $-\frac{6}{7}y - 6 \geq 42$

49. $4 + \frac{x}{2} > 2x$

50. $3x + 5 \leq 2x - 8$

51. $13.5a + 7.4 \leq 85.7$

52. $42w > 2(w + 7)$

53. Commission A salesperson earns $200 per week plus a commission equal to 4% of her sales. This week her goal is to earn no less than $450. Write and solve an inequality to find the amount of sales she must have to reach her goal.

1-8 Compound Inequalities

Quick Review

Two inequalities that are joined by the word *and* or the word *or* are called **compound inequalities**. A solution of a compound inequality involving *and* makes both inequalities true. A solution of an inequality involving *or* makes either inequality true.

Example

What are the solutions of $-3 \leq z - 1 < 3$?

$$-3 \leq z - 1 < 3$$

$$-2 \leq z < 4 \qquad \text{Add 1 to each part of the inequality.}$$

Exercises

Solve each compound inequality.

54. $-2 \leq d + \frac{1}{2} < 4\frac{1}{2}$

55. $0 < -8b \leq 12$

56. $2t \leq -4 \text{ or } 7t \geq 49$

57. $5m < -10 \text{ or } 3m > 9$

58. $-1 \leq a - 3 \leq 2$

59. $9.1 > 1.4p \geq -6.3$

60. Climate A town's high temperature for a given month is 88°F and the low temperature is 65°F. Write a compound inequality to represent the range of temperatures for the given month.

1-9 Absolute Value Equations and Inequalities

Quick Review

Solving an equation or inequality that contains an absolute value expression is similar to solving other equations and inequalities. You will need to write two equations or inequalities using positive and negative values. Then solve.

Example

What is the solution of $|x| - 7 = 3$?

$$|x| - 7 = 3$$

$$|x| = 10 \qquad \text{Add 7 to each side.}$$

$$x = 10 \text{ or } x = -10 \qquad \text{Definition of absolute value}$$

Exercises

Solve each equation or inequality. If there is no solution, write *no solution*.

61. $|y| = 3$ **62.** $|n + 2| = 4$

63. $4 + |r + 2| = 7$ **64.** $|x + 3| = -2$

65. $|5x| \leq 15$ **66.** $|3d + 5| < -2$

67. $|2x - 7| - 1 > 0$ **68.** $4|k + 5| > 8$

69. Manufacturing The ideal length of a certain nail is 20 mm. The actual length can vary from the ideal by at most 0.4 mm. Find the range of acceptable lengths of the nail.

Pull It **All Together**

Planning for a Fundraiser

Some students are planning to sell gourmet popcorn at a school fundraiser. They plan to offer cheese popcorn and peanut butter popcorn. The table shows the cost of the ingredients for each type of popcorn and the prices at which the students plan to sell the popcorn.

Gourmet Popcorn

Type of Popcorn	Cost of Ingredients per Container	Price per Container at Fundraiser
Cheese	$.65	$5.00
Peanut butter	$.40	$3.50

The students want to make and sell 100 containers of popcorn. They can spend at most $50 for the ingredients. Their goal is to take in at least $400 from selling the popcorn at the fundraiser.

Task Description

Find a range for the number of containers of each type of popcorn the students should make.

a. Let c = the number of containers of cheese popcorn the students make. Write an expression that represents the number of containers of peanut butter popcorn the students make.

b. Write and solve an inequality involving c that compares the total cost of the ingredients to the students' spending limit for the ingredients.

c. Write and solve an inequality involving c that compares the total amount of money the students will take in from selling the popcorn to the students' sales goal. (*Hint:* When you solve your inequality, remember that c must be a whole number of containers.)

d. Write a compound inequality for the number of containers of cheese popcorn c the students should make. Then write a compound inequality for the number of containers of peanut butter popcorn p the students should make.

CHAPTER

2

Get Ready!

Evaluating Expressions

Evaluate each expression for the given value(s) of the variable(s).

1. $3x - 2y; x = -1, y = 2$

2. $-w^2 + 3w; w = -3$

3. $\frac{3+k}{k}; k = 3$

4. $h - (h^2 - 1) \div 2; h = -1$

Graphing in the Coordinate Plane

Graph the ordered pairs in the same coordinate plane.

5. $(3, -3)$ **6.** $(0, -5)$ **7.** $(-2, 2)$ **8.** $(-2, 0)$

Solving Two-Step Equations

Solve each equation. Check your answer.

9. $5x + 3 = -12$ **10.** $\frac{n}{6} - 1 = 10$ **11.** $7 = \frac{x+8}{2}$ **12.** $\frac{x-1}{4} = \frac{3}{4}$

Solving Absolute Value Equations

Solve each equation. If there is no solution, write *no solution*.

13. $|r + 2| = 2$ **14.** $-3|d - 5| = -6$ **15.** $-3.2 = |8p|$ **16.** $5|2x - 7| = 20$

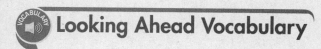

Looking Ahead Vocabulary

17. The amount of money you earn from a summer job is *dependent* upon the number of hours you work. What do you think it means when a variable is *dependent* upon another variable?

18. A *relation* is a person to whom you are related. If (1, 2), (3, 4), and (5, 6) form a mathematical *relation*, to which number is 3 related?

19. When a furnace runs *continuously*, there are no breaks or interruptions in its operation. What do you think a *continuous* graph looks like?

CHAPTER 2

An Introduction to Functions

Big Ideas

1 Functions
Essential Question How can you represent and describe functions?

2 Modeling
Essential Question Can functions describe real-world situations?

© Domains

- Interpreting Functions
- Building Functions

Chapter Preview

Interactive Digital Path

Log in to **pearsonsuccessnet.com** and click on Interactive Digital Path to access the Solve Its and animated Problems.

 Vocabulary

English/Spanish Vocabulary Audio Online:

English	Spanish
continuous graph, *p. 119*	gráfica continua
dependent variable, *p. 103*	variable dependiente
discrete graph, *p. 119*	gráfica discreta
domain, *p. 135*	dominio
function, *p. 105*	función
independent variable, *p. 103*	variable independiente
linear function, *p. 105*	función lineal
nonlinear function, *p. 110*	función no lineal
range, *p. 135*	rango
recursive formula, *p. 149*	fórmula recursiva
relation, *p. 135*	relación
sequence, *p. 146*	progresión

2-1

Using Graphs to Relate Two Quantities

F.IF.4 For a function that models a relationship between two quantities, interpret key features of graphs and tables in terms of the quantities, and sketch graphs showing key features given a verbal description . . .

Objective   To represent mathematical relationships using graphs

Solve It!   Write your solution to the Solve It in the space below.

As you may have noticed in the Solve It, the change in the height of the water as the volume increases is related to the shape of the container.

Essential Understanding   You can use graphs to visually represent the relationship between two variable quantities as they both change.

Problem 1   Analyzing a Graph

Got It?   What are the variables in each graph? Describe how the variables are related at various points on the graph.

Think

How can you analyze the relationship in a graph?

a.

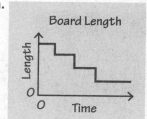

b.

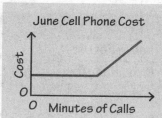

A Practice What are the variables in each graph? Describe how the variables are related at various points on the graph.

1.

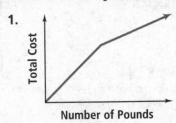

Total Cost

Number of Pounds

2.

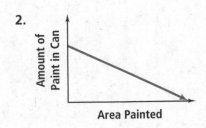

Amount of Paint in Can

Area Painted

Tables and graphs can both show relationships between variables. Data from a table are often displayed using a graph to visually represent the relationship.

Problem 2 Matching a Table and a Graph

Got It? The table shows the amount of sunscreen left in a can based on the number of times the sunscreen has been used. Which graph could represent the data shown in the table?

Sunscreen				
Number of Uses	0	1	2	3
Amount of Sunscreen (oz)	5	4.8	4.6	4.4

A.

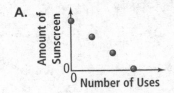

Amount of Sunscreen

Number of Uses

B.

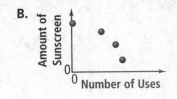

Amount of Sunscreen

Number of Uses

C.

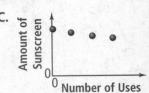

Amount of Sunscreen

Number of Uses

Practice Match each graph with its related table. Explain your answers.

3.

Temp (°F) / Time

4.
Temp (°F) / Time

5.
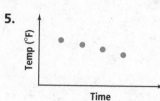
Temp (°F) / Time

A.

Time	Temperature (°F)
1 P.M.	91°
3 P.M.	89°
5 P.M.	81°
7 P.M.	64°

B.

Time	Temperature (°F)
1 P.M.	61°
3 P.M.	60°
5 P.M.	59°
7 P.M.	58°

C.

Time	Temperature (°F)
1 P.M.	24°
3 P.M.	26°
5 P.M.	27°
7 P.M.	21°

In Problem 2, the number of downloads, which is on the vertical axis of each graph, depends on the day, which is on the horizontal axis. When one quantity depends on another, show the independent quantity on the horizontal axis and the dependent quantity on the vertical axis.

Problem 3 **Sketching a Graph**

Think

How can you get started?

Got It? **a.** Suppose you start to swing yourself on a playground swing. You move back and forth and swing higher in the air. Then you slowly swing to a stop. What sketch of a graph could represent how your height from the ground might change over time? Label each section.

b. Reasoning If you jumped from the swing instead of slowly swinging to a stop, how would the graph in part (a) be different? Explain.

Practice Sketch a graph to represent each situation. Label each section.

6. hours of daylight each day over the course of one year

7. your distance from the ground as you ride a Ferris wheel

 Lesson Check

Do you know HOW?

8. What are the variables in the graph at the right? Use the graph to describe how the variables are related.

9. Describe the relationship between time and temperature in the table at the right.

Time (number of hours after noon)	1	3	5	7
Temperature (°F)	61	62	58	51

Do you UNDERSTAND?

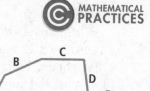

10. Match one of the labeled segments in the graph at the right with each of the following verbal descriptions: *rising slowly, constant,* and *falling quickly.*

Ⓒ **11. Reasoning** Describe a real-world relationship that could be represented by the graph sketched above in Exercise 10.

More Practice and Problem-Solving Exercises

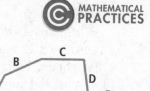
MATHEMATICAL
PRACTICES

🄱 Apply

Ⓒ **12. Think About a Plan** The *shishi-odoshi*, a popular Japanese garden ornament, was originally designed to frighten away deer. Using water, it makes a sharp rap each time a bamboo tube rises. Sketch a graph that could represent the volume of water in the bamboo tube as it operates.

Tube begins filling.

Full tube begins falling.

Tube falls and empties water.

Tube rises and hits rock, making noise.

- What quantities vary in this situation?
- How are these quantities related?

13. Error Analysis T-shirts cost $12.99 each for the first 5 shirts purchased. Each additional T-shirt costs $4.99. Describe and correct the error in the graph at the right that represents the relationship between total cost and number of shirts purchased.

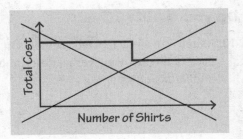

14. Open-Ended Describe a real-world relationship between the area of a rectangle and its width, as the width varies and the length stays the same. Sketch a graph to show this relationship.

15. Skiing Sketch a graph of each situation. Are the graphs the same? Explain.
   a. your speed as you travel on a ski lift from the bottom of a ski slope to the top
   b. your speed as you ski from the top of a ski slope to the bottom

16. Reasoning The diagram at the left below shows a portion of a bike trail.
   a. Explain whether the graph at the right is a reasonable representation of how the speed might change for the blue biker.

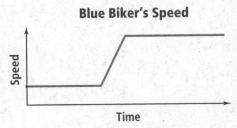

   b. Sketch two graphs that could represent a biker's speed over time. Sketch one graph for the blue biker, and the other for the red biker.

 **Challenge**

17. Track The sketch at the right shows the distance three runners travel during a race. Describe what occurs at times A, B, C, and D. In what order do the runners finish? Explain.

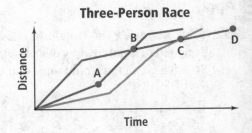

18. Reasoning The graph at the right shows the vertical distance traveled as Person A walks up a set of stairs and Person B walks up the steps of a moving escalator next to the stairs. Copy the graph. Then draw a line that could represent the vertical distance traveled as Person C rides the moving escalator while standing still. Explain your reasoning.

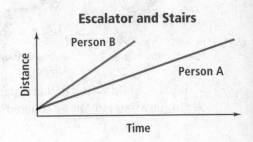

Patterns and Linear Functions

F.IF.4 For a function that models a relationship between two quantities, interpret key features of graphs and tables in terms of the quantities, and sketch graphs showing key features . . . Also **A.CED.2**

Objective To identify and represent patterns that describe linear functions

Solve It! Write your solution to the Solve It in the space below.

In the Solve It, you identified variables whose value *depends* on the value of another variable. In a relationship between variables, the **dependent variable** changes in response to another variable, the **independent variable.** Values of the independent variable are called **inputs.** Values of the dependent variable are called **outputs.**

Essential Understanding The value of one variable may be uniquely determined by the value of another variable. Such relationships may be represented using tables, words, equations, sets of ordered pairs, and graphs.

Problem 1 Representing a Geometric Relationship

Got It?

a. In the diagram below, what is the relationship between the number of triangles and the perimeter of the figure they form? Represent this relationship using a table, words, an equation, and a graph.

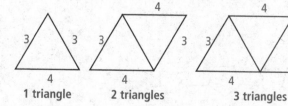
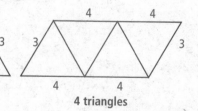

1 triangle 2 triangles 3 triangles 4 triangles

b. Reasoning Suppose you know the perimeter of *n* triangles. What would you do to find the perimeter of *n* + 1 triangles?

c. How does your answer to part (b) relate to the equation you wrote in part (a)?

Ⓐ Practice For each diagram, find the relationship between the number of shapes and the perimeter of the figures they form. Represent this relationship using a table, words, an equation, and a graph.

1.

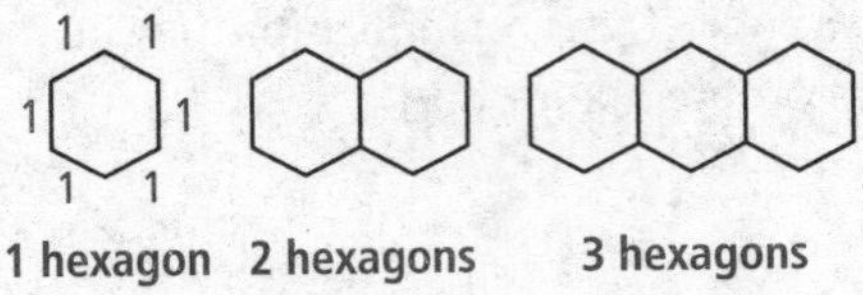

1 hexagon 2 hexagons 3 hexagons

2.

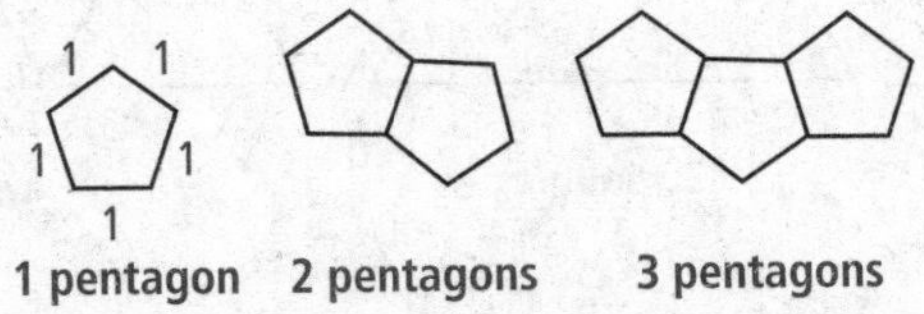

1 pentagon 2 pentagons 3 pentagons

You can describe the relationship in Problem 1 by saying that the perimeter is a function of the number of rectangles. A **function** is a relationship that pairs each input value with exactly one output value.

You have seen that one way to represent a function is with a graph. A **linear function** is a function whose graph is a nonvertical line or part of a nonvertical line.

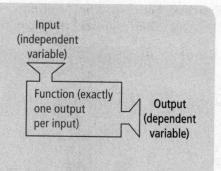

Problem 2   Representing a Linear Function

Got It?   **a.** Is the relationship in the table below a linear function? Describe the relationship using words, an equation, and a graph.

Think

How can you tell whether a relationship in a table is a function?

Input, x	0	1	2	3
Output, y	8	10	12	14

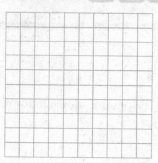

© **b. Reasoning** Does the set of ordered pairs (0, 2), (1, 4), (3, 5), and (1, 8) represent a linear function? Explain.

(A) Practice For each table, determine whether the relationship is a linear function. Then represent the relationship using words, an equation, and a graph.

3.

x	y
0	5
1	8
2	11
3	14

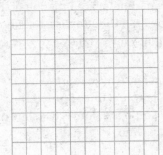

4.

x	y
0	43
1	32
2	21
3	10

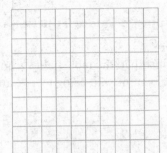

Lesson Check

Do you know HOW?

5. Graph each set of ordered pairs. Use words to describe the pattern shown in the graph.

a. (0, 0), (1, 1), (2, 2), (3, 3), (4, 4)

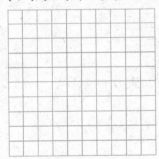

b. (0, 8), (1, 6), (2, 4), (3, 2), (4, 0)

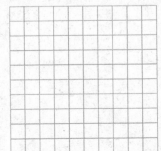

c. (3, 0), (3, 1), (3, 2), (3, 3), (3, 4)

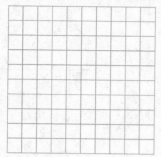

6. Use the diagram below. Complete the table showing the relationship between the number of squares and the perimeter of the figures they form.

1 □ 1
1 □ 1
1

1 square   2 squares   3 squares

Number of Squares	Perimeter
1	4
2	6
3	
4	
10	
	62
n	

Do you UNDERSTAND?

7. Vocabulary The amount of toothpaste in a tube decreases each time you brush your teeth. Identify the independent and dependent variables in this relationship.

8. Reasoning Tell whether each set of ordered pairs in Exercise 5 represents a function. Justify your answers.

9. **Reasoning** Does the graph at the right represent a linear function? Explain.

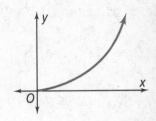

More Practice and Problem-Solving Exercises

B Apply

10. **Gardening** You can make 5 gal of liquid fertilizer by mixing 8 tsp of powdered fertilizer with water. Represent the relationship between the teaspoons of powder used and the gallons of fertilizer made using a table, an equation, and a graph. Is the amount of fertilizer made a function of the amount of powder used? Explain.

11. **Reasoning** Graph the set of ordered pairs $(-2, -3)$, $(0, -1)$, $(1, 0)$, $(3, 2)$, and $(4, 4)$. Determine whether the relationship is a linear function. Explain how you know.

12. **Think About a Plan** Gears are common parts in many types of machinery. In the diagram below, Gear A turns in response to the cranking of Gear B. Describe the relationship between the number of turns of Gear B and the number of turns of Gear A. Use words, an equation, and a graph.

- What are the independent and dependent variables?
- How much must you turn Gear B to get Gear A to go around once?

13. **Electric Car** An automaker makes a car that can travel 40 mi on its charged battery before it begins to use gas. Then the car travels 50 mi per gallon of gas used. Represent the relationship between the amount of gas used and the distance traveled using a table, an equation, and a graph. Is total distance traveled a function of the amount of gas used? What are the independent and dependent variables? Explain.

© **14. Reasoning** Suppose you know the perimeter of n octagons arranged as shown. What would you do to find the perimeter if 1 more octagon was added?

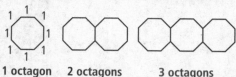

1 octagon   2 octagons   3 octagons

Challenge

15. Athletics The graph at the right shows the distance a runner has traveled as a function of the amount of time (in minutes) she has been running. Draw a graph that shows the time she has been running as a function of the distance she has traveled.

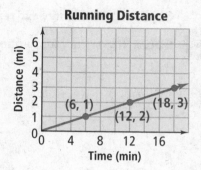

Running Distance

16. Movies When a movie on film is projected, a certain number of frames pass through the projector per minute. You say that the length of the movie in minutes is a function of the number of frames. Someone else says that the number of frames is a function of the length of the movie. Can you both be right? Explain.

2-3 Patterns and Nonlinear Functions

F.IF.4 For a function that models a relationship between two quantities, interpret key features of graphs and tables in terms of the quantities, and sketch graphs showing key features . . . Also **A.CED.2**

Objective To identify and represent patterns that describe nonlinear functions

Solve It! Write your solution to the Solve It in the space below.

The relationship in the Solve It is an example of a nonlinear function. A **nonlinear function** is a function whose graph is not a line or part of a line.

Essential Understanding Just like linear functions, nonlinear functions can be represented using words, tables, equations, sets of ordered pairs, and graphs.

take note

Concept Summary   Linear and Nonlinear Functions

Linear Function

A linear function is a function whose graph is a nonvertical line or part of a nonvertical line.

  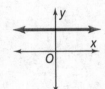

Nonlinear Function

A nonlinear function is a function whose graph is not a line or part of a line.

 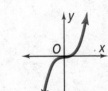 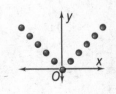

Problem 1 Classifying Functions as Linear or Nonlinear

Think

How can a graph tell you if a function is linear or nonlinear?

Got It? **a.** The table below shows the fraction *A* of the original area of a piece of paper that remains after the paper has been cut in half *n* times. Graph the function represented by the table. Is the function *linear* or *nonlinear*?

Cutting Paper				
Number of Cuts, *n*	1	2	3	4
Fraction of Original Area Remaining, *A*	$\frac{1}{2}$	$\frac{1}{4}$	$\frac{1}{8}$	$\frac{1}{16}$

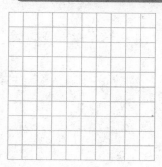

b. Reasoning Will the area *A* in part (a) ever reach zero? Explain.

Practice The cost *C*, in dollars, for pencils is a function of the number of pencils purchased, *n*. The length *L* of a pencil, in inches, is a function of the time *t*, in seconds, it has been sharpened. Graph the function shown by each table. Tell whether the function is *linear* or *nonlinear*.

1.

Pencil Cost					
Number of Pencils, *n*	6	12	18	24	30
Cost, *C*	$1	$2	$3	$4	$5

2.

Pencil Sharpening						
Time (s), *t*	0	3	6	9	12	15
Length (in.), *L*	7.5	7.5	7.5	7.5	7.4	7.3

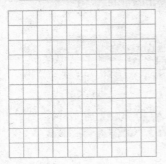

Problem 2   Representing Patterns and Nonlinear Functions

Got It?   The table shows the number of new branches in each figure of the pattern below. What is a pattern you can use to complete the table? Represent the relationship using words, an equation, and a graph.

1   2   3

Number of Figure, *x*	1	2	3	4	5
Number of New Branches, *y*	3	9	27		

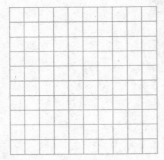

A Practice 3. For the diagram below, the table gives the total number of small triangles y in figure number x. What pattern can you use to complete the table? Represent the relationship using words, an equation, and a graph.

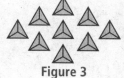

Figure 1

Figure 2

Figure 3

Figure Number, x	Total Small Triangles, y	Ordered Pair (x, y)
1	3	(1, 3)
2	12	(2, 12)
3	27	(3, 27)
4		
5		

A function can be thought of as a rule that you apply to the input in order to get the output. You can describe a nonlinear function with words or with an equation, just as you did with linear functions.

Problem 3 **Writing a Rule to Describe a Nonlinear Function**

Think

How can you use reasoning to write a rule?

Got It? What is a rule for the function represented by the ordered pairs (1, 1), (2, 4), (3, 9), (4, 16), and (5, 25)?

Ⓐ Practice Each set of ordered pairs represents a function. Write a rule that represents the function.

   4. (0, 0), (1, 4), (2, 16), (3, 36), (4, 64)

   5. (0, 0), (1, 0.5), (2, 2), (3, 4.5), (4, 8)

Lesson Check

Do you know HOW?

6. Graph the function represented by the table below. Is the function *linear* or *nonlinear*?

x	0	1	2	3	4
y	12	13	14	15	16

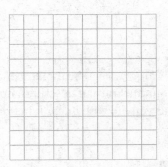

7. The ordered pairs (0, −2), (1, 1), (2, 4), (3, 7), and (4, 10) represent a function. What is a rule that represents this function?

8. Which rule could represent the function shown by the table below?

x	0	1	2	3	4
y	0	−1	−4	−9	−16

Ⓐ $y = x^2$ Ⓑ $y = -x^3$ Ⓒ $y = -x^2$

Do you UNDERSTAND?

9. Vocabulary Does each graph represent a *linear function* or a *nonlinear function*? Explain.

a.

b.

10. Error Analysis A classmate says that the function shown by the table at the right can be represented by the rule $y = x + 1$. Describe and correct your classmate's error.

x	y
0	1
1	2
2	5
3	10
4	17

B Apply

11. Writing The rule $V = \frac{4}{3}\pi r^3$ gives the volume V of a sphere as a function of its radius r. Identify the independent and dependent variables in this relationship. Explain your reasoning.

12. Open-Ended Write a rule for a nonlinear function such that y is negative when $x = 1$, positive when $x = 2$, negative when $x = 3$, positive when $x = 4$, and so on.

13. Think About a Plan Concrete forming tubes are used as molds for cylindrical concrete supports. The volume V of a tube is the product of its length ℓ and the area A of its circular base. You can make $\frac{2}{3}$ ft³ of cement per bag. Write a rule to find the number of bags of cement needed to fill a tube 4 ft long as a function of its radius r. How many bags are needed to fill a tube with a 4-in. radius? A 5-in. radius? A 6-in. radius?

- What is a rule for the volume V of any tube?
- What operation do you use to find the number of bags needed for a given volume?

14. Fountain A designer wants to make a circular fountain inside a square of grass as shown at the right. What is a rule for the area A of the grass as a function of r?

C Challenge

15. Reasoning What is a rule for the function represented by $\left(0, \frac{2}{19}\right)$, $\left(1, 1\frac{2}{19}\right)$, $\left(2, 4\frac{2}{19}\right)$, $\left(3, 9\frac{2}{19}\right)$, $\left(4, 16\frac{2}{19}\right)$, and $\left(5, 25\frac{2}{19}\right)$? Explain your reasoning.

16. Reasoning A certain function fits the following description: As the value of x increases by 1 each time, the value of y continually decreases by a smaller amount each time, and never reaches a value as low as 1. Is this function *linear* or *nonlinear*? Explain your reasoning.

Graphing a Function Rule

A.REI.10 Understand that the graph of an equation in two variables is the set of all its solutions plotted in the coordinate plane . . . Also **N.Q.1, F.IF.4**

Objective   To graph equations that represent functions

Solve It!   Write your solution to the Solve It in the space below.

You can use a table of values to help you make a graph in the Solve It.

Essential Understanding   The set of all solutions of an equation forms the equation's graph. A graph may include solutions that do not appear in a table. A real-world graph should only show points that make sense in the given situation.

Problem 1   Graphing a Function Rule

Got It?   What is the graph of the function rule $y = \frac{1}{2}x - 1$?

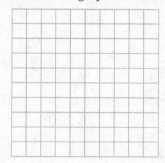

Think

How can a table of values help you draw the graph?

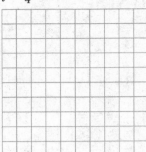

A **Practice** Graph each function rule.

1. $y = \frac{3}{4}x + 2$

2. $y = -\frac{1}{2}x + \frac{1}{2}$

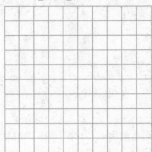

When you graph a real-world function rule, choose appropriate intervals for the units on the axes. Every interval on an axis should represent the same change in value. If all the data are nonnegative, show only the first quadrant.

Problem 2 **Graphing a Real-World Function Rule**

Got It? **a.** The function rule $W = 8g + 700$ represents the total weight W, in pounds, of a spa that contains g gallons of water. What is a reasonable graph of the function rule, given that the capacity of the spa is 250 gal?

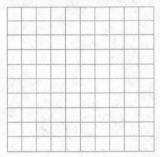

b. Reasoning What is the weight of the spa when empty? Explain.

118 **Chapter 2** An Introduction to Functions

3. Beverages The height h, in inches, of the juice in a 20-oz bottle depends on the amount of juice j, in ounces, that you drink. This situation is represented by the function rule $h = 6 - 0.3j$. Graph the function rule. Explain your choice of intervals on the axes of the graph.

In Problem 2, the truck could contain any amount of concrete from 0 to 200 ft³, such as 27.3 ft³ or $105\frac{2}{3}$ ft³. You can connect the data points from the table because any point between the data points has meaning.

Some graphs may be composed of isolated points. For example, in the Solve It you graphed only points that represent printing whole numbers of photos.

 take note

Key Concept   Continuous and Discrete Graphs

Continuous Graph

A **continuous graph** is a graph that is unbroken.

Discrete Graph

A **discrete graph** is composed of distinct, isolated points.

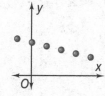

Got It? Graph each function rule. Is the graph *continuous* or *discrete*? Justify your answer.

Think

How can you decide if a graph is continuous or discrete?

a. The amount of water w in a wading pool, in gallons, depends on the amount of time t, in minutes, the wading pool has been filling, as related by the function rule $W = 3t$.

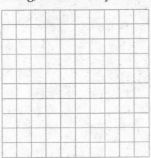

b. The cost C for baseball tickets, in dollars, depends on the number n of tickets bought, as related by the function rule $C = 16n$.

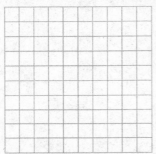

Practice Graph each function rule. Explain your choice of intervals on the axes of the graph. Tell whether the graph is *continuous* or *discrete*.

4. **Trucking** The total weight w, in pounds, of a tractor-trailer capable of carrying 8 cars depends on the number of cars c on the trailer. This situation is represented by the function rule $w = 37{,}000 + 4200c$.

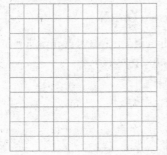

5. Food Delivery The cost C, in dollars, for delivered pizza depends on the number of pizzas ordered, p. This situation is represented by the function rule $C = 5 + 9p$.

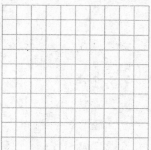

The function rules graphed in Problems 1–3 represent linear functions. You can also graph a nonlinear function rule. When a function rule does not represent a real-world situation, graph it as a continuous function.

Problem 4 **Graphing Nonlinear Function Rules**

Got It? What is the graph of the function rule $y = x^3 + 1$?

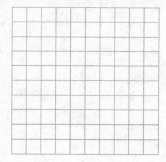

Practice Graph each function rule.

6. $y = -x^3$

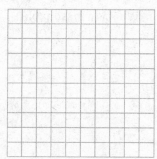

7. $y = |x - 3| - 1$

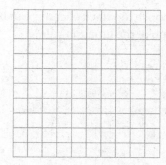

Lesson Check

Do you know HOW?

In Exercises 8–11, graph each function rule.

8. $y = 2x + 4$

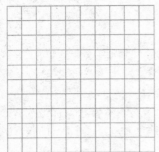

9. $y = \frac{1}{2}x - 7$

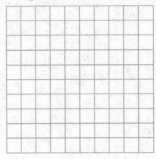

10. $y = 9 - x$

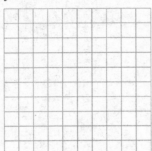

11. $y = -x^2 + 2$

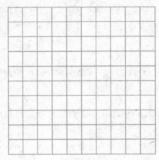

12. The function rule $h = 18 + 1.5n$ represents the height h, in inches, of a stack of traffic cones.

    a. Make a table for the function rule.

    b. Suppose the stack of cones can be no taller than 30 in. What is a reasonable graph of the function rule?

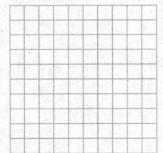

Do you UNDERSTAND?

Vocabulary Tell whether each relationship should be represented by a continuous or a discrete graph.

13. The number of bagels b remaining in a dozen depends on the number s that have been sold.

14. The amount of gas g remaining in the tank of a gas grill depends on the amount of time t the grill has been used.

15. Error Analysis Your friend graphs $y = x + 3$ at the right. Describe and correct your friend's error.

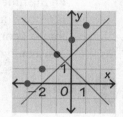

More Practice and Problem-Solving Exercises

B Apply

16. Error Analysis The graph at the right shows the distance d you run, in miles, as a function of time t, in minutes, during a 5-mi run. Your friend says that the graph is not continuous because it stops at $d = 5$, so the graph is discrete. Do you agree? Explain.

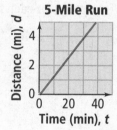

17. Writing Is the point $\left(2, 2\frac{1}{2}\right)$ on the graph of $y = x + 2$? How do you know?

18. Geometry The area A of an isosceles right triangle depends on the length ℓ of each leg of the triangle. This is represented by the rule $A = \frac{1}{2}\ell^2$. Graph the function rule. Is the graph *continuous* or *discrete*? How do you know?

19. Which function rule is graphed at the right?

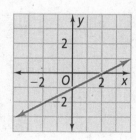

Ⓐ $y = -\frac{1}{2}x + 1$

Ⓑ $y = \frac{1}{2}x - 1$

Ⓒ $y = \left|\frac{1}{2}x\right| - 1$

Ⓓ $y = \frac{1}{2}x + 1$

20. Sporting Goods The amount a basketball coach spends at a sporting goods store depends on the number of basketballs the coach buys. The situation is represented by the function rule $a = 15b$.

 a. Make a table of values and graph the function rule. Is the graph *continuous* or *discrete*? Explain.

 b. Suppose the coach spent $120. How many basketballs did she buy?

21. Think About a Plan The height h, in inches, of the vinegar in the jars of pickle chips shown at the right depends on the number of chips p you eat. About how many chips must you eat to lower the level of the vinegar in the jar on the left to the level of the jar on the right? Use a graph to find the answer.

$$h = 4.75 - 0.22p$$

4 in.

- What should the maximum value of p be on the horizontal axis?
- What are reasonable values of p in this situation?

STEM 22. Falling Objects The height h, in feet, of an acorn that falls from a branch 100 ft above the ground depends on the time t, in seconds, since it has fallen. This is represented by the rule $h = 100 - 16t^2$. About how much time does it take for the acorn to hit the ground? Use a graph and give an answer between two consecutive whole-number values of t.

Challenge

23. Reasoning Graph the function rules below in the same coordinate plane.

$$y = |x| + 1 \qquad y = |x| + 4 \qquad y = |x| - 3$$

In the function rule $y = |x| + k$, how does changing the value of k affect the graph?

24. Reasoning Make a table of values and a graph for the function rules $y = 2x$ and $y = 2x^2$. How does the value of y change when you double the value of x for each function rule?

Graphing Functions and Solving Equations

A.REI.11 Explain why the *x*-coordinates of the points where . . . $y = f(x)$ and $y = g(x)$ intersect are the solutions of the equation $f(x) = g(x)$; find the solutions approximately . . .

MATHEMATICAL
PRACTICES

You have learned to graph function rules by making a table of values. You can also use a graphing calculator to graph function rules.

Example 1

Graph $y = \frac{1}{2}x - 4$ using a graphing calculator.

Step 1 Press the [y=] key. To the right of **Y₁ =**, enter $\frac{1}{2}x - 4$ by pressing [(] 1 [÷] 2 [)] [x,t,θ,n] [−] 4.

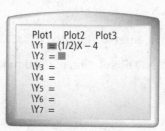

Step 2 The screen on the graphing calculator is a "window" that lets you look at only part of the graph. Press the [window] key to set the borders of the graph. A good window for this function rule is the standard viewing window, $-10 \le x \le 10$ and $-10 \le y \le 10$.

You can have the axes show 1 unit between tick marks by setting **Xscl** and **Yscl** to 1, as shown.

Step 3 Press the [graph] key. The graph of the function rule is shown.

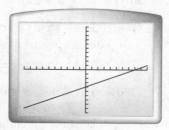

In Chapter 1 you learned how to solve equations in one variable. You can also solve equations by using a graphing calculator to graph each side of the equation as a function rule. The *x*-coordinate of the point where the graphs intersect is the solution of the equation.

Example 2

Solve $7 = -\frac{3}{4}k + 3$ using a graphing calculator.

Step 1 Press ⬛y=. Clear any equations. Then enter each side of the given equation. For $Y_1 =$, enter 7. For $Y_2 =$, enter $-\frac{3}{4}x + 3$ by pressing ⬛(⬛(-) 3 ⬛÷ 4 ⬛) ⬛x,t,θ,n ⬛+ 3. Notice that you must replace the variable k with x.

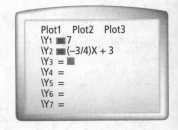

Step 2 Graph the function rules. Use a standard graphing window by pressing ⬛zoom 6. This gives a window defined by $-10 \le x \le 10$ and $-10 \le y \le 10$.

Step 3 Use the ⬛calc feature. Select **INTERSECT** and press ⬛enter to select the first line, then press ⬛enter to select the second line. Move the cursor near the point of intersection and press ⬛enter a third time.

The calculator's value for the x-coordinate of the point of intersection is -5.333333. The actual x-coordinate is $-5\frac{1}{3}$.

The solution of the equation $7 = -\frac{3}{4}k + 3$ is $-5\frac{1}{3}$.

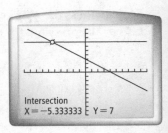

You cannot solve all equations using the methods of Chapter 1. In those cases, you can find approximate solutions by graphing.

Example 3

Solve $-x^2 + 6 = \frac{x + 4}{x + 2}$ using a graphing calculator.

Step 1 Press ⬛y=. Clear any equations. Then enter each side of the given equation. For $Y_1 =$, enter $-x^2 + 6$. For $Y_2 =$, enter $\frac{(x + 4)}{(x + 2)}$.

Step 2 Use the ⬛calc feature. Select **INTERSECT** and press ⬛enter to select the first curve, then press ⬛enter to select the second curve. Move the cursor near a point of intersection and press ⬛enter a third time.

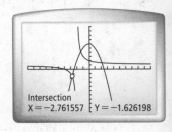

Step 3 Find the other points of intersection in a similar way.

The calculator's values for the x-coordinates of the points of intersection are -2.761557, -1.363328, and 2.1248854. These are the approximate solutions to the equation $-x^2 + 6 = \frac{x + 4}{x + 2}$.

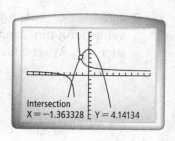

Intersection
X = −1.363328 Y = 4.14134

Exercises

Graph each function rule using a graphing calculator.

1. $y = 6x + 3$

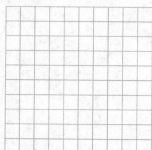

2. $y = -3x + 8$

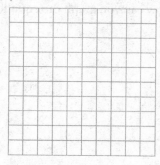

3. $y = 0.2x - 7$

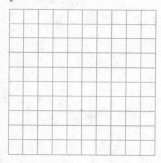

4. $y = -1.8x - 6$

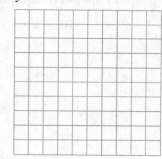

5. $y = -\frac{1}{3}x + 5$

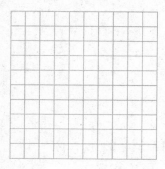

6. $y = \frac{8}{3}x - 5$

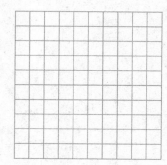

7. **Open-Ended** Graph $y = -0.4x + 8$. Using the (window) screen, experiment with values for **Xmin, Xmax, Ymin,** and **Ymax** until you can see the graph crossing both axes. What values did you use for **Xmin, Xmax, Ymin,** and **Ymax**?

8. **Reasoning** How can you graph the equation $2x + 3y = 6$ on a graphing calculator?

Use a graphing calculator to solve each equation.

9. $8a - 12 = 6$

10. $-4 = -3t + 2$

11. $-5 = -0.5x - 2$

12. $4 + \frac{3}{2}n = -7$

13. $\frac{5}{4}d - \frac{1}{2} = 6$

14. $-3y - 1 = 3.5$

15. $4 = |x - 2|$

16. $x^2 - 4 = |x|$

17. $x^2 - 5 = (x - 1)^3 + 4$

2-5 Writing a Function Rule

A.CED.2 Create equations in two or more variables . . .; graph equations on coordinate axes with labels and scales. Also **N.Q.2., A.SSE.1.a, F.BF.1.a**

Objective   To write equations that represent functions

Solve It!   Write your solution to the Solve It in the space below.

In the Solve It, you can see how the value of one variable depends on another. Once you see a pattern in a relationship, you can write a rule.

Essential Understanding   Many real-world functional relationships can be represented by equations. You can use an equation to find the solution of a given real-world problem.

Problem 1   **Writing a Function Rule**

Got It?   A landfill has 50,000 tons of waste in it. Each month it accumulates an average of 420 more tons of waste. What is a function rule that represents the total amount of waste after m months?

Think

How can a model help you visualize this real-world situation?

 Practice   Write a function rule that represents each situation.

   1. Wages   A worker's earnings e are a function of the number of hours n worked at a rate of $8.75 per hour.

2. **Baking** The almond extract a remaining in an 8-oz bottle decreases by $\frac{1}{6}$ oz for each batch b of waffle cookies made.

 **Problem 2** **Writing and Evaluating a Function Rule**

Got It? **a.** A kennel charges $15 per day to board a dog. Upon arrival, each dog must have a flea bath that costs $12. Write a function rule for the total cost for n days of boarding plus a bath. How much does a 10-day stay cost?

b. Reasoning Does a 5-day stay cost half as much as a 10-day stay? Explain.

 Practice **3. Aviation** A helicopter hovers 40 ft above the ground. Then the helicopter climbs at a rate of 21 ft/s. Write a rule that represents the helicopter's height h above the ground as a function of time t. What is the helicopter's height after 45 s?

4. Diving A team of divers assembles at an elevation of −10 ft relative to the surface of the water. Then the team dives at a rate of −50 ft/min. Write a rule that represents the team's depth *d* as a function of time *t*. What is the team's depth after 3 min?

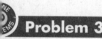 **Problem 3** **Writing a Nonlinear Function Rule**

Got It? **a.** Write a function rule for the area of a triangle whose height is 4 in. more than twice the length of its base. What is the area of the triangle when the length of its base is 16 in.?

Think

How can *drawing a diagram* help you write the rule?

Ⓒ**b. Reasoning** Graph the function rule from part (a). How do you know the rule is nonlinear?

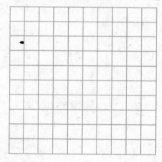

Ⓐ**Practice** **5.** Write a function rule for the area of a triangle with a base 3 cm greater than 5 times its height. What is the area of the triangle when its height is 6 cm?

6. Write a function rule for the volume of the cylinder shown at the right with a height 3 in. more than 4 times the radius of the cylinder's base. What is the volume of the cylinder when it has a radius of 2 in.?

$$V = \pi r^2 h$$

 ## Lesson Check

Do you know HOW?

Write a function rule to represent each situation.

7. the total cost C for p pounds of copper if each pound costs $3.57

8. the height f, in feet, of an object when you know the object's height h in inches

9. the amount y of your friend's allowance if the amount she receives is $2 more than the amount x you receive

10. the volume V of a cube-shaped box whose edge lengths are 1 in. greater than the diameter d of the ball that the box will hold

Do you UNDERSTAND?

11. Vocabulary Suppose you write an equation that gives a as a function of b. Which is the dependent variable and which is the independent variable?

12. Error Analysis A worker has dug 3 holes for fence posts. It will take 15 min to dig each additional hole. Your friend writes the rule $t = 15n + 3$ for the time t, in minutes, required to dig n additional holes. Describe and correct your friend's error.

13. Reasoning Is the graph of a function rule that relates a square's area to its side length *continuous* or *discrete*? Explain.

More Practice and Problem-Solving Exercises

MATHEMATICAL PRACTICES

B Apply

14. Open-Ended Write a function rule that models a real-world situation. Evaluate your function for an input value and explain what the output represents.

15. Writing What advantage(s) can you see of having a rule instead of a table of values to represent a function?

16. History of Math The golden ratio has been studied and used by mathematicians and artists for more than 2000 years. A golden rectangle, constructed using the golden ratio, has a length about 1.6 times its width. Write a rule for the area of a golden rectangle as a function of its width.

17. Whales From an elevation of 3.5 m below the surface of the water, a northern bottlenose whale dives at a rate of 1.8 m/s. Write a rule that gives the whale's depth d as a function of time in minutes. What is the whale's depth after 4 min?

◎ 18. Think About a Plan The height h, in inches, of the juice in the pitcher shown at the right is a function of the amount of juice j, in ounces, that has been poured out of the pitcher. Write a function rule that represents this situation. What is the height of the juice after 47 oz have been poured out?

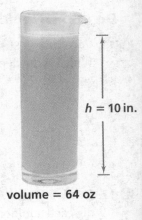

$h = 10$ in.

volume = 64 oz

- What is the height of the juice when half of it has been poured out?
- What fraction of the juice would you pour out to make the height decrease by 1 in.?

19. Tips You go to dinner and decide to leave a 15% tip for the server. You had $55 when you entered the restaurant.
- **a.** Make a table showing how much money you would have left after buying a meal that costs $15, $21, $24, or $30.
- **b.** Write a function rule for the amount of money m you would have left if the meal costs c dollars before the tip.
- **c.** Graph the function rule.

20. Car Rental A car rental agency charges $29 per day to rent a car and $13.95 per day for a global positioning system (GPS). Customers are charged for their full tank of gas at $3.80 per gallon.
- **a.** A car has a 12-gal tank and a GPS. Write a rule for the total bill b as a function of the number of days d the car is rented.
- **b.** What is the bill for a 9-day rental?

21. Projectors You consult your new projector's instruction manual before mounting it on the wall. The manual says to multiply the desired image width by 1.8 to find the correct distance of the projector lens from the wall.

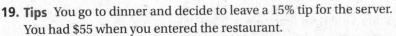

12 ft   ? ft

- **a.** Write a rule to describe the distance of the lens from the wall as a function of desired image width.
- **b.** The diagram shows the room in which the projector will be installed. Will you be able to project an image 7 ft wide? Explain.
- **c.** What is the maximum image width you can project in the room?

◎ 22. Reasoning Write a rule that is an example of a nonlinear function that fits the following description.

When d is 4, r is 9, and r is a function of d.

Ⓒ Challenge

Make a table and a graph of each set of ordered pairs (x, y). Then write a function rule to represent the relationship between x and y.

23. $(-4, 7), (-3, 6), (-2, 5), (-1, 4), (0, 3), (1, 2), (2, 1), (3, 0), (4, -1)$

24. $(-4, 15), (-3, 8), (-2, 3), (-1, 0), (0, -1), (1, 0), (2, 3), (3, 8), (4, 15)$

2-6

Formalizing Relations and Functions

F.IF.1 Understand that a function from one set (called the domain) to another set (called the range) assigns each element of the domain exactly one element of the range . . . Also **F.IF.2, F.IF.5**

Objectives To determine whether a relation is a function
To find domain and range and use function notation

Solve It! Write your solution to the Solve It in the space below.

A **relation** is a pairing of numbers in one set, called the **domain**, with numbers in another set, called the **range**. A relation is often represented as a set of ordered pairs (x, y). In this case, the domain is the set of x-values and the range is the set of y-values.

Essential Understanding A function is a special type of relation in which each value in the domain is paired with exactly one value in the range.

Problem 1 Identifying Functions Using Mapping Diagrams

Got It? Identify the domain and range of each relation. Represent the relation with a mapping diagram. Is the relation a function?

a. {(4.2, 1.5), (5, 2.2), (7, 4.8), (4.2, 0)}

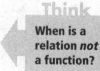

Think
When is a relation *not* a function?

b. {(−1, 1), (−2, 2), (4, −4), (7, −7)}

A **Practice** Identify the domain and range of each relation. Use a mapping diagram to determine whether the relation is a function.

   1. $\{(3, 7), (3, 8), (3, -2), (3, 4), (3, 1)\}$ **2.** $\{(0.04, 0.2), (0.2, 1), (1, 5), (5, -5)\}$

Another way to decide if a relation is a function is to analyze the graph of the relation using the **vertical line test**. If any vertical line passes through more than one point of the graph, then for some domain value there is more than one range value. So the relation is not a function.

Problem 2   **Identifying Functions Using the Vertical Line Test**

Got It?   Is the relation a function? Use the vertical line test.

Think

How can you use a pencil to apply the vertical line test?

   a. $\{(4, 2), (1, 2), (0, 1), (-2, 2), (3, 3)\}$

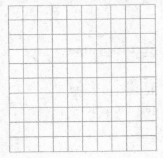

   b. $\{(0, 2), (1, -1), (-1, 4), (0, -3), (2, 1)\}$

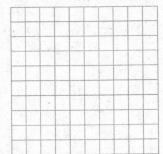

3.
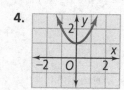

4.

You have seen functions represented as equations involving x and y, such as $y = -3x + 1$. Below is the same equation written using **function notation.**

$$f(x) = -3x + 1$$

Notice that $f(x)$ replaces y. It is read "f of x." The letter f is the name of the function, not a variable. Function notation is used to emphasize that the function value $f(x)$ depends on the independent variable x. Other letters besides f can also be used, such as g and h.

Problem 3   **Evaluating a Function**

Got It?   Use the function $w(x) = 250x$ from Problem 3, which represents the number of words you can read in x minutes. How many words can you read in 6 min?

5. **Shopping** You are buying orange juice for $4.50 per container and have a gift card worth $7. The function $f(x) = 4.50x - 7$ represents your total cost $f(x)$ if you buy x containers of orange juice and use the gift card. How much do you pay to buy 4 containers of orange juice?

STEM 6. **Physics** Light travels about 186,000 mi/s. The function $d(t) = 186,000t$ gives the distance $d(t)$, in miles, that light travels in t seconds. How far does light travel in 30 s?

Problem 4 **Finding the Range of a Function**

Got It?   The domain of $g(x) = 4x - 12$ is $\{1, 3, 5, 7\}$. What is the range?

Find the range of each function for the given domain.

7. $h(x) = x^2; \{-1.2, 0, 0.2, 1.2, 4\}$

8. $f(x) = 8x - 3; \left\{-\frac{1}{2}, \frac{1}{4}, \frac{3}{4}, \frac{1}{8}\right\}$

Problem 5 Identifying a Reasonable Domain and Range

Got It? **a.** What domain and range are reasonable if you have 7 qt of paint instead of 3 qt in Problem 5?

©**b. Reasoning** Why does it *not* make sense to have domain values less than 0 or greater than 3 in Problem 5?

A Practice Find a reasonable domain and range for each function. Then graph the function.

9. **Fuel** A car can travel 32 mi for each gallon of gasoline. The function $d(x) = 32x$ represents the distance $d(x)$, in miles, that the car can travel with x gallons of gasoline. The car's fuel tank holds 17 gal.

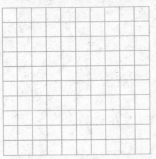

10. **Nutrition** There are 98 International Units (IUs) of vitamin D in 1 cup of milk. The function $V(c) = 98c$ represents the amount $V(c)$ of vitamin D, in IUs, you get from c cups of milk. You have a 16-cup jug of milk.

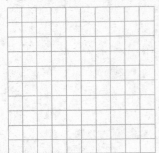

Lesson Check

Do you know HOW?

11. Identify the domain and range of the relation $\{(-2, 3), (-1, 4), (0, 5), (1, 6)\}$. Represent the relation with a mapping diagram. Is the relation a function?

12. Is the relation in the graph shown at the right a function? Use the vertical line test.

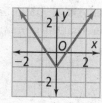

13. What is $f(2)$ for the function $f(x) = 4x + 1$?

14. The domain of $f(x) = \frac{1}{2}x$ is $\{-4, -2, 0, 2, 4\}$. What is the range?

Do you UNDERSTAND?

MATHEMATICAL PRACTICES

ⓒ **15. Vocabulary** Write $y = 2x + 7$ using function notation.

ⓒ **16. Compare and Contrast** You can use a mapping diagram or the vertical line test to tell if a relation is a function. Which method do you prefer? Explain.

17. Error Analysis A student drew the dashed line on the graph shown and concluded that the graph represented a function. Is the student correct? Explain.

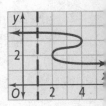

More Practice and Problem-Solving Exercises

MATHEMATICAL PRACTICES

B Apply

Determine whether the relation represented by each table is a function. If the relation is a function, state the domain and range.

18.

x	0	3	3	5
y	2	1	−1	3

19.

x	−4	−1	0	3
y	−4	−4	−4	−4

20. Open-Ended Make a table that represents a relation that is not a function. Explain why the relation is not a function.

21. Reasoning If $f(x) = 6x - 4$ and $f(a) = 26$, what is the value of a? Explain.

22. Think About a Plan In a factory, a certain machine needs 10 min to warm up. It takes 15 min for the machine to run a cycle. The machine can operate for as long as 6 h per day including warm-up time. Draw a graph showing the total time the machine operates during 1 day as a function of the number of cycles it runs.
  • What domain and range are reasonable?
  • Is the function a linear function?

23. Carwash A theater group is having a carwash fundraiser. The group can only spend $34 on soap, which is enough to wash 40 cars. Each car is charged $5.
  a. If c is the total number of cars washed and p is the profit, which is the independent variable and which is the dependent variable?
  b. Is the relationship between c and p a function? Explain.
  c. Write an equation that shows this relationship.
  d. Find a reasonable domain and range for the situation.

24. Open-Ended What value of x makes the relation $\{(1, 5), (x, 8), (-7, 9)\}$ a function?

Determine whether each relation is a function. Assume that each different variable has a different value.

25. $\{(a, b), (b, a), (c, c), (e, d)\}$

26. $\{(b, b), (c, d), (d, c), (c, a)\}$

27. $\{(c, e), (c, d), (c, b)\}$

28. $\{(a, b), (b, c), (c, d), (d, e)\}$

© **29. Reasoning** Can the graph of a function be a horizontal line? A vertical line? Explain.

Challenge

30. To form the inverse of a relation written as a set of ordered pairs, you switch the coordinates of each ordered pair. For example, the inverse of the relation $\{(1, 8), (3, 5), (7, 9)\}$ is $\{(8, 1), (5, 3), (9, 7)\}$. Give an example of a relation that is a function, but whose inverse is *not* a function.

Use the functions $f(x) = 2x$ and $g(x) = x^2 + 1$ to find the value of each expression.

31. $f(3) + g(4)$

32. $g(3) + f(4)$

33. $f(5) - 2 \cdot g(1)$

34. $f(g(3))$

TECHNOLOGY LAB

Use With Lesson 2-6

Even and Odd Functions

F.BF.3 . . . Recognize even and odd functions from their graphs and algebraic expressio for them.

Some functions can be classified as *even* or *odd*. You can determine whether a function is even or odd by its graph or by using algebra.

An **even function** is a function f such that $f(-x) = f(x)$. The graph of an even function is symmetric across the y-axis. This means that if the point (x, y) is on the graph of the function, so is the point $(-x, y)$.

An **odd function** is a function f such that $f(-x) = -f(x)$. The graph of an odd function is symmetric about the origin. This means that if the point (x, y) is on the graph of the function, so is the point $(-x, -y)$.

Example 1

Determine whether the function $f(x) = x^2$ is *even*, *odd*, or *neither* by graphing.

Step 1 Press the (y=) key. To the right of Y_1, enter x^2 by pressing
(x) [^] 2.

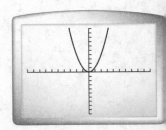

Step 2 Graph the function on your calculator. Press the (window) key to set the borders of the graph if needed.

The function is symmetric across the y-axis because the graph is a mirror image on each side of the y-axis. So, $f(x) = x^2$ is an even function.

Example 2

Determine whether the function $g(x) = x^3$ is *even*, *odd*, or *neither* algebraically.

$$g(-x) = (-x)^3 \qquad \text{Evaluate } g(-x).$$
$$= (-1)^3 \cdot x^3 \qquad \text{Raise each factor to the third power.}$$
$$= -x^3 \qquad \text{Simplify.}$$
$$= -g(x) \qquad \text{Subsitute } g(x) \text{ for } x^3.$$

Because $g(-x) = -g(x)$, the function is odd.

Exercises

Determine whether each function is *even, odd,* or *neither.*

1. $f(x) = x^2 - 3$

2. $g(x) = x^3 + 1$

3. $h(x) = |x|$

4. $g(x) = x^5$

5. $f(x) = x^5 - 2x^3 - x$

6. $h(x) = x^6 - 2x^4 - x^2 - 5$

© **7. Reasoning** Is it possible for a function to be both even and odd? Explain.

2-7 Arithmetic Sequences

F.IF.3 Recognize that sequences are functions, sometimes defined recursively . . . **A.SSE.1.a, A.SSE.1.b, F.BF.1.a, F.BF.2, F.LE.2**

Objectives To identify and extend patterns in sequences
To represent arithmetic sequences using function notation

Solve It! Write your solution to the Solve It in the space below.

In the Solve It, the numbers of pieces of wood used for 1 section of fence, 2 sections of fence, and so on, form a pattern, or a sequence. A **sequence** is an ordered list of numbers that often form a pattern. Each number in the list is called a **term of a sequence**.

Essential Understanding When you can identify a pattern in a sequence, you can use it to extend the sequence. You can also model some sequences with a function rule that you can use to find any term of the sequence.

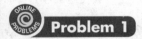 **Problem 1** **Extending Sequences**

Got It? Describe a pattern in each sequence. What are the next two terms of each sequence?

    a. 5, 11, 17, 23, . . .

    b. 400, 200, 100, 50, . . .

c. 2, −4, 8, −16, . . .

d. −15, −11, −7, −3, . . .

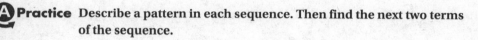

Practice **Describe a pattern in each sequence. Then find the next two terms of the sequence.**

1. 10, 4, −2, −8, . . .

2. 2, 20, 200, 2000, . . .

In an **arithmetic sequence**, the difference between consecutive terms is constant. This difference is called the **common difference**.

ONLINE PROBLEMS **Problem 2** Identifying an Arithmetic Sequence

Got It? Tell whether the sequence is arithmetic. If it is, what is the common difference?

Plan
How can you identify an arithmetic sequence?

a. 8, 15, 22, 30, . . .

b. 7, 9, 11, 13, . . .

c. 10, 4, −2, −8, . . .

d. 2, −2, 2, −2, . . .

Practice Tell whether the sequence is arithmetic. If it is, identify the common difference.

3. 10, 24, 36, 52, . . .

4. 15, 14.5, 14, 13.5, 13, . . .

A sequence is a function whose domain is the natural numbers, and whose outputs are the terms of the sequence.

You can write a sequence using a recursive formula. A **recursive formula** is a function rule that relates each term of a sequence after the first to the ones before it. Consider the sequence 7, 11, 15, 19, . . . You can use the common difference of the terms of an arithmetic sequence to write a recursive formula for the sequence. For the sequence 7, 11, 15, 19, . . . , the common difference is 4.

Let n = the term number in the sequence.

Let $A(n)$ = the value of the nth term of the sequence.

value of term 1 = $A(1) = 7$ The common difference is 4.

value of term 2 = $A(2) = A(1) + 4 = 11$

value of term 3 = $A(3) = A(2) + 4 = 15$

value of term 4 = $A(4) = A(3) + 4 = 19$ The value of the previous term plus 4

value of term n = $A(n) = A(n - 1) + 4$

The recursive formula for the arithmetic sequence above is $A(n) = A(n - 1) + 4$, where $A(1) = 7$.

Problem 3   **Writing a Recursive Formula**

Got It?   Write a recursive formula for each arithmetic sequence. What is the 9th term of each sequence?

   a. 3, 9, 15, 21, . . .

   b. 23, 35, 47, 59, . . .

   c. 7.3, 7.8, 8.3, 8.8, . . .

d. 97, 88, 79, 70, . . .

© **e. Reasoning** Is a recursive formula a useful way to find the value of an arithmetic sequence? Explain.

Ⓐ **Practice** Write a recursive formula for each sequence.

5. 2.3, 2.8, 3.3, 3.8, . . .

6. 4.6, 4.7, 4.8, 4.9, . . .

You can find the value of any term of an arithmetic sequence using a recursive formula. You can also write a sequence using an explicit formula. An **explicit formula** is a function rule that relates each term of a sequence to the term number.

take note

Key Concept   Explicit Formula For an Arithmetic Sequence

The nth term of an arithmetic sequence with first term $A(1)$ and common difference d is given by

$$A(n) = A(1) + (n - 1)d$$

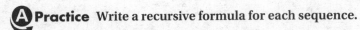
nth term   first term   term number   **common difference**

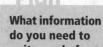Plan

What information
do you need to
write a rule for
an arithmetic
sequence?

Got It? **a.** A subway pass has a starting value of $100. After one ride, the value of the pass is $98.25. After two rides, its value is $96.50. After three rides, its value is $94.75. Write an explicit formula to represent the remaining value on the card as an arithmetic sequence. What is the value of the pass after 15 rides?

© b. Reasoning How many rides can be taken with the $100 pass?

Practice **7. Garage** After one customer buys 4 new tires, a garage recycling bin has 20 tires in it. After another customer buys 4 new tires, the bin has 24 tires in it. Write an explicit formula to represent the number of tires in the bin as an arithmetic sequence. How many tires are in the bin after 9 customers buy all new tires?

8. Cafeteria You have a cafeteria card worth $50. After you buy lunch on Monday, its value is $46.75. After you buy lunch on Tuesday, its value is $43.50. Write an explicit formula to represent the amount of money left on the card as an arithmetic sequence. What is the value of the card after you buy 12 lunches?

You can write an explicit formula from a recursive formula and vice versa.

Problem 5 **Writing an Explicit Formula From a Recursive Formula**

Got It? For each recursive formula, find an explicit formula that represents the same sequence.

　a. $A(n) = A(n - 1) + 2; A(1) = 21$

　b. $A(n) = A(n - 1) + 7; A(1) = 2$

Practice Write an explicit formula for each recursive formula.

　9. $A(n) = A(n - 1) + 3; A(1) = 6$

　10. $A(n) = A(n - 1) - 0.3; A(1) = 0.3$

Got It? For each explicit formula, find a recursive formula that represents the same sequence.

   a. $A(n) = 76 + (n - 1)(10)$

   b. $A(n) = 1 + (n - 1)(3)$

Practice Write a recursive formula for each explicit formula.

   11. $A(n) = -1 + (n - 1)(-2)$

   12. $A(n) = 4 + (n - 1)(1)$

Lesson Check

Do you know HOW?

Describe a pattern in each sequence. Then find the next two terms of the sequence.

13. 3, 11, 19, 27, . . .

14. 3, −6, 12, −24, . . .

Tell whether the sequence is arithmetic. If it is, identify the common difference.

15. 1, −7, −14, −21, . . .

16. 11, 20, 29, 38, . . .

17. Write a recursive and an explicit formula for the arithmetic sequence.

9, 7, 5, 3, 1, . . .

Do you UNDERSTAND?

18. Vocabulary Consider the following arithmetic sequence: 25, 19, 13, 7, . . .
Is the common difference 6 or −6? Explain.

19. Error Analysis Describe and correct the error at
the right in finding the tenth term of the arithmetic
sequence 4, 12, 20, 28, . . .

first term = 4
common difference = 8
tenth term = 4 + 10(8) = 84

20. Reasoning Can you use the explicit formula below to find the *n*th term of an
arithmetic sequence with a first term $A(1)$ and a common difference d? Explain.

$A(n) = A(1) + nd - d$

More Practice and Problem-Solving Exercises

B Apply

Tell whether each sequence is arithmetic. Justify your answer. If the sequence is arithmetic, write a recursive and an explicit formula to represent it.

21. 0.3, 0.9, 1.5, 2.1, . . .

22. $-3, -7, -11, -15,$ . . .

23. 1, 8, 27, 64, . . .

24. $-5, 5, -5, 5,$ . . .

25. 46, 31, 16, 2, . . .

26. $0.2, -0.6, -1.4, -2.2,$ . . .

Using the recursive formula for each arithmetic sequence, find the second, third, and fourth terms of the sequence. Then write the explicit formula that represents the sequence.

27. $A(n) = A(n - 1) - 4; A(1) = 8$

28. $A(n) = A(n - 1) + 1.2; A(1) = 8.8$

29. $A(n) = A(n - 1) + 3; A(1) = 13$

30. $A(n) = A(n - 1) - 2; A(1) = 0$

31. Reasoning An arithmetic sequence can be represented by the explicit function $A(n) = -10 + (n - 1)(4)$. Describe the relationship between the first term and the second term. Describe the relationship between the second term and the third term. Write a recursive formula to represent this sequence.

32. Open-Ended Write a function rule for a sequence that has 25 as the sixth term.

Write the first six terms in each sequence. Explain what the sixth term means in the context of the situation.

33. A cane of bamboo is 30 in. tall the first week and grows 6 in. per week thereafter.

34. You borrow $350 from a friend the first week and pay the friend back $25 each week thereafter.

35. Think About a Plan Suppose the first Friday of a new year is the fourth day of that year. Will the year have 53 Fridays regardless of whether or not it is a leap year?
- What is a rule that represents the sequence of the days in the year that are Fridays?
- How many full weeks are in a 365-day year?

36. Look For a Pattern The first five rows of Pascal's Triangle are shown at the right.
- **a.** Predict the numbers in the seventh row.
- **b.** Find the sum of the numbers in each of the first five rows. Predict the sum of the numbers in the seventh row.

37. Transportation Buses run every 9 min starting at 6:00 A.M. You get to the bus stop at 7:16 A.M. How long will you wait for a bus?

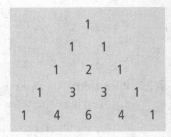

38. Multiple Representations Use the table at the right that shows an arithmetic sequence.

  a. Copy and complete the table.
  b. Graph the ordered pairs (x, y) on a coordinate plane.
  c. What do you notice about the points on your graph?

x	y
1	5
2	8
3	■
4	■

39. Number Theory The Fibonacci sequence is 1, 1, 2, 3, 5, 8, 13, . . . After the first two numbers, each number is the sum of the two previous numbers.

  a. What is the next term of the sequence? The eleventh term of the sequence?
  b. **Open-Ended** Choose two other numbers to start a Fibonacci-like sequence. Write the first seven terms of your sequence.

Challenge

Find the common difference of each arithmetic sequence. Then find the next term.

40. $4, x + 4, 2x + 4, 3x + 4, \ldots$

41. $a + b + c, 4a + 3b + c, 7a + 5b + c, \ldots$

42. a. Geometry Draw the next figure in the pattern.

  b. **Reasoning** What is the color of the twentieth figure? Explain.
  c. How many sides does the twenty-third figure have? Explain.

LESSON LAB

Use With Lesson 2-7

The Fibonacci Sequence

F.IF.3 Recognize that sequences are functions, sometimes defined recursively . . .

One famous mathematical sequence is the Fibonacci sequence. You can find each term of the sequence using addition, but the sequence is not arithmetic.

Example

The recursive formula for the Fibonacci sequence is $F_n = F_{n-2} + F_{n-1} = 1$, with $F_1 = 1$ and $F_2 = 1$. Using the formula, what are the first five terms of the sequence?

$F_1 = 1$

$F_2 = 1$

$F_3 = F_1 + F_2 = 1 + 1 = 2$

$F_4 = F_2 + F_3 = 1 + 2 = 3$

$F_5 = F_3 + F_4 = 2 + 3 = 5$

The first five terms of the Fibonacci sequence are 1, 1, 2, 3, 5.

Exercises

1. **Nature** The numbers of the Fibonacci sequence are often found in other areas, especially nature. Which term of the Fibonacci sequence does each picture represent?

   a.

   b.

   c.

   d.

2. a. Generate the first ten terms of the Fibonacci sequence.

b. Find the sum of the first ten terms of the Fibonacci sequence. Divide the sum by 11. What do you notice?

Ⓒ **c. Open-Ended** Choose two numbers other than 1 and 1. Generate a Fibonacci-like sequence from them. Write the first ten terms of your sequence, find the sum, and divide the sum by 11. What do you notice?

Ⓒ **d. Make a Conjecture** What is the sum of the first ten terms of any Fibonacci-like sequence?

3. a. Study the pattern at the right. Write the next line.

$$1^2 + 1^2 = 2 = 1 \cdot 2$$
$$1^2 + 1^2 + 2^2 = 6 = 2 \cdot 3$$
$$1^2 + 1^2 + 2^2 + 3^2 = 15 = 3 \cdot 5$$
$$1^2 + 1^2 + 2^2 + 3^2 + 5^2 = 40 = 5 \cdot 8$$

b. Without calculating, use the pattern to predict the sum of the squares of the first ten terms of the Fibonacci sequence.

c. Verify the prediction you made in part (b).

2 Chapter Review

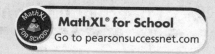

MathXL® for School
Go to pearsonsuccessnet.com

2-1 Using Graphs to Relate Two Quantities

Quick Review

You can use graphs to represent the relationship between two variables.

Example

A dog owner plays fetch with her dog. Sketch a graph to represent the distance between them and the time.

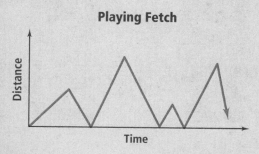

Playing Fetch

Exercises

1. **Travel** A car's speed increases as it merges onto a highway. The car travels at 65 mi/h on the highway until it slows to exit. The car then stops at two traffic lights before reaching its destination. Draw a sketch of a graph that shows the car's speed over time. Label each section.

2. **Surfing** A professional surfer paddles out past breaking waves, rides a wave, paddles back out past the breaking waves, rides another wave, and paddles back to the beach. Draw a sketch of a graph that shows the surfer's possible distance from the beach over time.

2-2 Patterns and Linear Functions

Quick Review

A **function** is a relationship that pairs each **input** value with exactly one **output** value. A **linear function** is a function whose graph is a line or part of a line.

Example

The number y of eggs left in a dozen depends on the number x of 2-egg omelets you make, as shown in the table. Represent this relationship using words, an equation, and a graph.

Number of Omelets Made, x	0	1	2	3
Number of Eggs Left, y	12	10	8	6

Look for a pattern in the table. Each time x increases by 1, y decreases by 2. The number y of eggs left is 12 minus the quantity 2 times the number x of omelets made: $y = 12 - 2x$.

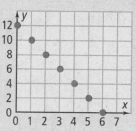

Exercises

For each table, identify the independent and dependent variables. Represent the relationship using words, an equation, and a graph.

3. **Paint in Can**

Number of Chairs Painted, p	Paint Left (oz), L
0	128
1	98
2	68
3	38

4. **Game Cost**

Number of Snacks Purchased, s	Total Cost, C
0	$18
1	$21
2	$24
3	$27

5. **Elevation**

Number of Flights of Stairs Climbed, n	0	1	2	3
Elevation (ft above sea level), E	311	326	341	356

2-3 Patterns and Nonlinear Functions

Quick Review

A **nonlinear function** is a function whose graph is *not* a line or part of a line.

Example

The area A of a square field is a function of the side length s of the field. Is the function *linear* or *nonlinear*?

Side Length (ft), s	10	15	20	25
Area (ft²), A	100	225	400	625

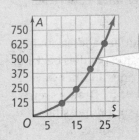

Graph the ordered pairs and connect the points. The graph is not a line, so the function is nonlinear.

Exercises

Graph the function shown by each table. Tell whether the function is *linear* or *nonlinear*.

6.

x	y
1	0
2	1
3	8
4	20

7.

x	y
1	0
2	4.5
3	9
4	13.5

8.

x	y
1	2
2	6
3	12
4	72

9.

x	y
1	-2
2	-9
3	-16
4	-23

2-4 Graphing a Function Rule

Quick Review

A **continuous graph** is a graph that is unbroken. A **discrete graph** is composed of distinct, isolated points. In a real-world graph, show only points that make sense.

Example

The total height h of a stack of cans is a function of the number n of layers of 4.5-in. cans used. This situation is represented by $h = 4.5n$. Graph the function.

n	h
0	0
1	4.5
2	9
3	13.5
4	18

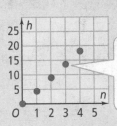

The graph is discrete because only whole numbers of layers make sense.

Exercises

Graph the function rule. Explain why the graph i *continuous* or *discrete*.

10. **Walnuts** Your cost c to buy w pounds of walnuts at $6/lb is represented by $c = 6w$.

11. **Moving** A truck originally held 24 chairs. You remove 2 chairs at a time. The number of chairs n remaining after you make t trips is represented by $n = 24 - 2t$.

12. **Flood** A burst pipe fills a basement with 37 ir of water. A pump empties the water at a rate of 1.5 in./h. The water level ℓ, in inches, after t hours is represented by $\ell = 37 - 1.5t$.

13. Graph $y = -|x| + 2$.

2-5 Writing a Function Rule

Quick Review

To write a function rule describing a real-world situation, it is often helpful to start with a verbal model of the situation.

Example

At a bicycle motocross (BMX) track, you pay $40 for a racing license plus $15 per race. What is a function rule that represents your total cost?

total cost = license fee + fee per race • number of races

$$C \quad = \quad 40 \quad + \quad 15 \quad • \quad r$$

A function rule is $C = 40 + 15 • r$.

Exercises

Write a function rule to represent each situation.

14. **Landscaping** The volume V remaining in a 243-ft^3 pile of gravel decreases by 0.2 ft^3 with each shovelful s of gravel spread in a walkway.

15. **Design** Your total cost C for hiring a garden designer is $200 for an initial consultation plus $45 for each hour h the designer spends drawing plans.

2-6 Formalizing Relations and Functions

Quick Review

A **relation** pairs numbers in the **domain** with numbers in the **range**. A relation may or may not be a function.

Example

Is the relation {(0, 1), (3, 3), (4, 4), (0, 0)} a function?

The x-values of the ordered pairs form the domain, and the y-values form the range. The domain value 0 is paired with two range values, 1 and 0. So the relation is not a function.

Exercises

Tell whether each relation is a function.

16. {(21, 7), (9, 4), (3, −2), (5, 3), (9, 1)}

17. {(2, 5), (3, 5), (4, −4), (5, 24), (6, 8)}

Evaluate each function for $x = 2$ and $x = 7$.

18. $f(x) = 2x - 8$ 19. $h(x) = -4x + 61$

20. The domain of $t(x) = -3.8x - 4.2$ is {−3, −1.4, 0, 8}. What is the range?

2-7 Arithmetic Sequences

Quick Review

A **sequence** is an ordered list of numbers, called **terms**, that often forms a pattern. A sequence can be represented by a **recursive formula** or an **explicit formula**.

Example

Tell whether the sequence is arithmetic.

2,   −1,   −4, ...

−3   −3   −3

The sequence has a common difference of −3, so it is arithmetic.

Exercises

For each sequence, write a recursive and an explicit formula.

21. 3, 8, 13, 18, ...   22. −2, −5, −8, −11, ...

23. 4, 6.5, 9, 11.5, ...   24. 18, 11, 4, −3, ...

For each recursive formula, find an explicit formula that represents the same sequence.

25. $A(n) = A(n - 1) + 3; A(1) = 4$

26. $A(n) = A(n - 1) + 11; A(1) = 13$

27. $A(n) = A(n - 1) - 1; A(1) = 19$

Pull It All Together

ASSESSMENT

Comparing the Growth of Two Blogs

Jayden and Keiko each start writing a blog at the same time. When Jayden starts his blog (Month 0), he gets 48 of his friends to subscribe. At the end of each month, he records the number of subscribers in a table. His data for the first few months are shown below.

Jayden's Blog

Number of Months	Number of Subscribers
0	48
1	56
2	64
3	72
4	80

Keiko finds that the number of subscribers K to her blog can be modeled by the function rule $K = m^2 + 10$, where m is the number of months since she started the blog.

Task Description

Determine which person's blog will be the first to have 200 subscribers.

  a. Let J = the number of subscribers to Jayden's blog.
     Let m = the number of months since he started the blog.

     Write a function rule for the relationship in the table, assuming the number of subscribers continues to grow at the same rate.

  b. Make a graph of the function rule you wrote in part (a). Did you draw a continuous graph or a discrete graph? Why?

  c. Make a graph of the function rule for the number of subscribers to Keiko's blog. How is this function different from the function you wrote in part (a)?

  d. Use your graphs to determine which person's blog will be the first to have 200 subscribers. About how many additional months will it take for the other blog to reach this level? Explain.

Get Ready!

Solutions of a Two-Variable Equation

Tell whether the given ordered pair is a solution of the equation.

1. $4y + 2x = 3; (1.5, 0)$ **2.** $y = 7x - 5; (0, 5)$ **3.** $y = -2x + 5; (2, 1)$

Transforming Equations

Solve each equation for y.

4. $2y - x = 4$ **5.** $3x = y + 2$ **6.** $-2y - 2x = 4$

Comparing Unit Rates

7. Transportation A car traveled 360 km in 6 h. A train traveled 400 km in 8 h. A boat traveled 375 km in 5 h. Which had the fastest average speed?

8. Plants A birch tree grew 2.5 in. in 5 months. A bean plant grew 8 in. in 10 months. A rose bush grew 5 in. in 8 months. Which grew the fastest?

Graphing a Function Rule

9. Make a table of values for the function $f(x) = x + 3$. Then graph the function.

Arithmetic Sequences

Write an explicit formula for each arithmetic sequence.

10. 2, 5, 8, 11, . . .   **11.** 13, 10, 7, 4, . . .   **12.** −3, −0.5, 2, 4.5, . . .

 # Looking Ahead Vocabulary

13. A steep hill has a greater *slope* than a flat plain. What does the *slope* of a line on a graph describe?

14. Two streets are *parallel* when they go the same way and do not cross. What does it mean in math to call two lines *parallel*?

CHAPTER 3

Linear Functions

Big Ideas

1 Proportionality

Essential Question: What does the slope of a line indicate about the line?

2 Functions

Essential Question: What information does the equation of a line give you?

Ⓒ Domains

- Interpreting Functions
- Building Functions
- Creating Equations

Chapter Preview

Interactive Digital Path

Log in to **pearsonsuccessnet.com** and click on Interactive Digital Path to access the Solve Its and animated Problems.

Vocabulary

English/Spanish Vocabulary Audio Online:

English	Spanish
direct variation, *p. 176*	variación directa
linear equation, *p. 186*	ecuación lineal
parallel lines, *p. 212*	rectas paralelas
perpendicular lines, *p. 213*	rectas perpendiculares
point-slope form, *p. 195*	forma punto-pendiente
rate of change, *p. 167*	tasa de cambio
slope, *p. 168*	pendiente
slope-intercept form, *p. 186*	forma pendiente-interce
standard form, *p. 203*	forma normal
x-intercept, *p. 203*	intercepto en *x*
y-intercept, *p. 186*	intercepto en *y*

3-1 | Rate of Change and Slope

F.LE.1.b Recognize situations in which one quantity changes at a constant rate . . . relative to another. **F.IF.6**

Objectives To find rates of change from tables
To find slope

Solve It! Write your solution to the Solve It in the space below.

Essential Understanding You can use ratios to show a relationship between changing quantities, such as vertical and horizontal change.

Rate of change shows the relationship between two changing quantities. When one quantity depends on the other, the following is true.

$$\text{rate of change} = \frac{\text{change in the dependent variable}}{\text{change in the independent variable}}$$

Problem 1 Finding Rate of Change Using a Table

Got It? In Problem 1, do you get the same rate of change if you use nonconsecutive rows of the table? Explain.

Ⓐ Practice Determine whether each rate of change is constant. If it is, find the rate of change and explain what it represents.

1. **Turtle Walking**

Time (min)	Distance (m)
1	6
2	12
3	15
4	21

2. **Airplane Descent**

Time (min)	Elevation (ft)
0	30,000
2	29,000
5	27,500
12	24,000

The graphs of the ordered pairs (time, distance) in Problem 1 lie on a line, as shown at the right. The relationship between time and distance is linear. When data are linear, the rate of change is constant.

Notice also that the rate of change found in Problem 1 is just the ratio of the vertical change (or *rise*) to the horizontal change (or *run*) between two points on the line. The rate of change is called the *slope* of the line.

$$\text{slope} = \frac{\text{vertical change}}{\text{horizontal change}} = \frac{\text{rise}}{\text{run}}$$

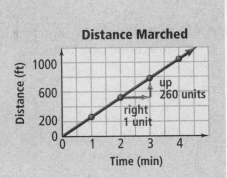
Distance Marched

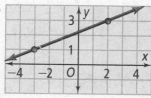 **Problem 2**   Finding Slope Using a Graph

Got It?   What is the slope of each line in parts (a) and (b)?

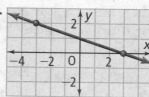

a.

b.

©c. **Reasoning**   In part (a) of Problem 2, pick two new points on the line to find the slope. Do you get the same slope?

A **Practice**   Find the slope of each line.

3.

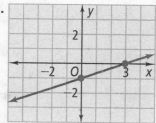

4.

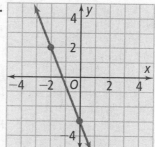

Notice that the line in part (A) of Problem 2 has a positive slope and slants upward from left to right. The line in part (B) of Problem 2 has a negative slope and slopes downward from left to right.

You can use any two points on a line to find its slope. Use subscripts to distinguish between the two points. In the diagram, (x_1, y_1) are the coordinates of point A, and (x_2, y_2) are the coordinates of point B. To find the slope of $\overleftrightarrow{AB}$, you can use the *slope formula*.

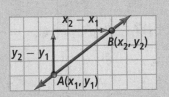

 take note

Key Concept The Slope Formula

$$\text{slope} = \frac{\text{rise}}{\text{run}} = \frac{y_2 - y_1}{x_2 - x_1}, \text{ where } x_2 - x_1 \neq 0$$

The x-coordinate you use first in the denominator must belong to the same ordered pair as the y-coordinate you use first in the numerator.

Problem 3 **Finding Slope Using Points**

Got It? **a.** What is the slope of the line through $(1, 3)$ and $(4, -1)$?

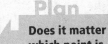

Plan

Does it matter which point is (x_1, y_1) and which is (x_2, y_2)?

b. Reasoning Plot the points in part (a) and draw a line through them. Does the slope of the line look as you expected it to? Explain.

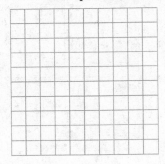

Ⓐ Practice Find the slope of the line that passes through each pair of points.

5. $(-6, 1), (4, 8)$

6. $(2, -3), (5, -4)$

Got It?   What is the slope of the line through the given points?

     a. $(4, -3), (4, 2)$ **b.** $(-1, -3), (5, -3)$

Practice   Find the slope of each line.

7.

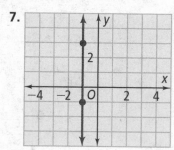

8.

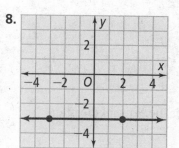

The following summarizes what you have learned about slope.

take note

Concept Summary   Slopes of Lines

A line with positive slope slants upward from left to right.

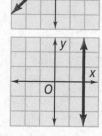

A line with negative slope slants downward from left to right.

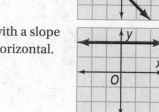

A line with an undefined slope is vertical.

A line with a slope of 0 is horizontal.

Lesson Check

Do you know HOW?

9. Is the rate of change in cost constant with respect to the number of pencils bought? Explain.

Cost of Pencils				
Number of Pencils	1	4	7	12
Cost ($)	0.25	1	1.75	3

10. What is the slope of the line?

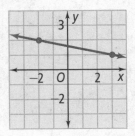

11. What is the slope of the line through $(-1, 2)$ and $(2, -3)$?

Do you UNDERSTAND?

12. Vocabulary What characteristic of a graph represents the rate of change? Explain.

13. Open-Ended Give an example of a real-world situation that you can model with a horizontal line. What is the rate of change for the situation? Explain.

14. Compare and Contrast How does finding a line's slope by counting units of vertical and horizontal change on a graph compare with finding it using the slope formula?

15. Error Analysis A student calculated the slope of the line at the right to be 2. Explain the mistake. What is the correct slope?

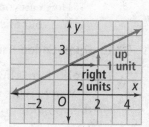

B Apply

Without graphing, tell whether the slope of a line that models each linear relationship is positive, negative, zero, or undefined. Then find the slope.

16. The length of a bus route is 4 mi long on the sixth day and 4 mi long on the seventeenth day.

17. A babysitter earns $9 for 1 h and $36 for 4 h.

18. A student earns a 98 on a test for answering one question incorrectly and earns a 90 for answering five questions incorrectly.

19. The total cost, including shipping, for ordering five uniforms is $66. The total cost, including shipping, for ordering nine uniforms is $114.

State the independent variable and the dependent variable in each linear relationship. Then find the rate of change for each situation.

20. Snow is 0.02 m deep after 1 h and 0.06 m deep after 3 h.

21. The cost of tickets is $36 for three people and $84 for seven people.

22. A car is 200 km from its destination after 1 h and 80 km from its destination after 3 h.

Use the slope formula to find the slope of the line that passes through each pair of points. Then plot the points and sketch the line that passes through them. Does the slope you found using the formula match the direction of the line you sketched?

23. $(-2, 1), (7, 1)$

24. $(4.25, 0), (3.5, 3)$

25. $\left(-\frac{1}{2}, \frac{4}{7}\right), \left(8, \frac{4}{7}\right)$

26. $(-5, 0.124), (-5, -0.584)$

27. $(-42.25, 5.2), (3.25, 3)$

28. $\left(-2, \frac{2}{11}\right), \left(-2, \frac{7}{13}\right)$

© 29. Think About a Plan The graph shows the average growth rates for three different animals. Which animal's growth shows the fastest rate of change? The slowest rate of change?
  • How can you use the graph to find the rates of change?
  • Are your answers reasonable?

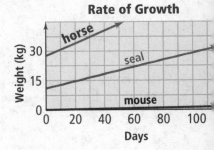

© 30. Open-Ended Find two points that lie on a line with slope -9.

31. Profit John's business made $4500 in January and $8600 in March. What is the rate of change in his profit for this time period?

Each pair of points lies on a line with the given slope. Find x or y.

32. $(2, 4), (x, 8)$; slope $= -2$

33. $(4, 3), (5, y)$; slope $= 3$

34. $(2, 4), (x, 8)$; slope $= -\frac{1}{2}$

35. $(3, y), (1, 9)$; slope $= -\frac{5}{2}$

36. $(-4, y), (2, 4y)$; slope $= 6$

37. $(3, 5), (x, 2)$; undefined slope

38. Reasoning Is it true that a line with slope 1 always passes through the origin? Explain your reasoning.

39. Arithmetic Sequences Use the arithmetic sequence 10, 15, 20, 25, ...
   a. Find the common difference of the sequence.
   b. Let $x =$ the term number, and let $y =$ the corresponding term of the sequence. Graph the ordered pairs (x, y) for the first eight terms of the sequence. Draw a line through the points.
   c. **Reasoning** How is the slope of a line from part (b) related to the common difference of the sequence?

Challenge

Do the points in each set lie on the same line? Explain your answer.

40. $A(1, 3), B(4, 2), C(-2, 4)$ **41.** $G(3, 5), H(-1, 3), I(7, 7)$

42. $D(-2, 3), E(0, -1), F(2, 1)$ **43.** $P(4, 2), Q(-3, 2), R(2, 5)$

44. $G(1, -2), H(-1, -5), I(5, 4)$ **45.** $S(-3, 4), T(0, 2), X(-3, 0)$

Find the slope of the line that passes through each pair of points.

46. $(a, -b), (-a, -b)$

47. $(-m, n), (3m, -n)$

48. $(2a, b), (c, 2d)$

A.CED.2 Create equations in two or more variables . . .; graph equations on coordinate axes with labels and scales.

Objective To write and graph an equation of a direct variation

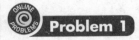
Solve It! Write your solution to the Solve It in the space below.

The time it takes to hear thunder *varies directly with* the distance from lightning.

Essential Understanding If the ratio of two variables is constant, then the variables have a special relationship, known as a *direct variation*.

A **direct variation** is a relationship that can be represented by a function in the form $y = kx$, where $k \neq 0$. The **constant of variation for a direct variation** k is the coefficient of x. By dividing each side of $y = kx$ by x, you can see that the ratio of the variables is constant: $\frac{y}{x} = k$.

To determine whether an equation represents a direct variation, solve it for y. If you can write the equation in the form $y = kx$, where $k \neq 0$, it represents a direct variation.

Problem 1 Identifying a Direct Variation

Got It? Does $4x + 5y = 0$ represent a direct variation? If so, find the constant of variation.

Think
How do you know if an equation represents a direct variation?

Practice Determine whether each equation represents a direct variation. If it does, find the constant of variation.

1. $2y = 5x + 1$ **2.** $-4 + 7x + 4 = 3y$

> To write an equation for a direct variation, first find the constant of variation k using an ordered pair, other than $(0, 0)$, that you know is a solution of the equation.

Problem 2 **Writing a Direct Variation Equation**

Plan

Got It? Suppose y varies directly with x, and $y = 10$ when $x = -2$. What direct variation equation relates x and y? What is the value of y when $x = -15$?

How can you find the constant of variation?

Ⓐ **Practice** Suppose y varies directly with x. Write a direct variation equation that relates x and y. Then find the value of y when $x = 12$.

3. $y = 10.4$ when $x = 4$.

4. $y = 9\frac{1}{3}$ when $x = -\frac{1}{2}$

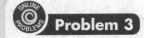

Problem 3 **Graphing a Direct Variation**

Got It? **a.** Weight on the moon y varies directly with weight on Earth x. A person who weighs 100 lb on Earth weighs 16.6 lb on the moon. What is an equation that relates weight on Earth x and weight on the moon y? What is the graph of this equation?

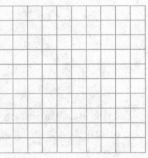

b. Reasoning What is the slope of the graph of $y = 0.38x$ in Problem 3? How is the slope related to the equation?

Practice **5. Travel Time** The distance d you bike varies directly with the amount of time t you bike. Suppose you bike 13.2 mi in 1.25 h. What is an equation that relates d and t? What is the graph of the equation?

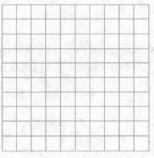

6. Geometry The perimeter p of a regular hexagon varies directly with the length ℓ of one side of the hexagon. What is an equation that relates p and ℓ? What is the graph of the equation?

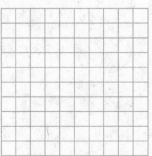

Concept Summary   Graphs of Direct Variations

The graph of a direct variation equation $y = kx$ is a
line with the following properties.
- The line passes through $(0, 0)$.
- The slope of the line is k.

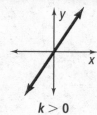

$k > 0$

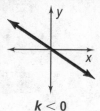

$k < 0$

You can rewrite a direct variation equation $y = kx$ as $\frac{y}{x} = k$. When a set of data pairs
(x, y) vary directly, $\frac{y}{x}$ is the constant of variation. It is the same for each data pair.

Problem 4   Writing a Direct Variation From a Table

Got It?   For the data in the table at the right, does y vary directly with x? If it does,
write an equation for the direct variation.

x	y
−3	2.25
1	−0.75
4	−3

Ⓐ Practice   For the data in each table, tell whether y varies directly with x. If it
does, write an equation for the direct variation. Check your answer by
plotting the points from the table and sketching the line.

7.

x	y
3	5.4
7	12.6
12	21.6

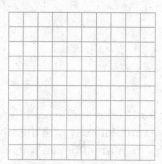

8.

x	y
−2	1
3	6
8	11

Lesson Check

Do you know HOW?

9. Does the equation $6y = 18x$ represent a direct variation? If it does, what is its constant of variation?

10. Suppose y varies directly with x, and $y = 30$ when $x = 3$. What direct variation equation relates x and y?

11. A recipe for 12 corn muffins calls for 1 cup of flour. The number of muffins you can make varies directly with the amount of flour you use. You have $2\frac{1}{2}$ cups of flour. How many muffins can you make?

12. Does y vary directly with x? If it does, what is an equation for the direct variation?

x	y
−2	1
2	−1
4	−2

Do you UNDERSTAND?

Vocabulary In Exercises 13–15, determine whether each statement is *always*, *sometimes*, or *never* true.

13. The ordered pair $(0, 0)$ is a solution of the direct variation equation $y = kx$.

14. You can write a direct variation in the form $y = k + x$, where $k \neq 0$.

15. The constant of variation for a direct variation represented by $y = kx$ is $\frac{y}{x}$.

16. Reasoning Suppose q varies directly with p. Does this imply that p varies directly with q? Explain.

More Practice and Problem-Solving Exercises

 Apply

Suppose y varies directly with x. Write a direct variation equation that relates x and y. Then graph the equation.

17. $y = \frac{1}{2}$ when $x = 3$ **18.** $y = -5$ when $x = \frac{1}{4}$

19. $y = \frac{6}{5}$ when $x = -\frac{5}{6}$ **20.** $y = 7.2$ when $x = 1.2$.

21. Think About a Plan The amount of blood in a person's body varies directly with body weight. A person who weighs 160 lb has about 4.6 qt of blood. About how many quarts of blood are in the body of a 175-lb person?
- How can you find the constant of variation?
- Can you write an equation that relates quarts of blood to weight?
- How can you use the equation to determine the solution?

STEM **22. Electricity** Ohm's Law $V = I \times R$ relates the voltage, current, and resistance of a circuit. V is the voltage measured in volts. I is the current measured in amperes. R is the resistance measured in ohms.
- **a.** Find the voltage of a circuit with a current of 24 amperes and a resistance of 2 ohms.
- **b.** Find the resistance of a circuit with a current of 24 amperes and a voltage of 18 volts.

Reasoning **Tell whether the two quantities vary directly. Explain your reasoning.**

23. the number of ounces of cereal and the number of Calories the cereal contains

24. the time it takes to travel a certain distance and the rate at which you travel

25. the perimeter of a square and the side length of the square

26. the amount of money you have left and the number of items you purchase

27. a. Graph the following direct variation equations in the same coordinate plane: $y = x$, $y = 2x$, $y = 3x$, and $y = 4x$.
- **b.** **Look for a Pattern** Describe how the graphs of the lines change as the constant of variation increases.
- **c.** Predict how the graph of $y = \frac{1}{2}x$ would appear.

28. Error Analysis Use the table at the right. A student says that y varies directly with x because as x increases by 1, y also increases by 1. Explain the student's error.

29. Writing Suppose y varies directly with x. Explain how the value of y changes in each situation.
- **a.** The value of x is doubled.
- **b.** The value of x is halved.

x	y
0	3
1	4
2	5

30. Physics The force you need to apply to a lever varies directly with the weight you want to lift. Suppose you can lift a 50-lb weight by applying 20 lb of force to a certain lever.

   a. What is the ratio of force to weight for the lever?

   b. Write an equation relating force and weight. What is the force you need to lift a friend who weighs 130 lb?

ⓒ Challenge

The ordered pairs in each exercise are for the same direct variation. Find each missing value.

31. $(3, 4)$ and $(9, y)$ **32.** $(1, y)$ and $\left(\frac{3}{2}, -9\right)$ **33.** $(-5, 3)$ and $(x, -4.8)$

34. Gas Mileage A car gets 32 mi per gallon. The number of gallons g of gas used varies directly with the number of miles m traveled.

   a. Suppose the price of gas is $3.85 per gallon. Write a function giving the cost c for g gallons of gas. Is this a direct variation? Explain your reasoning.

   b. Write a direct variation equation relating the cost of gas to the miles traveled.

   c. How much will it cost to buy gas for a 240-mi trip?

Investigating $y = mx + b$

F.IF.7.a Graph . . . functions and show intercepts, maxima, and minima.
Also **F.IF.7, F.BF.3**

MATHEMATICAL
PRACTICES

You can use a graphing calculator to explore the graph of an equation in the form $y = mx + b$. For this activity, choose a standard screen by pressing (zoom) 6.

1. Graph these equations on the same screen. Then complete each statement.

$$y = x + 3 \qquad\qquad y = 2x + 3 \qquad\qquad y = \tfrac{1}{2}x + 3$$

  a. The graph of _____ is steepest.

  b. The graph of _____ is the least steep.

2. Match each equation with the best choice for its graph.

  A. $y = \tfrac{1}{4}x - 2$ **B.** $y = 4x - 2$ **C.** $y = x - 2$

  I.
  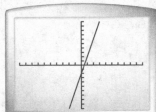
       II.
  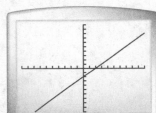
       III.
  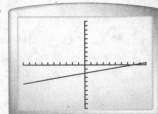

3. Graph these equations on the same screen.

$$y = 2x + 3 \qquad\qquad y = -2x + 3$$

  How does the sign of m affect the graph of the equation?

4. Reasoning How does changing the value of *m* affect the graph of an equation in the form $y = mx + b$?

5. Graph these equations on the same screen.

$$y = 2x + 3 \qquad\qquad y = 2x - 3 \qquad\qquad y = 2x + 2$$

Where does the graph of each equation cross the *y*-axis? (*Hint:* Use the **ZOOM** feature to better see the points of intersection.)

6. Match each equation with the best choice for its graph.

A. $y = \frac{1}{3}x - 3$ **B.** $y = \frac{1}{3}x + 1$ **C.** $y = \frac{1}{3}x$

I. 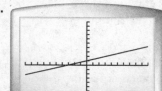   **II.** 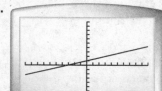   **III.**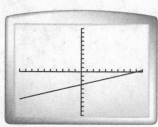

7. Reasoning How does changing the value of *b* affect the graph of an equation in the form $y = mx + b$?

3-3 Slope-Intercept Form

F.IF.7.a Graph . . . functions and show intercepts, maxima, and minima. Also F.IF.4, F.LE.2, F.LE.5

Objectives To write linear equations using slope-intercept form
To graph linear equations in slope-intercept form

 Solve It! Write your solution to the Solve It in the space below.

The function in the Solve It is a linear function, but it is not a direct variation. Direct variations are only part of the family of linear functions.

A family of functions is a group of functions with common characteristics. A **parent function** is the simplest function with these characteristics. The **linear parent function** is $y = x$ or $f(x) = x$. The graphs of three linear functions are shown at the right.

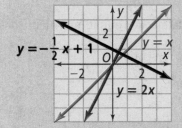

A **linear equation** is an equation that models a linear function. In a linear equation, the variables cannot be raised to a power other than 1. So $y = 2x$ is a linear equation, but $y = x^2$ and $y = 2^x$ are not. The graph of a linear equation contains all the ordered pairs that are solutions of the equation.

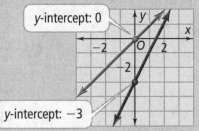

Graphs of linear functions may cross the y-axis at any point. A **y-intercept** of a graph is the y-coordinate of a point where the graph crosses the y-axis.

Essential Understanding You can use the slope and y-intercept of a line to write and graph an equation of the line.

Key Concept   Slope-Intercept Form of a Linear Equation

The **slope-intercept form** of a linear equation of a nonvertical line is $y = mx + b$.

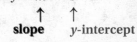

Problem 1 Identifying Slope and y-Intercept

Got It? **a.** What are the slope and y-intercept of the graph of $y = -\frac{1}{2}x + \frac{2}{3}$?

©**b. Reasoning** How do the graph of the line and the equation in part (a) change if the y-intercept is moved down 3 units?

Ⓐ**Practice** Find the slope and y-intercept of the graph of each equation.

1. $y = -x + 4$

2. $y = \frac{1}{4}x - \frac{1}{3}$

Problem 2 Writing an Equation in Slope-Intercept Form

Got It? What is an equation of the line with slope $\frac{3}{2}$ and y-intercept -1?

A Practice Write an equation in slope-intercept form of the line with the given slope *m* and *y*-intercept *b*.

    3. $m = -0.5, b = 1.5$ **4.** $m = -2, b = \frac{8}{5}$

Problem 3   **Writing an Equation From a Graph**

Got It?   **a.** What do you expect the slope of the line to be from looking at the graph? Explain.

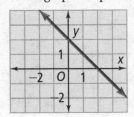

Think

What does the graph tell you about the slope?

       b. What is an equation of the line shown above?

      c. Reasoning Does the equation of the line depend on the points you use to find the slope? Explain.

A Practice Write an equation in slope-intercept form of each line.

5.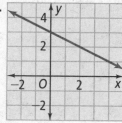

6.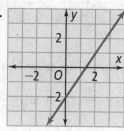

Problem 4 **Writing an Equation From Two Points**

Got It? What equation in slope-intercept form represents the line that passes through the points $(3, -2)$ and $(1, -3)$?

A Practice Write an equation in slope-intercept form of the line that passes through the given points.

7. $(-2, 4)$ and $(3, -1)$

8. $(-3, 3)$ and $(1, 2)$

You can use the slope and y-intercept from an equation to graph a line.

 Problem 5 **Graphing a Linear Equation**

Got It? What is the graph of each linear equation?

Think
What information can you get from each equation?

a. $y = -3x + 4$

b. $y = 4x - 8$

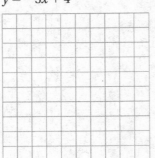 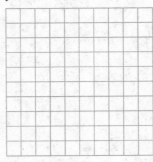

Practice Graph each equation.

9. $y = 3x + 4$

10. $y = -2x + 1$

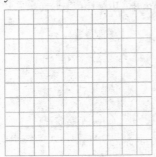 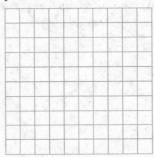

Slope-intercept form is useful for modeling real-life situations where you are given a starting value (the y-intercept) and a rate of change (the slope).

 Problem 6 **Modeling a Function**

Got It? A plumber charges a \$65 fee for a repair plus \$35 per hour. Write an equation to model the total cost y of a repair that takes x hours. What graph models the total cost?

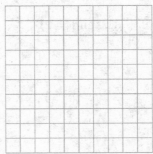

11. Retail Sales Suppose you have a $5-off coupon at a fabric store. You buy fabric that costs $7.50 per yard. Write an equation that models the total amount of money y you pay if you buy x yards of fabric. What is the graph of the equation?

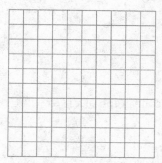

12. Temperature The temperature at sunrise is 65°F. Each hour during the day, the temperature rises 5°F. Write an equation that models the temperature y, in degrees Fahrenheit, after x hours during the day. What is the graph of the equation?

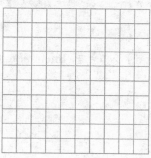

Lesson Check

Do you know HOW?

13. What is an equation of the line with slope 6 and y-intercept -4?

14. What equation in slope-intercept form represents the line that passes through the points $(-3, 4)$ and $(2, -1)$?

15. What is the graph of $y = 5x + 2$?

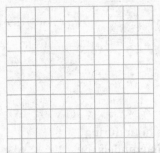

Do you UNDERSTAND?

16. Vocabulary Is $y = 5$ a linear equation? Explain.

17. Reasoning Is it *always, sometimes,* or *never* true that an equation in slope-intercept form represents a direct variation? Support your answer with examples.

© **18. Writing** Describe two different methods you can use to graph the equation $y = 2x + 4$. Which method do you prefer? Explain.

More Practice and Problem-Solving Exercises

© MATHEMATICAL PRACTICES

B Apply

19. Using the tables at the right, predict whether the two graphs will intersect. Plot the points and sketch the lines. Do the two lines appear to intersect? Explain.

Find the slope and y-intercept of the graph of each equation.

20. $y - 2 = -3x$

21. $y + \frac{1}{2}x = 0$

22. $y - 9x = \frac{1}{2}$

23. $2y - 6 = 3x$

24. $-2y = 6(5 - 3x)$

25. $y - d = cx$

26. $y = (2 - a)x + a$

27. $2y + 4n = -6x$

x	y
-2	9
-1	7
0	5
1	3
2	1

x	y
-2	-18
-1	-14
0	-10
1	-6
2	-2

© **28. Think About a Plan** Polar bears are listed as a threatened species. In 2005, there were about 25,000 polar bears in the world. If the number of polar bears declines by 1000 each year, in what year will polar bears become extinct?
- What equation models the number of polar bears?
- How can graphing the equation help you solve the problem?

© **29. Error Analysis** A student drew the graph at the right for the equation $y = -2x + 1$. What error did the student make? Draw the correct graph.

© **30. Computers** A computer repair service charges $50 for diagnosis and $35 per hour for repairs. Let x be the number of hours it takes to repair a computer. Let y be the total cost of the repair.
- **a.** Write an equation in slope-intercept form that relates x and y.
- **b.** Graph the equation.
- **c. Reasoning** Explain why you should draw the line only in Quadrant I.

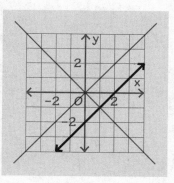

Use the slope and y-intercept to graph each equation.

31. $y = 7 - 3x$

32. $2y + 4x = 0$

33. $3y + 6 = -2x$

34. $y + 2 = 5x - 4$

35. $4x + 3y = 2x - 1$

36. $-2(3x + 4) + y = 0$

Write a recursive formula and an explicit formula in slope-intercept form that model each arithmetic sequence. How does the recursive formula relate to the slope-intercept form?

37. 3, 5, 7, 9, . . .   **38.** −1, 3, 7, 11, . . .   **39.** 0.7, 0.3, −0.1, −0.5, . . .

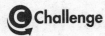 **40. Writing** Describe two ways you can determine whether an equation is linear.

41. Hobbies Suppose you are doing a 5000-piece puzzle. You have already placed 175 pieces. Every minute you place 10 more pieces.
   a. Write an equation in slope-intercept form to model the number of pieces placed. Graph the equation.
   b. After 50 more minutes, how many pieces will you have placed?

Ⓒ Challenge

Find the value of a such that the graph of the equation has the given slope m.

42. $y = 2ax + 4$, $m = -1$ **43.** $y = -\frac{1}{2}ax - 5$, $m = \frac{5}{2}$ **44.** $y = \frac{3}{4}ax + 3$, $m = \frac{9}{16}$

45. Sailing A sailboat begins a voyage with 145 lb of food. The crew plans to eat a total of 15 lb of food per day.
   a. Write an equation in slope-intercept form relating the remaining food supply y to the number of days x.
   b. Graph your equation.
   c. The crew plans to have 25 lb of food remaining when they end their voyage. How many days does the crew expect their voyage to last?

Point-Slope Form

F.LE.2 Construct linear and exponential functions, including arithmetic and geometric sequences, given a graph, a description of a relationship, or two input-output pairs . . . Also **A.CED.2, F.IF.7, F.BF.1**

Objective To write and graph linear equations using point-slope form

Solve It! Write your solution to the Solve It in the space below.

You have learned how to write an equation of a line by using its *y*-intercept. In this lesson, you will learn how to write an equation *without* using the *y*-intercept.

Essential Understanding You can use the slope of a line and any point on the line to write and graph an equation of the line. Any two equations for the same line are equivalent.

take note

Key Concept Point-Slope Form of a Linear Equation

Definition

The **point-slope form** of an equation of a nonvertical line with slope m and through point (x_1, y_1) is $y - y_1 = m(x - x_1)$.

Symbols

$$y - y_1 = m(x - x_1)$$
$$\uparrow \qquad \uparrow \qquad \uparrow$$
y-coordinate slope *x*-coordinate

Graph

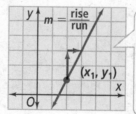

When you use $y - y_1 = m(x - x_1)$, (x_1, y_1) represents a *specific* point and (x, y) represents *any* point.

Here's Why It Works Given a point (x_1, y_1) on a line and the line's slope m, you can use the definition of slope to derive point-slope form.

$\dfrac{y_2 - y_1}{x_2 - x_1} = m$	Use the definition of slope.
$\dfrac{y - y_1}{x - x_1} = m$	Let (x, y) be any point on the line. Substitute (x, y) for (x_2, y_2).
$\dfrac{y - y_1}{x - x_1} \cdot (x - x_1) = m(x - x_1)$	Multiply each side by $(x - x_1)$.
$y - y_1 = m(x - x_1)$	Simplify the left side of the equation.

Problem 1 **Writing an Equation in Point-Slope Form**

Got It? A line passes through $(8, -4)$ and has slope $\frac{2}{3}$. What is an equation in point-slope form of the line?

A Practice Write an equation in point-slope form of the line that passes through the given point and with the given slope m.

1. $(4, 2); m = -\frac{5}{3}$

2. $(-2, -7); m = \frac{4}{5}$

Problem 2 **Graphing Using Point-Slope Form**

Got It? What is the graph of the equation $y + 7 = -\frac{4}{5}(x - 4)$?

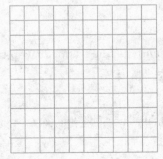

Plan

How does the equation help you make a graph?

A Practice Graph each equation.

3. $y + 5 = -(x + 2)$

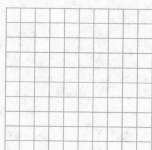

4. $y - 2 = \frac{4}{9}(x - 3)$

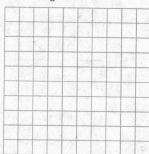

You can write the equation of a line given any two points on the line. First use the two given points to find the slope. Then use the slope and one of the points to write the equation.

Problem 3 **Using Two Points to Write an Equation**

Got It? **a.** In the last step of Problem 3, use the point $(-2, -3)$ instead of $(1, 4)$ to write an equation of the line.

Think

What variables do you substitute for?

ⓒ b. Reasoning Rewrite the equations in Problem 3 and part (a) in slope-intercept form. Compare the two rewritten equations. What can you conclude?

A Practice Write an equation in point-slope form for each line.

5.
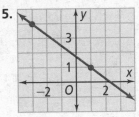

6.
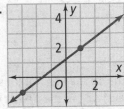

Problem 4 **Using a Table to Write an Equation**

Got It? **a.** The table shows the number of gallons of water y in a tank after x hours. The relationship is linear. What is an equation in point-slope form that models the data? What does the slope represent?

Volume of Water in Tank

Time, x (h)	Water, y (gal)
2	3320
3	4570
5	7070
8	10,820

b. Reasoning Write the equation from part (a) in slope-intercept form. What does the y-intercept represent?

Model the data in each table with a linear equation in slope-intercept form. Then tell what the slope and y-intercept represent.

7.

Time Painting, x (days)	Volume of Paint, y (gal)
2	56
3	44
5	20

8.

Time Worked, x (h)	Wages Earned, y ($)
1	8.50
3	25.50
6	51.00

Lesson Check

Do you know HOW?

9. What are the slope and one point on the graph of $y - 12 = \frac{4}{9}(x + 7)$?

10. What is an equation of the line that passes through the point $(3, -8)$ and has slope -2?

11. What is the graph of the equation $y - 4 = 3(x + 2)$?

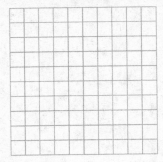

12. What is an equation of the line that passes through the points $(-1, -2)$ and $(2, 4)$?

Do you UNDERSTAND?

⊚ **13. Vocabulary** What features of the graph of the equation $y - y_1 = m(x - x_1)$ can you identify?

14. Reasoning Is $y - 4 = 3(x + 1)$ an equation of a line through $(-2, 1)$? Explain.

15. Reasoning Can any equation in point-slope form also be written in slope-intercept form? Give an example to explain.

More Practice and Problem-Solving Exercises

Apply

Graph the line that passes through the given point and has the given slope *m*.

16. $(-3, -2)$; $m = 2$ **17.** $(6, -1)$; $m = -\frac{5}{3}$ **18.** $(-3, 1)$; $m = \frac{1}{3}$

19. Think About a Plan The relationship of degrees Fahrenheit (°F) and degrees Celsius (°C) is linear. When the temperature is 50°F, it is 10°C. When the temperature is 77°F, it is 25°C. Write an equation giving the Celsius temperature *C* in terms of the Fahrenheit temperature *F*. What is the Celsius temperature when it is 59°F?
- How can point-slope form help you write the equation?
- What are two points you can use to find the slope?

20. a. Geometry Figure *ABCD* is a rectangle. Write equations in point-slope form of the lines containing the sides of *ABCD*.
   b. Reasoning Make a conjecture about the slopes of parallel lines.
   c. Use your conjecture to write an equation of the line that passes through $(0, -4)$ and is parallel to $y - 9 = -7(x + 3)$.

21. Boiling Point The relationship between altitude and the boiling point of water is linear. At an altitude of 8000 ft, water boils at 197.6°F. At an altitude of 4500 ft, water boils at 203.9°F. Write an equation giving the boiling point *b* of water, in degrees Fahrenheit, in terms of the altitude *a*, in feet. What is the boiling point of water at 2500 ft?

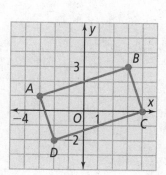

22. Using a graphing calculator, graph $f(x) = 3x + 2$.

   a. If $f(x) = 3x + 2$ and $g(x) = 4f(x)$, write the equation for $g(x)$. Graph $g(x)$ and compare it to the graph of $f(x)$.

   b. If $f(x) = 3x + 2$ and $h(x) = f(4x)$, write the equation for $h(x)$. Graph $h(x)$ and compare it to the graph of $f(x)$.

   c. Compare how multiplying a function by a number and multiplying the x-value of a function by a number change the graphs of the functions.

23. Using a graphing calculator, graph $f(x) = 2x - 5$.

   a. If $f(x) = 2x - 5$ and $j(x) = f(x) + 3$, write the equation for $j(x)$. Graph $j(x)$ and compare it to the graph of $f(x)$.

   b. If $f(x) = 2x - 5$ and $k(x) = f(x + 3)$, write the equation for $k(x)$. Graph $k(x)$ and compare it to the graph of $f(x)$.

   c. Compare how adding a number to a function and adding a number to the x-value of a function change the graphs of the functions.

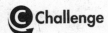 Challenge

24. Forestry A forester plants a tree and measures its circumference yearly over the next four years. The table shows the forester's measurements.

Tree Growth				
Time (yr)	1	2	3	4
Circumference (in.)	2	4	6	8

   a. Show that the data are linear, and write an equation that models the data.

   b. Predict the circumference of the tree after 10 yr.

   c. The circumference of the tree after 10 yr was actually 43 in. After four more years, the circumference was 49 in. Based on this new information, does the relationship between time and circumference continue to be linear? Explain.

3-5 Standard Form

A.CED.2 Create equations in two or more variables . . .; graph equations on coordinate axes with labels and scales. Also F.IF.4, F.IF.7.a, F.IF.9

Objectives To graph linear equations using intercepts
To write linear equations in standard form

Solve It! Write your solution to the Solve It in the space below.

In this lesson, you will learn to use intercepts to graph a line. Recall that a *y*-intercept is the *y*-coordinate of a point where a graph crosses the *y*-axis. The **x-intercept** is the *x*-coordinate of a point where a graph crosses the *x*-axis.

Essential Understanding One form of a linear equation, called *standard form*, allows you to find intercepts quickly. You can use the intercepts to draw the graph.

take note

Key Concept Standard Form of a Linear Equation

The **standard form of a linear equation** is $Ax + By = C$, where *A*, *B*, and *C* are real numbers, and *A* and *B* are not both zero.

Problem 1 Finding *x*- and *y*-Intercepts

Got It? What are the *x*- and *y*-intercepts of the graph of each equation?

a. $5x - 6y = 60$

b. $3x + 8y = 12$

Think
What do you substitute for *y* when you are finding the *x*-intercept?

Ⓐ Practice Find the *x*- and *y*-intercepts of the graph of each equation.

1. $7x - y = 21$

2. $-5x + 3y = -7.5$

Problem 2 **Graphing a Line Using Intercepts**

Think

How can you use the intercepts to help you graph a line?

Got It? What is the graph of $2x + 5y = 20$?

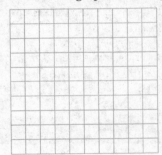

Ⓐ Practice Graph each equation using *x*- and *y*-intercepts.

3. $x - y = -8$

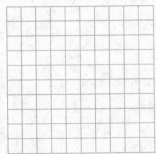

4. $6x - 2y = 18$

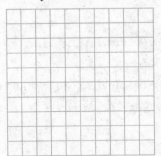

If $A = 0$ in the standard form $Ax + By = C$, then you can write the equation in the form $y = b$, where b is a constant. If $B = 0$, you can write the equation in the form $x = a$, where a is a constant. The graph of $y = b$ is a horizontal line, and the graph of $x = a$ is a vertical line.

Problem 3 Graphing Horizontal and Vertical Lines

Got It? What is the graph of each equation?

a. $x = 4$

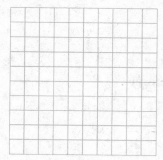

b. $x = -1$

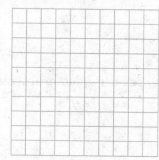

c. $y = 0$

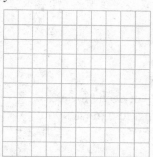

d. $y = 1$

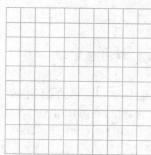

Practice Graph each equation.

5. $y = -2$

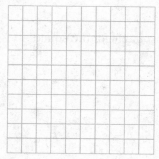

6. $x = 7$

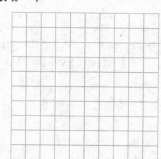

Given an equation in slope-intercept form or point-slope form, you can rewrite the equation in standard form using only integers.

Problem 4 **Transforming to Standard Form**

Got It? Write $y - 2 = -\frac{1}{3}(x + 6)$ in standard form using integers.

A Practice Write each equation in standard form using integers.

7. $y = \frac{1}{4}x - 2$

8. $y = -\frac{2}{3}x - 1$

Problem 5 **Using Standard Form as a Model**

Got It? **a.** In Problem 5, suppose the store charged $15 for each movie. What equation describes the numbers of songs and movies you can purchase for $60?

© **b. Reasoning** What domain and range are reasonable for the equation in part (a)? Explain.

9. Video Games In a video game, you earn 5 points for each jewel you find. You earn 2 points for each star you find. Write and graph an equation that represents the numbers of jewels and stars you must find to earn 250 points. What are three combinations of jewels and stars you can find that will earn you 250 points?

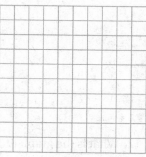

10. Clothing A store sells T-shirts for $12 each and sweatshirts for $15 each. You plan to spend $120 on T-shirts and sweatshirts. Write and graph an equation that represents this situation. What are three combinations of T-shirts and sweatshirts you can buy for $120?

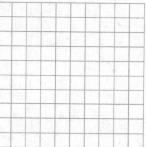

note

Concept Summary Linear Equations

You can describe any line using one or more of these forms of a linear equation. Any two equations for the same line are equivalent.

Graph

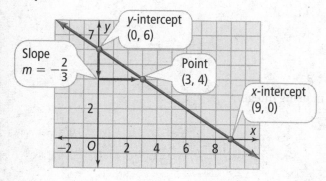

Forms

Slope-Intercept Form
$$y = mx + b$$

$$y = -\frac{2}{3}x + 6$$

Point-Slope Form
$$y - y_1 = m(x - x_1)$$

$$y - 4 = -\frac{2}{3}(x - 3)$$

Standard Form
$$Ax + By = C$$

$$2x + 3y = 18$$

Lesson Check

Do you know HOW?

11. What are the *x*- and *y*-intercepts of the graph of $3x - 4y = 9$?

12. What is the graph of $5x + 4y = 20$?

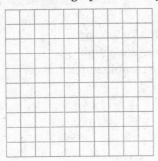

13. Is the graph of $y = -0.5$ a *horizontal line*, a *vertical line*, or *neither*?

14. What is $y = \frac{1}{2}x + 3$ written in standard form using integers?

15. A store sells gift cards in preset amounts. You can purchase gift cards for $10 or $25. You have spent $285 on gift cards. Write an equation in standard form to represent this situation. What are three combinations of gift cards you could have purchased?

Do you UNDERSTAND?

16. Vocabulary Tell whether each linear equation is in *slope-intercept form, point-slope form,* or *standard form.*

   a. $y + 5 = -(x - 2)$ **b.** $y = -2x + 5$

   c. $y - 10 = -2(x - 1)$ **d.** $2x + 4y = 12$

17. Reasoning Which form would you use to write an equation of the line at the right: *slope-intercept form, point-slope form,* or *standard form*? Explain.

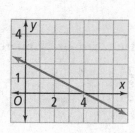

More Practice and Problem-Solving Exercises

Ⓑ Apply

Ⓒ **18. Writing** The three forms of linear equations you have studied are slope-intercept form, point-slope form, and standard form. Explain when each form is most useful.

Ⓒ **19. Think About a Plan** You are preparing a fruit salad. You want the total carbohydrates from pineapple and watermelon to equal 24 g. Pineapple has 3 g of carbohydrates per ounce and watermelon has 2 g of carbohydrates per ounce. What is a graph that shows all possible combinations of ounces of pineapple and ounces of watermelon?
   • Can you write an equation to model the situation?
   • What domain and range are reasonable for the graph?

Ⓒ **20. Compare and Contrast** Graph $3x + y = 6$, $3x - y = 6$, and $-3x + y = 6$. How are the graphs similar? How are they different?

Ⓒ **21. Reasoning** What are the slope and y-intercept of the graph of $Ax + By = C$?

Ⓒ **22. Error Analysis** A student says the equation $y = 4x + 1$ can be written in standard form as $4x - y = 1$. Describe and correct the student's error.

Ⓒ **23. Reasoning** The coefficients of x and y in the standard form of a linear equation cannot both be zero. Explain why.

Graphing Calculator Use a graphing calculator to graph each equation. Make a sketch of the graph. Include the x- and y-intercepts.

24. $2x - 8y = -16$ **25.** $-3x - 4y = 0$ **26.** $x + 3.5y = 7$

27. $-x + 2y = -8$ **28.** $3x + 3y = -15$ **29.** $4x - 6y = 9$

Ⓒ **30. Compare and Contrast** The graph below represents one function, and the table represents a different function. How are the functions similar? How are they different?

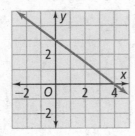

x	-4	-2	0	2	4
y	5	4	3	2	1

Find the x- and y-intercepts of the line that passes through the given points.

31. $(-6, 4), (3, -5)$ **32.** $(-5, -5), (4, -2)$ **33.** $(-7, 6), (-4, 11)$

34. $(-2, 8), (4, 2)$ **35.** $(3, -8), (-4, 13)$ **36.** $(5, 0.4), (-1, -2)$

37. Sports The scoreboard for a football game is shown at the right. All of the points the home team scored came from field goals worth 3 points and touchdowns with successful extra-point attempts worth 7 points. Write and graph a linear equation that represents this situation. List every possible combination of field goals and touchdowns the team could have scored.

Challenge

38. Geometry Graph $x + 4y = 8$, $4x - y = -1$, $x + 4y = -12$, and $4x - y = 20$ in the same coordinate plane. What figure do the four lines appear to form?

Write an equation of each line in standard form.

39. The line contains the point $(-4, -7)$ and has the same slope as the graph of $y + 3 = 5(x + 4)$.

40. The line has the same slope as $4x - y = 5$ and the same y-intercept as the graph of $3y - 13x = 6$.

41. a. Graph $2x + 3y = 6$, $2x + 3y = 12$, and $2x + 3y = 18$ in the same coordinate plane.
　　b. How are the lines from part (a) related?
　　c. As C increases, what happens to the graph of $2x + 3y = C$?

© 42. a. Fundraising Suppose your school is having a talent show to raise money for new band supplies. You think that 200 students and 150 adults will attend. It will cost $200 to put on the talent show. What is an equation that describes the ticket prices you can set for students and adults to raise $1000?
　　b. Open-Ended Graph your equation. What are three possible prices you could set for student and adult tickets?

Slopes of Parallel and Perpendicular Lines

G.GPE.5 Prove the slope criteria for parallel and perpendicular lines and use them . . . to solve problems . . .
Also **A.CED.2, F.IF.7.a, F.LE.2**

Objectives To determine whether lines are parallel, perpendicular, or neither
To write equations of parallel lines and perpendicular lines

Solve It! Write your solution to the Solve It in the space below.

Two distinct lines in a coordinate plane either intersect or are *parallel*. **Parallel lines** are lines in the same plane that never intersect.

Essential Understanding You can determine the relationship between two lines by comparing their slopes and y-intercepts.

Key Concept Slopes of Parallel Lines

Words

Nonvertical lines are parallel if they have the same slope and different y-intercepts. Vertical lines are parallel if they have different x-intercepts.

Graph

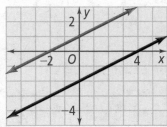

Example

The graphs of $y = \frac{1}{2}x + 1$ and $y = \frac{1}{2}x - 2$ are lines that have the same slope, $\frac{1}{2}$, and different y-intercepts. The lines are parallel.

You can use the fact that the slopes of parallel lines are the same to write an equation of a line parallel to a given line.

Got It? A line passes through $(-3, -1)$ and is parallel to the graph of $y = 2x + 3$. What equation represents the line in slope-intercept form?

Practice Write an equation in slope-intercept form of the line that passes through the given point and is parallel to the graph of the given equation.

1. $(2, -1)$; $y = -\frac{3}{2}x + 6$

2. $(0, 0)$; $y = \frac{2}{3}x + 1$

You can also use slope to determine whether two lines are *perpendicular*. **Perpendicular lines** are lines that intersect to form right angles.

take note

Key Concept Slopes of Perpendicular Lines

Words

Two nonvertical lines are perpendicular if the product of their slopes is -1. A vertical line and a horizontal line are also perpendicular.

Graph

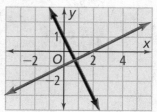

Example

The graph of $y = \frac{1}{2}x - 1$ has a slope of $\frac{1}{2}$. The graph of $y = -2x + 1$ has a slope of -2. Since $\frac{1}{2}(-2) = -1$, the lines are perpendicular.

Two numbers whose product is -1 are **opposite reciprocals**. So, the slopes of perpendicular lines are opposite reciprocals. To find the opposite reciprocal of $-\frac{3}{4}$, for example, first find the reciprocal, $-\frac{4}{3}$. Then write its opposite, $\frac{4}{3}$. Since $-\frac{3}{4} \cdot \frac{4}{3} = -1$, $\frac{4}{3}$ is the opposite reciprocal of $-\frac{3}{4}$.

Problem 2 Classifying Lines

Got It? Are the graphs of the equations *parallel*, *perpendicular*, or *neither*? Explain.

    a. $y = \frac{3}{4}x + 7$ and $4x - 3y = 9$

    b. $6y = -x + 6$ and $y = -\frac{1}{6}x + 6$

Practice Determine whether the graphs of the given equations are *parallel, perpendicular*, or *neither*. Explain.

    3. $y = -7$
       $x = 2$

    4. $y = 4x - 2$
       $-x + 4y = 0$

Problem 3   Writing an Equation of a Perpendicular Line

Got It?   A line passes through $(1, 8)$ and is perpendicular to the graph of $y = 2x + 1$. What equation represents the line in slope-intercept form?

 **Practice**   Write an equation in slope-intercept form of the line that passes through the given point and is perpendicular to the graph of the given equation.

   5. $(5, 0)$; $y + 1 = 2(x - 3)$

   6. $(1, -6)$; $x - 2y = 4$

Problem 4   Solving a Real-World Problem

Got It?   What equation could the architect in Problem 4 enter to represent a second beam whose graph will pass through the corner at $(0, 10)$ and be parallel to the existing beam? Give your answer in slope-intercept form.

Practice

7. **Urban Planning** A path for a new city park will connect the park entrance to Main Street. The path should be perpendicular to Main Street. What is an equation that represents the path?

8. **Bike Path** A bike path is being planned for the park in Exercise 7. The bike path will be parallel to Main Street and will pass through the park entrance. What is an equation of the line that represents the bike path?

 Lesson Check

Do you know HOW?

9. Which equations below have graphs that are parallel to one another? Which have graphs that are perpendicular to one another?

   $y = -\frac{1}{6}x$
   $y = 6x$
   $y = 6x - 2$

10. What is an equation of the line that passes through $(3, -1)$ and is parallel to $y = -4x + 1$? Give your answer in slope-intercept form.

11. What is an equation of the line that passes through $(2, -3)$ and is perpendicular to $y = x - 5$? Give your answer in slope-intercept form.

Do you UNDERSTAND?

12. Vocabulary Tell whether the two numbers in each pair are opposite reciprocals.

   a. $-2, \frac{1}{2}$ **b.** $\frac{1}{4}, 4$ **c.** $5, -5$

13. Open-Ended Write equations of two parallel lines.

14. Compare and Contrast How is determining if two nonvertical lines are parallel similar to determining if they are perpendicular? How are the processes different?

B Apply

15. Identify each pair of parallel lines. Then identify each pair of perpendicular lines.

   line *a*: $y = 3x + 3$ line *b*: $x = -1$ line *c*: $y - 5 = \frac{1}{2}(x - 2)$

   line *d*: $y = 3$ line *e*: $y + 4 = -2(x + 6)$ line *f*: $9x - 3y = 5$

Determine whether each statement is *always, sometimes,* or *never* true. Explain.

16. A horizontal line is parallel to the *x*-axis.

17. Two lines with positive slopes are parallel.

18. Two lines with the same slope and different *y*-intercepts are perpendicular.

© 19. **Reasoning** For an arithmetic sequence, the first term is $A(1) = 3$. Each successive term adds 2 to the previous term. Another arithmetic sequence has the rule $B(n) = 5 + (n - 1)d$, where *n* is the term number and *d* is the common difference. If the graphs of the two sequences are parallel, what is the value of *d*? Explain.

© 20. **Reasoning** Will the graph of the line represented by the table intersect the graph of $y = 4x + 5$? Explain.

x	−1	0	1	2
y	−1	3	7	11

© 21. **Think About a Plan** A designer is creating a new logo, as shown at the right. The designer wants to add a line to the logo that will be perpendicular to the blue line and pass through the red point. What equation represents the new line?
   • What is the slope of the blue line?
   • What is the slope of the new line?

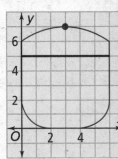

© 22. **Reasoning** For what value of *k* are the graphs of $12y = -3x + 8$ and $6y = kx - 5$ parallel? For what value of *k* are they perpendicular?

23. **Agriculture** Two farmers use combines to harvest corn from their fields. One farmer has 600 acres of corn, and the other has 1000 acres of corn. Each farmer's combine can harvest 100 acres per day. Write two equations for the number of acres *y* of corn *not* harvested after *x* days. Are the graphs of the equations *parallel, perpendicular,* or *neither*? How do you know?

C Challenge

24. **Geometry** In a rectangle, opposite sides are parallel and adjacent sides are perpendicular. Figure *ABCD* has vertices $A(-3, 3)$, $B(-1, -2)$, $C(4, 0)$, and $D(2, 5)$. Show that *ABCD* is a rectangle.

25. **Geometry** A right triangle has two sides that are perpendicular to each other. Triangle *PQR* has vertices $P(4, 3)$, $Q(2, -1)$, and $R(0, 1)$. Determine whether *PQR* is a right triangle. Explain your reasoning.

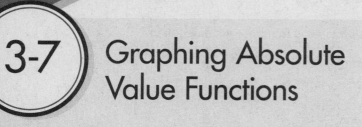

3-7 Graphing Absolute Value Functions

F.IF.7 Graph functions expressed symbolically and show key features of the graph . . . Also **F.IF.4, F.BF.3**

Objectives To graph an absolute value function
To translate the graph of an absolute value function

Solve It! Write your solution to the Solve It in the space below.

In the Solve It you described how one line could be shifted to result in a second line. You can use a similar method to graph *absolute value functions.* An **absolute value function** has a V-shaped graph that opens up or down. The parent function for the family of absolute value functions is $y = |x|$.

A **translation** is a shift of a graph horizontally, vertically, or both. The result is a graph of the same size and shape, but in a different position.

Essential Understanding You can quickly graph absolute value equations by shifting the graph of $y = |x|$.

Problem 1   Describing Translations

Got It?   **a.** How is the graph below related to the graph of $y = |x|$?

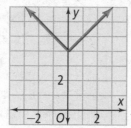

Ⓒ **b. Reasoning** What are the domain and range of each function in Problem 1?

Ⓐ **Practice** Describe how each graph is related to the graph of $y = |x|$.

1.

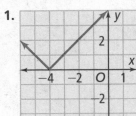

2.

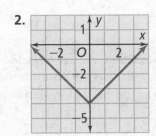

The graph of $y = |x| + k$ is a translation of $y = |x|$. Let k be a positive number. Then $y = |x| + k$ translates the graph of $y = |x|$ up k units, while $y = |x| - k$ translates the graph of $y = |x|$ down k units.

Problem 2 **Graphing a Vertical Translation**

Got It? What is the graph of $y = |x| - 7$?

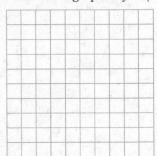

Think

How can the graph of $y = |x|$ help you graph this equation?

A Practice Graph each function by translating $y = |x|$.

3. $y = |x| + 3$

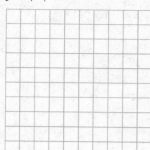

4. $y = |x| - 6$

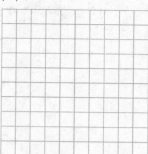

If you know the direction of the translation and the number of units the function is to be translated, you can write an equation to describe the translation.

Problem 3 **Writing Equations of Vertical Translations**

Got It? What is an equation for each translation of $y = |x|$?

   a. 8 units up

   b. 5 units down

A Practice Write an equation for each translation of $y = |x|$.

   5. 0.25 unit up

   6. 3.25 units down

The graphs below show what happens when you graph $y = |x + 2|$ and $y = |x - 2|$.

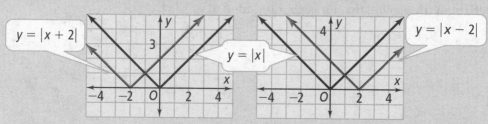

For a positive number h, $y = |x + h|$ translates the graph of $y = |x|$ left h units, and $y = |x - h|$ translates the graph of $y = |x|$ right h units.

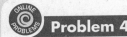 **Problem 4** Graphing a Horizontal Translation

Think

How can you check that the graph is correct?

Got It? What is the graph of $y = |x - 5|$?

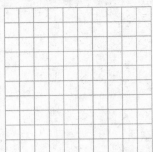

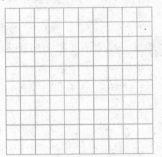**Practice** Graph each function by translating $y = |x|$.

7. $y = |x - 3|$

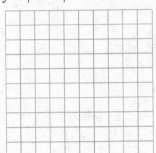

8. $y = |x + 6|$

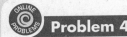 **Problem 5** Writing Equations of Horizontal Translations

Got It? What is an equation for each translation of $y = |x|$?

    a. 8 units right

                                b. 6 units left

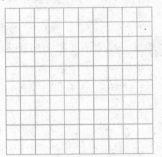**Practice** Write an equation for each translation of $y = |x|$.

    9. left $\frac{5}{2}$ units

                               10. right 8.2 units

Lesson Check

Do you know HOW?

11. How is the graph of $y = |x| - 8$ different from the graph of $y = |x|$? How is it the same?

12. What is the equation for the translation 9 units up of the graph of $y = |x|$?

13. What is the graph of $y = |x + 7|$?

Do you UNDERSTAND?

MATHEMATICAL PRACTICES

14. Compare and Contrast How are the graphs of $y = |x| - 4$ and $y = |x - 4|$ the same? How are they different?

© 15. **Error Analysis** A student is graphing the equation $y = |x - 10|$ and translates the graph of $y = |x|$ to the left 10 units. Describe the student's error.

More Practice and Problem-Solving Exercises

Ⓑ **Apply**

At the right is the graph of $y = -|x|$. Graph each function by translating $y = -|x|$.

16. $y = -|x| + 3$ **17.** $y = -|x| - 3$

18. $y = -|x + 3|$ **19.** $y = -|x - 3|$

Write an equation for each translation of $y = -|x|$.

20. 2 units up   **21.** 2.25 units left

22. 15 units down   **23.** 4 units right

© 24. **Think About a Plan** What point(s) do the graphs of $y = |x - 2|$ and $y = |x + 4|$ have in common?
- How are these graphs related?
- Could a graph or a table help you solve this problem?

25. What point(s) do the graphs of $y = -|x| + 7$ and $y = |x - 3|$ have in common?

© 26. **a.** Graph $y = |x - 2| + 3$.
     b. The *vertex* of an absolute value function is the point at which its graph changes direction. What is the vertex of the graph of $y = |x - 2| + 3$?
     c. **Reasoning** What relationship do you see between the vertex and the equation? What is the vertex of the graph of $y = |x - h| + k$?

27. A car travels on a straight road at 60 mi/h. It goes under an overpass, then three minutes later, goes under another overpass. The car then continues on the straight road.
     a. Make a table showing the number of minutes since going under the first overpass, and the distance in miles from the second overpass.
     b. Write a function that models the situation.
     c. Graph the function. What is the significance of the vertex of the graph?

Ⓒ **Challenge**

28. **a.** Graph $y = |2x|$ by making a table of values.
     b. Translate $y = |2x|$ to graph $y = |2x| + 3$.
     c. Translate $y = |2x|$ to graph $y = |2(x - 1)|$.
     d. Translate $y = |2x|$ to graph $y = |2(x - 1)| + 3$.

3-1 Rate of Change and Slope

Quick Review

Rate of change shows the relationship between two changing quantities. The **slope** of a line is the ratio of the vertical change (the rise) to the horizontal change (the run).

$$\text{slope} = \frac{\text{rise}}{\text{run}} = \frac{y_2 - y_1}{x_2 - x_1}$$

The slope of a horizontal line is 0, and the slope of a vertical line is undefined.

Example

What is the slope of the line that passes through the points (1, 12) and (6, 22)?

$$\text{slope} = \frac{y_2 - y_1}{x_2 - x_1} = \frac{22 - 12}{6 - 1} = \frac{10}{5} = 2$$

Exercises

Find the slope of the line that passes through each pair of points.

1. (2, 2), (3, 1) **2.** (4, 2), (0, 2)

3. (−1, 2), (0, 5) **4.** (−3, −2), (−3, 2)

Find the slope of each line.

5. 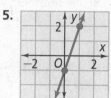 **6.**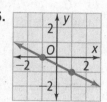

3-2 Direct Variation

Quick Review

A function represents a **direct variation** if it has the form $y = kx$, where $k \neq 0$. The coefficient k is the **constant of variation**.

Example

Suppose y varies directly with x, and $y = 15$ when $x = 5$. Write a direct variation equation that relates x and y. What is the value of y when $x = 9$?

$y = kx$ Start with the general form of a direct variation.

$15 = k(5)$ Substitute 5 for x and 15 for y.

$3 = k$ Divide each side by 5 to solve for k.

$y = 3x$ Write an equation. Substitute 3 for k in $y = kx$.

The equation $y = 3x$ relates x and y. When $x = 9$, $y = 3(9)$, or 27.

Exercises

Suppose y varies directly with x. Write a direct variation equation that relates x and y. Then find the value of y when $x = 7$.

7. $y = 8$ when $x = -4$. **8.** $y = 15$ when $x = 6$.

9. $y = 3$ when $x = 9$. **10.** $y = -4$ when $x = 4$.

For the data in each table, tell whether y varies directly with x. If it does, write an equation for the direct variation.

11.

x	y
−1	−6
2	3
5	12
9	24

12.

x	y
−3	7.5
−1	2.5
2	−5
5	−12.5

3-3, 3-4, and 3-5 Forms of Linear Equations

Quick Review

The graph of a linear equation is a line. You can write a linear equation in different forms.

The **slope-intercept form** of a linear equation is $y = mx + b$, where m is the slope and b is the **y-intercept**.

The **point-slope form** of a linear equation is $y - y_1 = m(x - x_1)$, where m is the slope and (x_1, y_1) is a point on the line.

The **standard form** of a linear equation is $Ax + By = C$, where A, B, and C are real numbers, and A and B are not both zero.

Example

What is an equation of the line that has slope -4 and passes through the point $(-1, 7)$?

$y - y_1 = m(x - x_1)$ Use point-slope form.

$y - 7 = -4(x - (-1))$ Substitute $(-1, 7)$ for (x_1, y_1) and -4 for m.

$y - 7 = -4(x + 1)$ Simplify inside grouping symbols.

An equation of the line is $y - 7 = -4(x + 1)$.

Exercises

Write an equation in slope-intercept form of the line that passes through the given points.

13. $(-3, 4), (1, 4)$ **14.** $(3, -2), (6, 1)$

Write an equation of each line.

15. 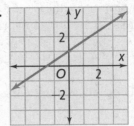   **16.**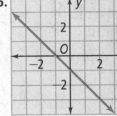

Graph each equation.

17. $y = 4x - 3$ **18.** $y = 2$

19. $y + 3 = 2(x - 1)$ **20.** $x + 4y = 10$

3-6 Slopes of Parallel and Perpendicular Lines

Quick Review

Parallel lines are lines in the same plane that never intersect. Two lines are **perpendicular** if they intersect to form right angles.

Example

Are the graphs of $y = \frac{4}{3}x + 5$ and $y = -\frac{3}{4}x + 2$ *parallel*, *perpendicular*, or *neither*? Explain.

The slope of the graph of $y = \frac{4}{3}x + 5$ is $\frac{4}{3}$.

The slope of the graph of $y = -\frac{3}{4}x + 2$ is $-\frac{3}{4}$.

$$\frac{4}{3}\left(-\frac{3}{4}\right) = -1$$

The slopes are opposite reciprocals, so the graphs are perpendicular.

Exercises

Write an equation of the line that passes through the given point and is parallel to the graph of the given equation.

21. $(2, -1); y = 5x - 2$ **22.** $(0, -5); y = 9x$

Determine whether the graphs of the two equations are *parallel*, *perpendicular*, or *neither*. Explain.

23. $y = 6x + 2$ **24.** $2x - 5y = 0$

$18x - 3y = 15$ $y + 3 = \frac{5}{2}x$

Write an equation of the line that passes through the given point and is perpendicular to the graph of the given equation.

25. $(3, 5); y = -3x + 7$ **26.** $(4, 10); y = 8x - 1$

3-7 Graphing Absolute Value Functions

Quick Review

The graph of an **absolute value function** is a V-shaped graph that opens upward or downward.

A **translation** shifts a graph either vertically, horizontally, or both. To graph an absolute value function, you can translate $y = |x|$.

Example

Graph the absolute value function $y = |x - 4|$.

Start with the graph of $y = |x|$. Translate the graph right 4 units.

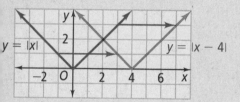

Exercises

Graph each function by translating $y = |x|$.

27. $y = |x| + 2$ **28.** $y = |x| - 3$

29. $y = |x + 3|$ **30.** $y = |x - 6|$

Write an equation for each translation of $y = |x|$.

31. 5.5 units down   **32.** 11 units left

33. 13 units up   **34.** 6.5 units right

35. Write an equation for the graph of the absolute value function at the right.

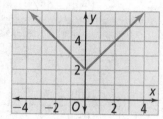

Pull It All Together

Analyzing Advertising Revenue

A local weekly newspaper offers advertising in its print edition and on its Web site. The table shows the amount of revenue the newspaper received from print advertising for various years.

Print Advertising

Year	Revenue
2000	$95,000
2006	$77,000
2009	$68,000
2010	$65,000
2012	$59,000

In 2010, the newspaper's revenue from online advertising was $31,000. The revenue from online advertising has been increasing steadily at a rate of $2500 per year.

Task Description

Determine the first year in which revenue from online advertising will exceed revenue from print advertising, and find the total advertising revenue in that year.

a. Is the rate of change in revenue from print advertising with respect to time constant? If so, what does the rate of change represent?

b. Let x = the number of years since 2000.
Let y = the revenue from print advertising in thousands of dollars.

Write an equation in slope-intercept form that models the revenue from print advertising, in thousands of dollars, x years after 2000.

c. Explain how you can use point-slope form to write an equation that models the revenue from online advertising, in thousands of dollars, x years after 2000. Describe what the point you use represents and what the slope represents. Then write the equation.

d. What is the first year in which revenue from online advertising will exceed revenue from print advertising? What is the total advertising revenue for that year? Justify your answer with tables and/or graphs.

Get Ready!

Solving Equations

Solve each equation. If the equation is an identity, write *identity*.
If it has no solution, write *no solution*.

1. $3(2 - 2x) = -6(x - 1)$ **2.** $3p + 1 = -p + 5$ **3.** $4x - 1 = 3(x + 1) + x$

4. $\frac{1}{2}(6c - 4) = 4 + c$ **5.** $5x = 2 - (x - 7)$ **6.** $v + 5 = v - 5$

Solving Inequalities

Solve each inequality.

7. $5x + 3 < 18$ **8.** $-\frac{r}{5} + 1 \geq -6$ **9.** $-3t - 5 < 34$

10. $-(7f + 18) - 2f \leq 0$ **11.** $8s + 7 > -3(5s - 4)$ **12.** $\frac{1}{2}(x + 6) + 1 \geq -5$

Writing Functions

13. The height of a triangle is 1 cm less than twice the length of the base.
Let $x =$ the length of the base.

  a. Write an expression for the height of the triangle.

  b. Write a function rule for the area of the triangle.

  c. What is the area of such a triangle if the length of its base is 16 cm?

Graphing Linear Equations

Graph each equation.

14. $2x + 4y = -8$ **15.** $y = -\frac{2}{3}x + 3$ **16.** $y + 5 = -2(x - 2)$

 ## Looking Ahead Vocabulary

17. Two answers to a question are said to be *inconsistent* if they could not both be true. Two answers to a question are said to be *consistent* if they could both be true. If there is no solution that makes both equations in a system of two linear equations true, do you think the system is *inconsistent* or *consistent*?

18. After a team loses a game, they're *eliminated* from a tournament. The *elimination method* is a way to solve a system of equations. Do you think using the elimination method adds or deletes a variable from a system of equations?

CHAPTER 4

Systems of Equations and Inequalities

Big Ideas

1 Solving Equations and Inequalities
Essential Question: How can you solve a system of equations or inequalities?

2 Modeling
Essential Question: Can systems of equations model real-world situations?

©Domains

- Creating Equations
- Reasoning with Equations and Inequalities

Chapter Preview

Interactive Digital Path

Log in to **pearsonsuccessnet.com** and click on Interactive Digital Path to access the Solve Its and animated Problems.

 Vocabulary

English/Spanish Vocabulary Audio Online:

English	Spanish
consistent, *p. 233*	consistente
dependent, *p. 233*	dependiente
elimination method, *p. 247*	eliminación
inconsistent, *p. 233*	inconsistente
independent, *p. 233*	independiente
linear inequality, *p. 263*	desigualdad lineal
solution of an inequality, *p. 263*	solución de una desigua
solution of a system of linear equations, *p. 231*	solución de un sistema ecuaciones lineales
solution of a system of linear inequalities, *p. 271*	solución de un sistema desigualdades lineales
substitution method, *p. 240*	método de sustitución

 **4-1** Solving Systems by Graphing

A.REI.6 Solve systems of linear equations . . . focusing on pairs of linear equations in two variables.
Also A.CED.3

Objectives To solve systems of equations by graphing
To analyze special systems

Solve It! Write your solution to the Solve It in the space below.

Two or more linear equations form a **system of linear equations**. Any ordered pair that makes *all* of the equations in a system true is a **solution of a system of linear equations**.

Essential Understanding You can use systems of linear equations to model problems. Systems of equations can be solved in more than one way. One method is to graph each equation and find the intersection point, if one exists.

Problem 1 Solving a System of Equations by Graphing

Got It? What is the solution of the system? Check your answer.

$y = 2x + 4$
$y = x + 2$

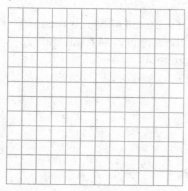

Think

How does graphing each equation help you find the solution?

 **Practice** Solve each system by graphing. Check your solution.

1. $y = 2x$

$y = -2x + 8$

2. $y = \frac{1}{2}x + 7$

$y = \frac{3}{2}x + 3$

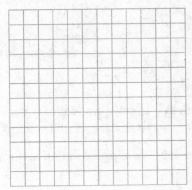 **Problem 2** **Writing a System of Equations**

Got It? One satellite radio service charges $10 per month plus an activation fee of $20. A second service charges $11 per month plus an activation fee of $15. In what month was the cost of both services the same?

Think

What are the initial cost and the rate of change for each service?

 Practice **3. Student Statistics** The number of right-handed students in a mathematics class is nine times the number of left-handed students. The total number of students in the class is 30. How many right-handed students are in the class? How many left-handed students are in the class?

4. Plants A plant nursery is growing a tree that is 3 ft tall and grows at an average rate of 1 ft per year. Another tree at the nursery is 4 ft tall and grows at an average rate of 0.5 ft per year. After how many years will the trees be the same height?

A system of equations that has at least one solution is **consistent**. A consistent system can be either *independent* or *dependent*.

A consistent system that is **independent** has exactly one solution. For example, the systems in Problems 1 and 2 are consistent and independent. A consistent system that is **dependent** has infinitely many solutions.

A system of equations that has no solution is **inconsistent**.

Problem 3   Systems with Infinitely Many Solutions or No Solution

Got It?   What is the solution of each system in parts (a) and (b)? Describe the number of solutions.

a. $y = -x - 3$
 $y = -x + 5$

b. $y = 3x - 3$
 $3y = 9x - 9$

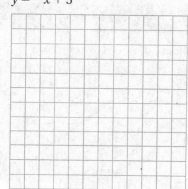
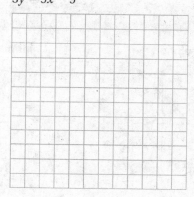

c. Reasoning Before graphing the equations, how can you determine whether a system of equations has exactly one solution, infinitely many solutions, or no solution?

Practice Solve each system by graphing. Tell whether the system has *one solution, infinitely many solutions,* or *no solution.*

5. $2x + 2y = 4$
   $12 - 3x = 3y$

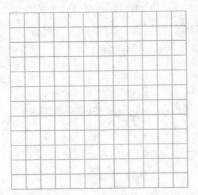

6. $2y = x - 2$
   $3y = \frac{3}{2}x - 3$

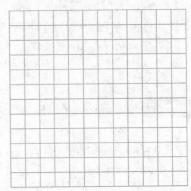

---

take note

Concept Summary   Systems of Linear Equations

One solution

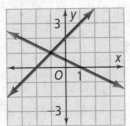

The lines intersect at one point. The lines have different slopes. The equations are consistent and independent.

Infinitely many solutions

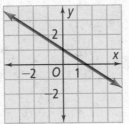

The lines are the same. The lines have the same slope and *y*-intercept. The equations are consistent and dependent.

No solution

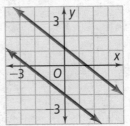

The lines are parallel. The lines have the same slope and different *y*-intercepts. The equations are inconsistent.

Lesson Check

Do you know HOW?

Solve each system by graphing.

7. $y = x + 7$
   $y = 2x + 1$

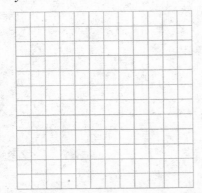

8. $y = \frac{1}{2}x + 6$
   $y = x - 2$

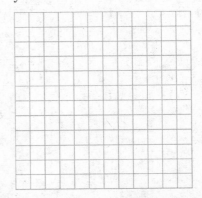

9. $y = -3x - 3$
$y = 2x + 2$

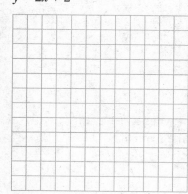

10. $y = -x - 4$
$4x - y = -1$

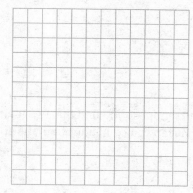

11. Concert Tickets Tickets for a concert cost $10 each if you order them online, but you must pay a service charge of $8 per order. The tickets are $12 each if you buy them at the door on the night of the concert.

   a. Write a system of equations to model the situation. Let c be the total cost. Let t be the number of tickets.

   b. Graph the equations and find the intersection point. What does this point represent?

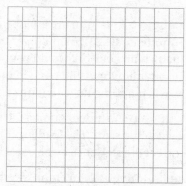

Do you UNDERSTAND?

MATHEMATICAL PRACTICES

12. Vocabulary Match each type of system with the number of solutions the system has.

   A. inconsistent

   B. consistent and dependent

   C. consistent and independent

   I. exactly one

   II. infinitely many

   III. no solution

13. Writing Suppose you graph a system of linear equations. If a point is on only one of the lines, is it a solution of the system? Explain.

14. Reasoning Can a system of two linear equations have exactly two solutions? Explain.

15. Reasoning Suppose you find that two linear equations are true when $x = -2$ and $y = 3$. What can you conclude about the graphs of the equations? Explain.

More Practice and Problem-Solving Exercises

B Apply

16. Think About a Plan You are looking for an after-school job. One job pays $9 per hour. Another pays $12 per hour, but you must buy a uniform that costs $39. After how many hours of work would your net earnings from either job be the same?
- What equations can you write to model the situation?
- How will graphing the equations help you solve the problem?

17. Error Analysis A student graphs the system $y = -x + 3$ and $y = -2x - 1$ as shown at the right. The student concludes there is no solution. Describe and correct the student's error.

18. Reasoning Suppose you graph a system of linear equations and the intersection point appears to be (3, 7). Can you be sure that the ordered pair (3, 7) is the solution? What must you do to be sure?

19. Cell Phone Plans A cell phone provider offers a plan that costs $40 per month plus $.20 per text message sent or received. A comparable plan costs $60 per month but offers unlimited text messaging.
- **a.** How many text messages would you have to send or receive in order for the plans to cost the same each month?
- **b.** If you send or receive an average of 50 text messages each month, which plan would you choose? Why?

Without graphing, decide whether each system has one solution, infinitely many solutions, or no solution. Justify your answer.

20. $y = x - 4$
   $y = x - 3$

21. $x - y = -\frac{1}{2}$
   $2x - 2y = -1$

22. $y = 5x - 1$
   $10x = 2y + 2$

23. $3x + 2y = 1$
   $4y = 6x + 2$

24. Banking The graph at the right shows the balances in two bank accounts over time. Use the graph to write a system of equations giving the amount in each account over time. Let t = the time in weeks and let b = the balance in dollars. If the accounts continue to grow as shown, when will they have the same balance?

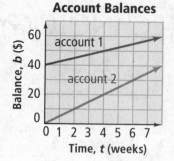

Account Balances

© **25. Open-Ended** One equation in a system is $y = \frac{1}{2}x - 2$.
   a. Write a second equation so that the system has one solution.
   b. Write a second equation so that the system has no solution.
   c. Write a second equation so that the system has infinitely many solutions.

Challenge

© **26. Reasoning** Consider the system at the right.
$$y = gx + 3$$
$$y = hx + 7$$
   a. If $g \geq h$, will the system *always*, *sometimes*, or *never* have exactly one solution? Explain your reasoning.
   b. If $g \leq h$, will the system *always*, *sometimes*, or *never* have infinitely many solutions? Explain your reasoning.

27. Hiking Two hikers are walking along a marked trail. The first hiker starts at a point 6 mi from the beginning of the trail and walks at a speed of 4 mi/h. At the same time, the second hiker starts 1 mi from the beginning and walks at a speed of 3 mi/h.
   a. What is a system of equations that models the situation?
   b. Graph the two equations and find the intersection point.
   c. Is the intersection point meaningful in this situation? Explain.

TECHNOLOGY LAB

Use With Lesson 4-1

Solving Systems Using Tables and Graphs

A.REI.11 Explain why the x-coordinates of the points where the graphs of the equations $y = f(x)$ and $y = g(x)$ intersect are the solutions of the equation $f(x) = g(x)$; find the solutions approximately . . . Also **A.REI.6**

Activity 1

MATHEMATICAL PRACTICES

Solve the system using a table. $\quad y = 3x - 7$
$$y = -0.5x + 7$$

Step 1
Enter the equations in the (y=) screen.

Step 2
Use the (tblset) function. Set TblStart to 0 and Δ Tbl to 1.

Step 3
Press (table) to show the table on the screen.

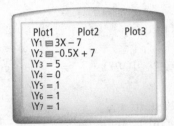

```
Plot1   Plot2   Plot3
\Y1 ⊟ 3X − 7
\Y2 ⊟ −0.5X + 7
\Y3 = 5
\Y4 = 0
\Y5 = 1
\Y6 = 1
\Y7 = 1
```

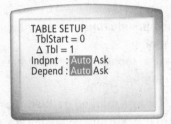

```
TABLE SETUP
  TblStart = 0
  Δ Tbl = 1
  Indpnt : Auto Ask
  Depend : Auto Ask
```

X	Y1	Y2
0	−7	7
1	−4	6.5
2	−1	6
3	2	5.5
4	5	5
5	8	4.5
6	11	4

X=0

1. Which x-value gives the same value for Y_1 and Y_2?

2. What ordered pair is the solution of the system?

Activity 2

Solve the system using a graph. $\quad y = -5x + 6$
$$y = -x - 2$$

Step 1 Enter the equations in the (y=) screen.

Step 2 Graph the equations. Use a standard graphing window.

Step 3 Use the (calc) feature. Choose **INTERSECT** to find the point where the lines intersect.

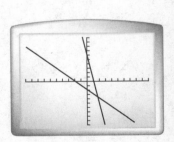

3. Complete: The lines intersect at (_____, _____), so this point is the solution of the system.

4. How can you use the graph to find the solution of the equation $-5x + 6 = -x - 2$?

Exercises

Use the table and graph to solve each system. Sketch your graph.

5. $y = 5x - 3$
$y = 3x + 1$

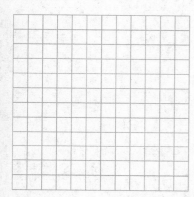

6. $y = 2x - 13$
$y = x - 9$

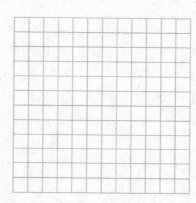

7. $2x - y = 1.5$
$y = -\frac{1}{2}x - 1.5$

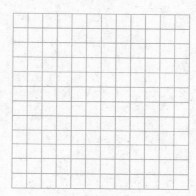

8. How can you use the graph of a system to find the solution of the equation $5x - 3 = 3x + 1$?

4-2 Solving Systems Using Substitution

A.REI.6 Solve systems of linear equations . . . focusing on pairs of linear equations in two variables. Also **A.CED.3**

Objective To solve systems of equations using substitution

Solve It! Write your solution to the Solve It in the space below.

You can solve linear systems by solving one of the equations for one of the variables. Then substitute the expression for the variable into the other equation. This is called the **substitution method**.

Essential Understanding Systems of equations can be solved in more than one way. When a system has at least one equation that can be solved quickly for a variable, the system can be solved efficiently using substitution.

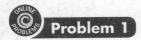 **Problem 1** **Using Substitution**

Got It? What is the solution of the system? Use substitution. Check your answer.

$y = 2x + 7$
$y = x - 1$

Think
Which variable should you substitute for?

1. $x + y = 8$
   $y = 3x$

2. $2x + 2y = 38$
   $y = x + 3$

> To use substitution to solve a system of equations, one of the equations must be solved for a variable.

Problem 2 Solving for a Variable and Using Substitution

Got It? **a.** What is the solution of the system? Use substitution. $6y + 5x = 8$
   $x + 3y = -7$

b. Reasoning In your first step in part (a), which variable did you solve for? Which equation did you use to solve for the variable?

Practice Solve each system using substitution. Check your answer.

3. $4x = 3y - 2$
   $18 = 3x + y$

4. $2 = 2y - x$
   $23 = 5y - 4x$

Got It? You pay $22 to rent 6 video games. The store charges $4 for new games and $2 for older games. How many new games did you rent?

 Practice

5. **Transportation** A school is planning a field trip for 142 people. The trip will use six drivers and two types of vehicles: buses and vans. A bus can seat 51 passengers. A van can seat 10 passengers. Write and solve a system of equations to find how many buses and how many vans will be needed.

6. **Geometry** The measure of one acute angle in a right triangle is four times the measure of the other acute angle. Write and solve a system of equations to find the measures of the acute angles.

If you get an identity, like $2 = 2$, when you solve a system of equations, then the system has infinitely many solutions. If you get a false statement, like $8 = 2$, then the system has no solution.

Problem 4 Systems With Infinitely Many Solutions or No Solution

Got It? How many solutions does the system have? Explain.

$6y + 5x = 8$
$2.5x + 3y = 4$

Think

How many solutions can a system of linear equations have?

Practice **Tell whether the system has *one solution, infinitely many solutions,* or *no solution.***

7. $5 = \frac{1}{2}x + 3y$
$10 - x = 6y$

8. $17 = 11y + 12x$
$12x + 11y = 14$

Lesson Check

Do you know HOW?

Solve each system using substitution. Check your solution.

9. $4y = x$
$3x - y = 70$

10. $-2x + 5y = 19$
$3x - 4 = y$

Tell whether the system has *one solution, infinitely many solutions,* or *no solution.*

11. $y = 2x + 1$
$4x - 2y = 6$

12. $-x + \frac{1}{2}y = 13$
$x + 15 = \frac{1}{2}y$

13. Talent Show In a talent show of singing and comedy acts, singing acts are 5 min long and comedy acts are 3 min long. The show has 12 acts and lasts 50 min. How many singing acts and how many comedy acts are in the show?

Do you UNDERSTAND?

MATHEMATICAL PRACTICES

Ⓒ **14. Vocabulary** When is the substitution method a better method than graphing for solving a system of linear equations?

For each system, tell which equation you would first use to solve for a variable in the first step of the substitution method. Explain your choice.

15. $-2x + y = -1$
$4x + 2y = 12$

16. $2.5x - 7y = 7.5$
$6x - y = 1$

Tell whether each statement is *true* or *false*. Explain.

17. When solving a system using substitution, if you obtain an identity, then the system has no solution.

18. You cannot use substitution to solve a system that does not have a variable with a coefficient of 1 or −1.

More Practice and Problem-Solving Exercises

MATHEMATICAL PRACTICES

Apply

19. **Geometry** The rectangle shown has a perimeter of 34 cm and the given area. Its length is 5 more than twice its width. Write and solve a system of equations to find the dimensions of the rectangle.

ℓ

w | $A = 52$ cm²

20. **Writing** What would your first step be in solving the system below? Explain.
    $$1.2x + y = 2$$
    $$1.4y = 2.8x + 1$$

21. **Coins** You have $3.70 in dimes and quarters. You have 5 more quarters than dimes. How many of each type of coin do you have?

22. **Error Analysis** Describe and correct the error at the right in finding the solution of the following system:
    $$7x + 5y = 14$$
    $$x + 8y = 21$$

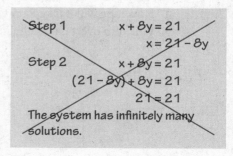

Step 1 $x + 8y = 21$
                    $x = 21 - 8y$
Step 2 $x + 8y = 21$
              $(21 - 8y) + 8y = 21$
                    $21 = 21$
The system has infinitely many solutions.

23. Art An artist is going to sell two sizes of prints at an art fair. The artist will charge $20 for a small print and $45 for a large print. The artist would like to sell twice as many small prints as large prints. The booth the artist is renting for the day costs $510. How many of each size print must the artist sell in order to break even at the fair?

24. Think About a Plan At a certain high school, 350 students are taking an algebra course. The ratio of boys to girls taking algebra is 33 : 37. How many more girls are taking algebra than boys?
  - How can you write a system of equations to model the situation?
  - Which equation will you solve for a variable in the first step of solving the system? Why?
  - How can you interpret the solution in the context of the problem?

25. a. Compare and Contrast Using a graph, how can you tell when a system of linear equations has no solution?
  b. Using substitution, how can you tell when a system of linear equations has no solution?
  c. How can you tell by looking at a table of values if two lines will intersect in one point, no points, or an infinite number of points?

26. Fireworks A pyrotechnician plans for two fireworks to explode together at the same height in the air. They travel at the speeds shown at the right. Firework B is launched 0.25 s before Firework A. How many seconds after Firework B launches will both fireworks explode?

Firework A   Firework B
220 ft/s   200 ft/s

27. Writing Let a be any real number. Will the system at the right *always*, *sometimes*, or *never* have a solution? Explain.

$y = ax$
$y = ax + 4$

28. Reasoning Explain how you can use substitution to show that the system at the right has no solution.

$y + x = x$
$\dfrac{3x}{2y} = 4$

Challenge

29. Agriculture A farmer grows corn, tomatoes, and sunflowers on a 320-acre farm. This year, the farmer wants to plant twice as many acres of tomatoes as acres of sunflowers. The farmer also wants to plant 40 more acres of corn than of tomatoes. How many acres of each crop should the farmer plant?

30. Track and Field Michelle and Pam are running a 200-m race. Michelle runs at an average of 7.5 m/s. Pam averages 7.8 m/s, but she starts 1 s after Michelle.
  a. How long will it take Pam to catch up to Michelle?
  b. Will Pam overtake Michelle before the finish line? Explain.

4-3 Solving Systems Using Elimination

A.REI.5 Prove that, given . . . two equations . . . replacing one equation by the sum of that equation and a multiple of the other produces a system with the same solutions. Also **A.CED.3, A.REI.6**

Objective   To solve systems by adding or subtracting to eliminate a variable

Solve It!   Write your solution to the Solve It in the space below.

By the Addition and Subtraction Properties of Equality, if $a = b$ and $c = d$, then $a + c = b + d$ and $a - c = b - d$. For example, $5 + 1 = 6$ and $3 + 4 = 7$, so $(5 + 1) + (3 + 4) = 6 + 7$. In the **elimination method**, you use these properties to add or subtract equations in order to eliminate a variable in a system.

Essential Understanding   There is more than one way to solve a system of equations. Some systems are written in a way that makes eliminating a variable a good method to use.

Problem 1   **Solving a System by Adding Equations**

Got It?   What is the solution of each system? Use elimination.

a. $5x - 6y = -32$
    $3x + 6y = 48$

b. $-3x - 3y = 9$
    $3x - 4y = 5$

Think

Which variable should you eliminate?

Practice Solve each system using elimination.

    1. $3x + 3y = 27$
        $x - 3y = -11$

    2. $4x - 7y = 3$
        $x - 7y = -15$

 Problem 2   **Solving a System by Subtracting Equations**

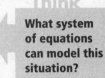

Think
What system of equations can model this situation?

Got It?   Washing 2 cars and 3 trucks takes 130 min. Washing 2 cars and 5 trucks takes 190 min. How long does it take to wash each type of vehicle?

 Practice   **3. Talent Show** Your school's talent show will feature 12 solo acts and 2 ensemble acts. The show will last 90 min. The 6 solo performers judged best will give a repeat performance at a second 60-min show, which will also feature the 2 ensemble acts. Each solo act lasts x minutes, and each ensemble act lasts y minutes.

    a. Write a system of equations to model the situation.

    b. Solve the system from part (a). How long is each solo act? How long is each ensemble act?

4. Furniture A carpenter is designing a drop-leaf table with two drop leaves of equal size. The lengths of the table when one leaf is folded up and when both leaves are folded up are shown. How long is the table when no leaves are folded up?

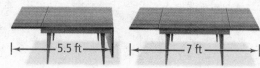

In Problems 1 and 2, a variable is eliminated because the sum or difference of its coefficients is zero. From the Multiplication Property of Equality, you know that you can multiply each side of an equation to get a new equation that is equivalent to the original. That is, $a + b = c$ is equivalent to $d(a + b) = dc$, or $da + db = dc$.

Since this is true, you can eliminate a variable by adding or subtracting, if you first multiply an equation by an appropriate number. You can prove that the results are the same simply by substituting the values for the variables in the original equations to show that the equations are true.

Problem 3   **Solving a System by Multiplying One Equation**

Got It?   **a.** How can you use the Multiplication Property of Equality to change an equation in the system at the right in order to solve it using elimination?

$-5x - 2y = 6$
$3x + 6y = 6$

b. Write and solve a revised system.

c. Show that the solution of the revised system is a solution of the original system.

5. $3x + y = 5$
   $2x - 2y = -2$

6. $6x + 4y = 42$
   $-3x + 3y = -6$

Problem 4   **Solving a System by Multiplying Both Equations**

Got It?   **a.** How can you use the Multiplication Property of Equality to $4x + 3y = -19$
change the equations in the system at the right in order to solve $3x - 2y = -10$
it using elimination?

b. Write and solve a revised system.

c. Show that the solution of the revised system is a solution of the original system.

 Practice Solve each system using elimination.

7. $6x - 3y = 15$
   $7x + 4y = 10$

8. $5x - 9y = -43$
   $3x + 8y = 68$

Recall that if you get a false statement as you solve a system, then the system has no solution. If you get an identity, then the system has infinitely many solutions.

Problem 5 Finding the Number of Solutions

Got It? How many solutions does the system at the right have?
$$-2x + 5y = 7$$
$$-2x + 5y = 12$$

 Practice Tell whether the system has *one solution, infinitely many solutions*, or *no solution*.

9. $5x - 3y = 10$
$10x + 6y = 20$

10. $4x - 7y = 15$
$-8x + 14y = -30$

The flowchart below can help you decide which steps to take when solving a system of equations using elimination.

Can I eliminate a variable by adding or subtracting the given equations? — yes — Do so.

no

Can I multiply one of the equations by a number, and then add or subtract the equations? — yes — Do so.

no

Multiply both equations by different numbers. Then add or subtract the equations.

Lesson Check

Do you know HOW?

Solve each system using elimination.

11. $3x - 2y = 0$
     $4x + 2y = 14$

12. $3p + q = 7$
     $2p - 2q = -6$

13. $3x - 2y = 1$
     $8x + 3y = 2$

Do you UNDERSTAND?

14. Vocabulary If you add two equations in two variables and the sum is an equation in one variable, what method are you using to solve the system? Explain.

15. Reasoning Explain how the Addition Property of Equality allows you to add equations.

16. Writing Explain how you would solve a system of equations using elimination.

More Practice and Problem-Solving Exercises

B Apply

© **17. Think About a Plan** A photo studio offers portraits in 8×10 and wallet-sized formats. One customer bought two 8×10 portraits and four wallet-sized portraits and paid $52. Another customer bought three 8×10 portraits and two wallet-sized portraits and paid $50. What is the cost of an 8×10 portrait? What is the cost of a wallet-sized portrait?
- Can you eliminate a variable simply by adding or subtracting?
- If not, how many of the equations do you need to multiply by a constant?

© **18. Reasoning** A toy store worker packed two boxes of identical dolls and plush toys for shipping in boxes that weigh 1 oz when empty. One box held 3 dolls and 4 plush toys. The worker marked the weight as 12 oz. The other box held 2 dolls and 3 plush toys. The worker marked the weight as 10 oz. Explain why the worker must have made a mistake.

© **19. Error Analysis** A student solved a system of equations by elimination. Describe and correct the error made in the part of the solution shown.

20. Nutrition Half a pepperoni pizza plus three fourths of a ham-and-pineapple pizza contains 765 Calories. One fourth of a pepperoni pizza plus a whole ham-and-pineapple pizza contains 745 Calories. How many Calories are in a whole pepperoni pizza? How many Calories are in a whole ham-and-pineapple pizza?

$$5x + 4y = 2 \quad \text{—} \times 3 \rightarrow 15x + 12y = 6$$
$$3x + 3y = -3 \quad \text{—} \times 4 \rightarrow 12x + 12y = -3$$
$$3x + 0 = 9$$
$$x = 3$$

© **21. Open-Ended** Write a system of equations that can be solved efficiently by elimination. Explain what you would do to eliminate one of the variables. Then solve the system.

Solve each system using any method. Explain why you chose the method you used.

22. $y = 2.5x$
$2y + 3x = 32$

23. $2x + y = 4$
$6x + 7y = 12$

24. $3x + 2y = 5$
$4x + 5y = 16$

25. $y = \frac{2}{3}x + 1$
$2x + 3y = 27$

26. $x + y = 1.5$
$2x + y = 1$

27. $\frac{1}{3}x + \frac{1}{2}y = 0$
$\frac{1}{2}x + \frac{1}{5}y = \frac{11}{5}$

© **28. Compare and Contrast** What do the substitution method and the elimination method have in common? Explain. Give an example of a system that you would prefer to solve using one method instead of the other. Justify your choice.

29. Vacations A hotel offers two activity packages. One costs $192 and includes 3 h of horseback riding and 2 h of parasailing. The second costs $213 and includes 2 h of horseback riding and 3 h of parasailing. What is the cost for 1 h of each activity?

30. Geometry Each of the squares in the figures shown at the right has the same area, and each of the triangles has the same area. The total area of Figure A is 141 cm². The total area of Figure B is 192 cm². What is the area of each square and each triangle?

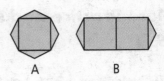

A   B

31. In parts (a)–(c), show that given a system of two equations in two variables, replacing one equation by the sum of that equation and a multiple of the other produces a system with the same solutions.

   a. What is the solution to the following system of equations with the variables x and y, where a, b, c, d, e, and f are real numbers?

$$ax + by = c$$
$$dx + ey = f$$

   b. What is the sum of the second equation and k times the first equation?

   c. Solve the system that results when you replace the second equation with your answer from part (b).

 **Challenge**

Solve each system using elimination.

32. $\dfrac{2}{x} - \dfrac{3}{y} = -5$

    $\dfrac{4}{x} + \dfrac{6}{y} = 14$

33. $2x = 5(2 - y)$

    $y = 3(-x + 5)$

34. $2x - 3y + z = 0$

    $2x + y + z = 12$

    $y - z = 4$

© 35. Reasoning The dartboard at the right shows the number of points you score for hitting each region. Can you score exactly 100 points with seven darts that all land on the board? Explain.

4-4 | Applications of Linear Systems

A.CED.3 Represent constraints by equations or inequalities, and by systems of equations and inequalities, and interpret solutions as viable or non-viable . . . Also **N.Q.2, N.Q.3, A.REI.6**

Objective To choose the best method for solving a system of linear equations

Solve It! Write your solution to the Solve It in the space below.

Essential Understanding You can solve systems of linear equations using a graph, the substitution method, or the elimination method. The best method to use depends on the forms of the given equations and how precise the solution should be.

take note

Concept Summary | Choosing a Method for Solving Linear Systems

Method	When to Use
Graphing	When you want a visual display of the equations, or when you want to estimate a solution
Substitution	When one equation is already solved for one of the variables, or when it is easy to solve for one of the variables
Elimination	When the coefficients of one variable are the same or opposites, or when it is not convenient to use graphing or substitution

Systems of equations are useful for modeling problems involving mixtures, rates, and break-even points.

The break-even point for a business is the point at which income equals expenses. The graph shows the break-even point for one business.

Notice that the values of y on the red line represent dollars spent on expenses. The values of y on the blue line represent dollars received as income. So y is used to represent both expenses and income.

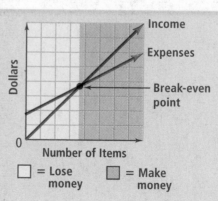

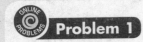

Problem 1   Finding a Break-Even Point

Think
What equations should you write?

Got It?   A puzzle expert wrote a new sudoku puzzle book. His initial costs are $864. Binding and packaging each book costs $.80. The price of the book is $2. How many copies must be sold to break even?

 Practice

1. **Business** A bicycle store costs $2400 per month to operate. The store pays an average of $60 per bike. The average selling price of each bicycle is $120. How many bicycles must the store sell each month to break even?

2. **Theater** Producing a musical costs $88,000 plus $5900 per performance. One sold-out performance earns $7500 in revenue. If every performance sells out, how many performances are needed to break even?

In real-world situations, you need to consider the constraints described in the problem in order to write equations. Once you solve an equation, you need to consider the viability of the solution. For example, a solution that has a negative number of hours is not a viable solution.

Problem 2   Identifying Constraints and Viable Solutions

Got It?   The zoo has two water tanks that are leaking. One tank contains 10 gal of water and is leaking at a constant rate of 2 gal/h. The second tank contains 6 gal of water and is leaking at a constant rate of 4 gal/h. When will the tanks have the same amount of water? Explain.

Practice   **3. Investment** You split $1500 between two savings accounts. Account A pays 5% annual interest and Account B pays 4% annual interest. After one year, you have earned a total of $69.50 in interest. How much money did you invest in each account? Explain.

STEM 4. Biology A group of scientists studied the effect of a chemical on various strains of bacteria. Strain A started with 6000 cells and decreased at a constant rate of 2000 cells per hour after the chemical was applied. Strain B started with 2000 cells and decreased at a constant rate of 1000 cells per hour after the chemical was applied. When will the strains have the same number of cells? Explain.

When a plane travels from west to east across the United States, the steady west-to-east winds act as tailwinds. This increases the plane's speed relative to the ground. When a plane travels from east to west, the winds act as headwinds. This decreases the plane's speed relative to the ground.

From West to East

air speed + wind speed = ground speed

├──── a ────→├─ w ─→│

├──────── g ────────┤

From East to West

air speed − wind speed = ground speed

│←──── a ────→│

├─w─→│←─ g ─┤

Problem 3 Solving a Wind or Current Problem

Think
How are the speeds related?

Got It?   **a.** You row upstream at a speed of 2 mi/h. You travel the same distance downstream at a speed of 5 mi/h. What would be your rowing speed in still water? What is the speed of the current?

ⓒ b. Reasoning Suppose your rowing speed in still water is 3 mi/h and the speed of the current is 4 mi/h. What happens when you try to row upstream?

5. **Airports** A traveler is walking on a moving walkway in an airport. The traveler must walk back on the walkway to get a bag he forgot. The traveler's ground speed is 2 ft/s against the walkway and 6 ft/s with the walkway. What is the traveler's speed off the walkway? What is the speed of the moving walkway?

6. **Kayaking** A kayaker paddles upstream from camp to photograph a waterfall and returns. The kayaker's speed while traveling upstream is 4 miles per hour and downstream is 7 miles per hour. What is the kayaker's speed in still water? What is the speed of the current?

Lesson Check

Do you know HOW?

7. **Newsletters** Printing a newsletter costs $1.50 per copy plus $450 in printer's fees. The copies are sold for $3 each. How many copies of the newsletter must be sold to break even?

8. **Jewelry** A metal alloy is a metal made by blending 2 or more types of metal. A jeweler has supplies of two metal alloys. One alloy is 30% gold and the other is 10% gold. How much of each alloy should the jeweler combine to create 4 kg of an alloy containing 15% gold?

9. **Flying** With a tailwind, a bird flew at a ground speed of 3 mi/h. Flying the same path against the same wind, the bird travels at a ground speed of 1.5 mi/h. What is the bird's air speed? What is the wind speed?

Do you UNDERSTAND?

MATHEMATICAL PRACTICES

Ⓒ 10. **Vocabulary** What is the relationship between income and expenses before a break-even point is reached? What is the relationship between income and expenses after a break-even point is reached?

Ⓒ 11. **Reasoning** Which method would you use to solve the following system? Explain.
$$3x + 2y = 9$$
$$-2x + 3y = 5$$

© **12. Reasoning** One brand of cranberry-apple drink is 15% cranberry juice. Another brand is 40% cranberry juice. You would like to combine the brands to make a drink that is 25% cranberry juice. Without calculating, which brand of juice will you need more of to make your drink? Explain.

More Practice and Problem-Solving Exercises

B Apply

13. Money You have a jar of pennies and quarters. You want to choose 15 coins that are worth exactly $4.35.
  a. Write and solve a system of equations that models the situation.
  b. Is your solution reasonable in terms of the original problem? Explain.

Solve each system. Explain why you chose the method you used.

14. $4x + 5y = 3$
$3x - 2y = 8$

15. $2x + 7y = -20$
$y = 3x + 7$

16. $5x + 2y = 17$
$x - 2y = 8$

© **17. Reasoning** Find A and B so that the system below has the solution (2, 3).
$$Ax - 2By = 6$$
$$3Ax - By = -12$$

© **18. Think About a Plan** A tugboat can pull a boat 24 mi downstream in 2 h. Going upstream, the tugboat can pull the same boat 16 mi in 2 h. What is the speed of the tugboat in still water? What is the speed of the current?
  • How can you use the formula $d = rt$ to help you solve the problem?
  • How are the tugboat's speeds when traveling upstream and downstream related to its speed in still water and the speed of the current?

© **Open-Ended** Without solving, decide which method you would use to solve each system: graphing, substitution, or elimination. Explain.

19. $y = 3x - 1$
$y = 4x$

20. $3m - 4n = 1$
$3m - 2n = -1$

21. $4s - 3t = 8$
$t = -2s - 1$

22. Business A perfume maker has stocks of two perfumes on hand. Perfume A sells for $15 per ounce. Perfume B sells for $35 per ounce. How much of each should be combined to make a 3-oz bottle of perfume that can be sold for $63?

EM **23. Chemistry** In a chemistry lab, you have two vinegars. One is 5% acetic acid, and one is 6.5% acetic acid. You want to make 200 mL of a vinegar with 6% acetic acid. How many milliliters of each vinegar do you need to mix together?

24. Boating A boat is traveling in a river with a current that has a speed of 1.5 km/h. In one hour, the boat can travel twice the distance downstream that it can travel upstream. What is the boat's speed in still water?

© **25. Reasoning** A student claims that the best way to solve the system below is by substitution. Do you agree? Explain.

$$y - 3x = 4$$
$$y - 6x = 12$$

26. Entertainment A contestant on a quiz show gets 150 points for every correct answer and loses 250 points for each incorrect answer. After answering 20 questions, the contestant has 200 points. How many questions has the contestant answered correctly? Incorrectly?

© **Challenge**

27. Number Theory You can represent the value of any two-digit number with the expression $10a + b$, where a is the tens' place digit and b is the ones' place digit. For example, if a is 5 and b is 7, then the value of the number is $10(5) + 7$, or 57. What two-digit number is described below?

- The ones' place digit is one more than twice the tens' place digit.
- The value of the number is two more than five times the ones' place digit.

28. Mixed Nuts You want to sell 1-lb jars of mixed peanuts and cashews for $5. You pay $3 per pound for peanuts and $6 per pound for cashews. You plan to combine 4 parts peanuts and 1 part cashews to make your mix. You have spent $70 on materials to get started. How many jars must you sell to break even?

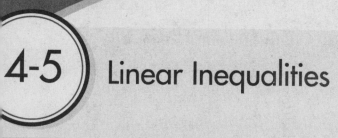

4-5 Linear Inequalities

A.REI.12 Graph the solutions to a linear inequality in two variables as a half-plane . . . and graph the solution . . . to a system of linear inequalities in two variables as the intersection of the corresponding half-planes. Also **A.CED.3**

Objectives   To graph linear inequalities in two variables
To use linear inequalities when modeling real-world situations

Solve It!   Write your solution to the Solve It in the space below.

> A **linear inequality** in two variables, such as $y > x - 3$, can be formed by replacing the equal sign in a linear equation with an inequality symbol. A **solution of an inequality** in two variables is an ordered pair that makes the inequality true.
>
> **Essential Understanding**   A linear inequality in two variables has an infinite number of solutions. These solutions can be represented in the coordinate plane as the set of all points on one side of a boundary line.

Problem 1   Identifying Solutions of a Linear Inequality

Got It?   **a.** Is $(3, 6)$ a solution of $y \leq \frac{2}{3}x + 4$? Explain.

© **b. Reasoning**   Suppose an ordered pair is not a solution of $y > x + 10$.
Must it be a solution of $y < x + 10$? Explain.

Practice Determine whether the ordered pair is a solution of the linear inequality.

1. $y \le -2x + 1$; $(2, 2)$

2. $3y > 5x - 12$; $(-6, 1)$

The graph of a linear inequality in two variables consists of all points in the coordinate plane that represent solutions. The graph is a region called a *half-plane* that is bounded by a line. All points on one side of the boundary line are solutions, while all points on the other side are not solutions.

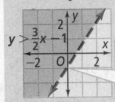

$y > \frac{3}{2}x - 1$

Each point on a *dashed* line is not a solution. A dashed line is used for inequalities with $>$ or $<$.

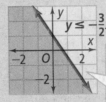

$y \le -\frac{3}{2}x + 1$

Each point on a *solid* line is a solution. A solid line is used for inequalities with $\ge$ or $\le$.

Problem 2 **Graphing an Inequality in Two Variables**

Got It? What is the graph of $y \le \frac{1}{2}x + 1$?

Think

What is the boundary line for the graph?

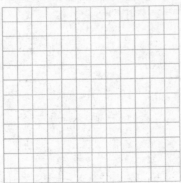

A Practice Graph each linear inequality.

3. $y \geq 3x - 2$

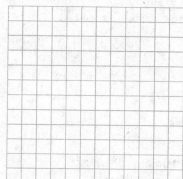

4. $y < -4x - 1$

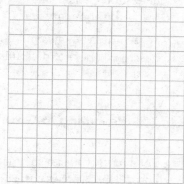

An inequality in one variable can be graphed on a number line or in the coordinate plane. When graphed in a coordinate plane, the boundary line will be a horizontal or vertical line.

Problem 3 Graphing a Linear Inequality in One Variable

Got It? What is the graph of each inequality?

a. $x < -5$

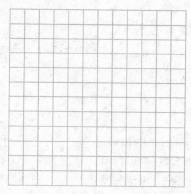

b. $y \leq 2$

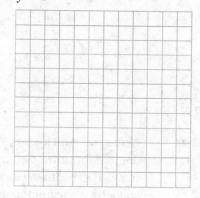

A Practice Graph each inequality in the coordinate plane.

5. $x \leq 4$

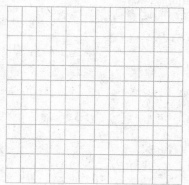

6. $x > -2$

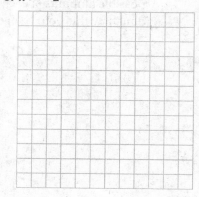

When a linear inequality is solved for *y*, the direction of the inequality symbol determines which side of the boundary line to shade. If the symbol is < or ≤, shade below the boundary line. If the symbol is > or ≥, shade above it.

Sometimes you must first solve an inequality for *y* before using the method described above to determine where to shade.

 **Problem 4** Rewriting to Graph an Inequality

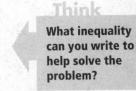

Think
What inequality can you write to help solve the problem?

Got It? For a party, you can spend no more than $12 on nuts. Peanuts cost $2/lb. Cashews cost $4/lb. What are three possible combinations of peanuts and cashews you can buy?

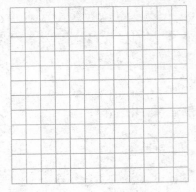

Practice 7. **Carpentry** You budget $200 for wooden planks for outdoor furniture. Cedar costs $2.50 per foot and pine costs $1.75 per foot. Let *x* = the number of feet of cedar and let *y* = the number of feet of pine. What is an inequality that shows how much of each type of wood you can buy? Graph the inequality. What are three possible amounts of each type of wood that can be bought within your budget?

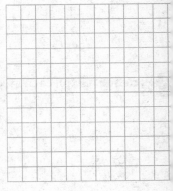

8. Business A fish market charges $9 per pound for cod and $12 per pound for flounder. Let x = the number of pounds of cod. Let y = the number of pounds of flounder. What is an inequality that shows how much of each type of fish the store must sell today to reach a daily quota of at least $120? Graph the inequality. What are three possible amounts of each fish that would satisfy the quota?

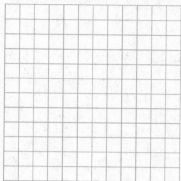

Problem 5   **Writing an Inequality From a Graph**

Got It?   You are writing an inequality from a graph. The boundary line is dashed and has slope $\frac{1}{3}$ and y-intercept -2. The area above the line is shaded. What inequality should you write?

Practice Write a linear inequality that represents each graph.

9.

10.

11.

Lesson Check

Do you know HOW?

12. Is $(-1, 4)$ a solution of the inequality $y < 2x + 5$? Explain.

Graph each linear inequality.

13. $y \le -2x + 3$

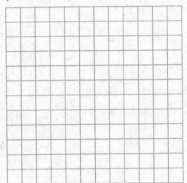

14. $x < -1$

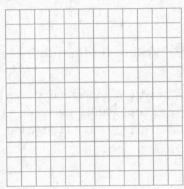

15. What is an inequality that represents the graph at the right?

Do you UNDERSTAND?

MATHEMATICAL PRACTICES

16. Vocabulary How is a linear inequality in two variables like a linear equation in two variables? How are they different?

17. Writing To graph the inequality $y < \frac{3}{2}x + 3$ inequality, do you shade above or below the boundary line? Explain.

18. Reasoning Write an inequality that describes the region of the coordinate plane *not* included in the graph of $y < 5x + 1$.

More Practice and Problem-Solving Exercises

Apply

19. Think About a Plan A truck that can carry no more than 6400 lb is being used to transport refrigerators and upright pianos. Each refrigerator weighs 250 lb and each piano weighs 475 lb. Write and graph an inequality to show how many refrigerators and how many pianos the truck could carry. Will 12 refrigerators and 8 pianos overload the truck? Explain.
- Which inequality symbol should you use?
- Which side of the boundary line should you shade?

20. Employment A student with two summer jobs earns $10 per hour at a cafe and $8 per hour at a market. The student would like to earn at least $800 per month.
 a. Write and graph an inequality to represent the situation.
 b. The student works at the market for 60 h per month and can work at most 90 h per month. Can the student earn at least $800 each month? Explain how you can use your graph to determine this.

21. Error Analysis A student graphed $y \geq 2x + 3$ as shown at the right. Describe and correct the student's error.

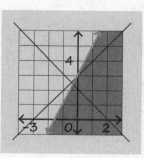

22. Writing When graphing an inequality, can you always use $(0, 0)$ as a test point to determine where to shade? If not, how would you choose a test point?

23. **Music Store** A music store sells used CDs for $5 each and buys used CDs for $1.50 each. You go to the store with $20 and some CDs to sell. You want to have at least $10 left when you leave the store. Write and graph an inequality to show how many CDs you could buy and sell.

24. **Groceries** At your grocery store, milk normally costs $3.60 per gallon. Ground beef costs $3 per pound. Today there are specials: Milk is discounted $.50 per gallon, and ground beef is 20% off. You want to spend no more than $20. Write and graph a linear inequality to show how many gallons of milk and how many pounds of ground beef you can buy today.

© 25. **Reasoning** You are graphing a linear inequality of the form $y > mx + b$. The point $(1, 2)$ is not a solution, but $(3, 2)$ is. Is the slope of the boundary line *positive*, *negative*, *zero*, or *undefined*? Explain.

4-6 Systems of Linear Inequalities

A.REI.12 Graph the solutions to a linear inequality in two variables as a half-plane . . . and graph the solution . . . to a system of linear inequalities in two variables as the intersection of the corresponding half-planes. Also **A.CED.3**

Objectives To solve systems of linear inequalities by graphing
To model real-world situations using systems of linear inequalities

Solve It! Write your solution to the Solve It in the space below.

A **system of linear inequalities** is made up of two or more linear inequalities. A **solution of a system of linear inequalities** is an ordered pair that makes all the inequalities in the system true. The graph of a system of linear inequalities is the set of points that represent all of the solutions of the system.

Essential Understanding You can graph the solutions of a system of linear inequalities in the coordinate plane. The graph of the system is the region where the graphs of the individual inequalities overlap.

Problem 1 Graphing a System of Inequalities

Think
What boundary lines should you graph first?

Got It? What is the graph of the system at the right? $y \geq -x + 5$
$-3x + y \leq -4$

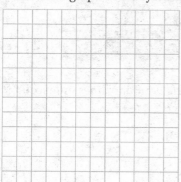

A **Practice** Solve each system of inequalities by graphing.

1. $y < 2x + 4$
   $-3x - 2y \geq 6$

2. $y \leq 0.75x - 2$
   $y > 0.75x - 3$

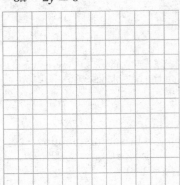

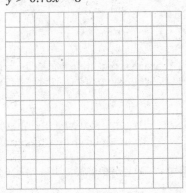

Determine whether the ordered pair is a solution of the given system.

3. $(2, 12)$;
   $y > 2x + 4$
   $y < 3x + 7$

4. $(8, 2)$;
   $3x - 2y \leq 17$
   $0.3x + 4y > 9$

You can combine your knowledge of linear equations with your knowledge of inequalities to describe a graph using a system of inequalities.

ONLINE PROBLEMS

Problem 2 **Writing a System of Inequalities From a Graph**

Got It? **a.** What system of inequalities is represented by the graph?

Think

How can you break this down into two simpler problems?

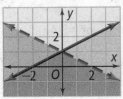

b. Reasoning In part (a), is the point where the boundary lines intersect a solution of the system? Explain.

A Practice Write a system of inequalities for each graph.

5.

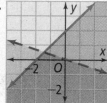

6.

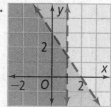

7.

You can model many real-world situations by writing and graphing systems of linear inequalities. Some real-world situations involve three or more restrictions, so you must write a system of at least three inequalities.

Problem 3 Using a System of Inequalities

Got It? You want to build a fence for a rectangular dog run. You want the run to be at least 10 ft wide. The run can be at most 50 ft long. You have 126 ft of fencing. What is a graph showing the possible dimensions of the dog run?

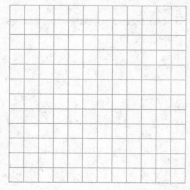

8. Earnings Suppose you have a job mowing lawns that pays $12 per hour. You also have a job at a clothing store that pays $10 per hour. You need to earn at least $350 per week, but you can work no more than 35 h per week. You must work a minimum of 10 h per week at the clothing store. What is a graph showing how many hours per week you can work at each job?

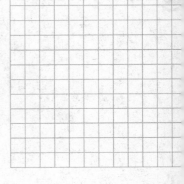

9. Driving Two friends agree to split the driving on a road trip from Philadelphia, Pennsylvania, to Denver, Colorado. One friend drives at an average speed of 60 mi/h. The other friend drives at an average speed of 55 mi/h. They want to drive at least 500 mi per day. They plan to spend no more than 10 h driving each day. The friend who drives slower wants to drive fewer hours. What is a graph showing how they can split the driving each day?

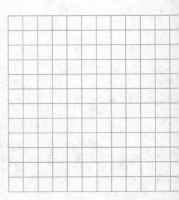

 Lesson Check

Do you know HOW?

10. What is the graph of the system at the right? $y > 3x - 2$
$2y - x \le 6$

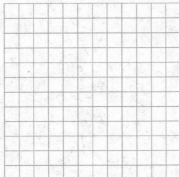

11. What system of inequalities is represented by the graph at the right?

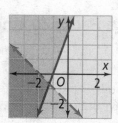

12. Cherries cost $4/lb. Grapes cost $2.50/lb. You can spend no more than $15 on fruit, and you need at least 4 lb in all. What is a graph showing the amount of each fruit you can buy?

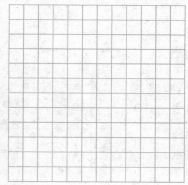

Do you UNDERSTAND?

MATHEMATICAL
PRACTICES

© 13. Vocabulary How can you determine whether an ordered pair is a solution of a system of linear inequalities?

© 14. Reasoning Suppose you are graphing a system of two linear inequalities, and the boundary lines for the inequalities are parallel. Does that mean that the system has no solution? Explain.

© 15. Writing How is finding the solution of a system of inequalities different from finding the solution of a system of equations? How is it the same? Explain.

More Practice and Problem-Solving Exercises

B Apply

© 16. **Think About a Plan** You are fencing in a rectangular area for a garden. You have only 150 ft of fence. You want the length of the garden to be at least 40 ft. You want the width of the garden to be at least 5 ft. What is a graph showing the possible dimensions your garden could have?
   • What variables will you use? What will they represent?
   • How many inequalities do you need to write?

© 17. **a.** Graph the system $y > 3x + 3$ and $y \le 3x - 5$.
   b. Writing Will the boundary lines $y = 3x + 3$ and $y = 3x - 5$ ever intersect? How do you know?
   c. Do the shaded regions in the graph from part (a) overlap?
   d. Does the system of inequalities have any solutions? Explain.

© 18. **Error Analysis** A student graphs the system as shown at the right. Describe and correct the student's error.

19. **Gift Certificates** You received a $100 gift certificate to a clothing store. The store sells T-shirts for $15 and dress shirts for $22. You want to spend no more than the amount of the gift certificate. You want to leave at most $10 of the gift certificate unspent. You need at least one dress shirt. What are all of the possible combinations of T-shirts and dress shirts you could buy?

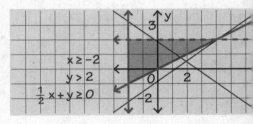

$$x \ge -2$$
$$y > 2$$
$$\tfrac{1}{2}x + y \ge 0$$

20. **a. Geometry** Graph the system of linear inequalities.
   b. Describe the shape of the solution region.
   c. Find the vertices of the solution region.
   d. Find the area of the solution region.

   $x \ge 2$
   $y \ge -3$
   $x + y \le 4$

21. Which region represents the solution of the system?
   Ⓐ I   Ⓑ II
   Ⓒ III   Ⓓ IV

   $y \le -\tfrac{3}{2}x - 2$
   $3y - 9x \ge 6$

© **Open-Ended** Write a system of linear inequalities with the given characteristic.

22. All solutions are in Quadrant III.   23. There are no solutions.

24. Business A jeweler plans to produce a ring made of silver and gold. The price of gold is about $25 per gram. The price of silver is approximately $.40 per gram. She considers the following in deciding how much gold and silver to use in the ring.
  - The total mass must be more than 10 g but less than 20 g.
  - The ring must contain at least 2 g of gold.
  - The total cost of the gold and silver must be less than $90.
  a. Write and graph the inequalities that describe this situation.
  b. For one solution, find the mass of the ring and the cost of the gold and silver.

25. Solve $|y| \geq x$. (Hint: Write two inequalities and then graph them.)

Ⓒ **26. Student Art** A teacher wants to post a row of student artwork on a wall that is 20 ft long. Some pieces are 8.5 in. wide. Other pieces are 11 in. wide. She is going to leave 3 in. of space to the left of each art piece. She wants to post at least 16 pieces of art. Write and graph a system of inequalities that describes how many pieces of each size she can post.

MathXL® for School
Go to pearsonsuccessnet.com

4-1 Solving Systems by Graphing

Quick Review

One way to solve a system of linear equations is by graphing each equation and finding the intersection point of the graph, if one exists.

Example

What is the solution of the system? $y = -2x + 2$
$$y = 0.5x - 3$$

$y = -2x + 2$ Slope is -2; y-intercept is 2.

$y = 0.5x - 3$ Slope is 0.5; y-intercept is -3.

The lines appear to intersect at $(2, -2)$. Check if $(2, -2)$ makes both equations true.

$-2 = -2(2) + 2$ ✓

$-2 = 0.5(2) - 3$ ✓

So, the solution is $(2, -2)$.

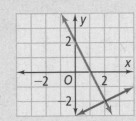

Exercises

Solve each system by graphing. Check your answe

1. $y = 3x + 13$
$y = x - 3$

2. $y = -x + 4$
$y = 3x + 12$

3. $y = 2x + 3$
$y = \frac{1}{3}x - 2$

4. $y = 1.5x + 2$
$4.5x - 3y = -9$

5. $y = -2x - 21$
$y = x - 7$

6. $y = x + 1$
$2x - 2y = -2$

7. Songwriting Jay has written 24 songs to date
He writes an average of 6 songs per year. Jenn
started writing songs this year and expects to
write about 12 songs per year. How many yea
from now will Jenna have written as many
songs as Jay? Write and graph a system of
equations to find your answer.

8. Reasoning Describe the graph of a system o
equations that has no solution.

4-2 Solving Systems Using Substitution

Quick Review

You can solve a system of equations by solving one equation for one variable and then substituting the expression for that variable into the other equation.

Example

What is the solution of the system? $y = -\frac{1}{3}x$
$$3x + 3y = -18$$

$3x + 3y = -18$ Write the second equation.

$3x + 3(-\frac{1}{3}x) = -18$ Substitute $-\frac{1}{3}x$ for y.

$2x = -18$ Simplify.

$x = -9$ Solve for x.

$y = -\frac{1}{3}(-9)$ Substitute -9 for x in the first equation.

$y = 3$

The solution is $(-9, 3)$.

Exercises

Solve each system using substitution. Tell whether the system has *one solution*, *infinitely many solutions*, or *no solution*.

9. $y = 2x - 1$
$2x + 2y = 22$

10. $-x + y = -13$
$3x - y = 19$

11. $2x + y = -12$
$-4x - 2y = 30$

12. $\frac{1}{3}y = \frac{7}{3}x + \frac{5}{3}$
$x - 3y = 5$

13. $y = x - 7$
$3x - 3y = 21$

14. $3x + y = -13$
$-2x + 5y = -54$

15. Business The owner of a hair salon charges $
more per haircut than the assistant. Yesterday
the assistant gave 12 haircuts. The owner gave
6 haircuts. The total earnings from haircuts
were $750. How much does the owner charge
for a haircut? Solve by writing and solving a
system of equations.

4-3 and 4-4
Solving Systems Using Elimination; Applications of Systems

Quick Review

You can add or subtract equations in a system to eliminate a variable. Before you add or subtract, you may have to multiply one or both equations by a constant to make eliminating a variable possible.

Example

What is the solution of the system? $3x + 2y = 41$
$$5x - 3y = 24$$

$3x + 2y = 41$ Multiply by 3. $9x + 6y = 123$
$5x - 3y = 24$ Multiply by 2. $\underline{10x - 6y = 48}$
$$19x + 0 = 171$$
$$x = 9$$

$3x + 2y = 41$ Write the first equation.

$3(9) + 2y = 41$ Substitute 9 for x.

$y = 7$ Solve for y.

The solution is (9, 7).

Exercises

Solve each system using elimination. Tell whether the system has *one solution, infinitely many solutions*, or *no solution*.

16. $x + 2y = 23$
$5x + 10y = 55$

17. $7x + y = 6$
$5x + 3y = 34$

18. $5x + 4y = -83$
$3x - 3y = -12$

19. $9x + \frac{1}{2}y = 51$
$7x + \frac{1}{3}y = 39$

20. $4x + y = 21$
$-2x + 6y = 9$

21. $y = 3x - 27$
$x - \frac{1}{3}y = 9$

22. Flower Arranging It takes a florist 3 h 15 min to make 3 small centerpieces and 3 large centerpieces. It takes 6 h 20 min to make 4 small centerpieces and 7 large centerpieces. How long does it take to make each small centerpiece and each large centerpiece? Write and solve a system of equations to find your answer.

4-5 and 4-6 Linear Inequalities and Systems of Inequalities

Quick Review

A *linear inequality* describes a region of the coordinate plane with a boundary line. Two or more inequalities form a *system of inequalities*. The system's solutions lie where the graphs of the inequalities overlap.

Example

What is the graph of the system? $y > 2x - 4$
$$y \le -x + 2$$

Graph the boundary lines $y = 2x - 4$ and $y = -x + 2$. For $y > 2x - 4$, use a dashed boundary line and shade above it. For $y \le -x + 2$, use a solid boundary line and shade below. The region of overlap contains the system's solutions.

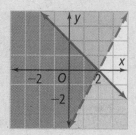

Exercises

Solve each system of inequalities by graphing.

23. $y \ge x + 4$
$y < 2x - 1$

24. $4y < -3x$
$y < -\frac{3}{4}x$

25. $2x - y > 0$
$3x + 2y \le -14$

26. $x + 0.5y \ge 5.5$
$0.5x + y < 6.5$

27. $y < 10x$
$y > x - 5$

28. $4x + 4 > 2y$
$3x - 4y \ge 1$

29. Downloads You have 60 megabytes (MB) of space left on your portable media player. You can choose to download song files that use 3.5 MB or video files that use 8 MB. You want to download at least 12 files. What is a graph showing the numbers of song and video files you can download?

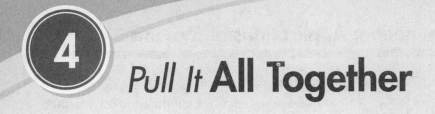

Pull It All Together

 ASSESSMEN

Planning an Exercise Program

You use the rowing machine and the stair machine at the gym for your exercise program. You want an exercise program that meets these three conditions:

(1) You can spend at most 60 minutes at the gym.
(2) After 10 minutes of stretching you exercise for at least 30 minutes, dividing your time between the rowing machine and the stair machine.
(3) You want to spend at least twice as much time on the stair machine as on the rowing machine.

Task Description

Find the greatest length of time you can spend on the rowing machine and meet conditions (1)–(3) above.

a. The least amount of time you exercise after stretching is 30 minutes. What is the greatest amount of time you can exercise after stretching?

b. Let x = the number of minutes spent on the rowing machine.
Let y = the number of minutes spent on the stair machine.
Write a system of two inequalities that describes the total amount of time you spend on the two machines.

c. Write a third inequality that describes condition (3).

d. Graph your system of three inequalities from parts (b) and (c) to show the set of all possible combinations of times that meet your conditions. Explain why the graph should use only the first quadrant.

e. Which point of the solution region represents the greatest length of time you can spend on the rowing machine? Solve a system of equations to find the coordinates of this point. What is the greatest length of time you can spend on the rowing machine?

Get Ready!

Converting Fractions to Decimals

Write as a decimal.

1. $\frac{7}{10}$ **2.** $6\frac{2}{5}$ **3.** $\frac{8}{1000}$ **4.** $\frac{7}{2}$ **5.** $\frac{3}{11}$

Using Order of Operations

Simplify each expression.

6. $(9 \div 3 + 4)^2$ **7.** $5 + (0.3)^2$ **8.** $3 - (1.5)^2$ **9.** $64 \div 2^4$

10. $4 \div (0.5)^2$ **11.** $(0.25)4^2$ **12.** $2(3 + 7)^3$ **13.** $-3(4 + 6 \div 2)^2$

Evaluating Expressions

Evaluate each expression for $a = -2$ and $b = 5$.

14. $(ab)^2$ **15.** $(a - b)^2$ **16.** $a^3 + b^3$ **17.** $b - (3a)^2$

Finding Percent Change

Tell whether each percent change is an increase or decrease. Then find the percent change. Round to the nearest percent.

18. \$15 to \$20   **19.** \$20 to \$15

20. \$600 to \$500   **21.** \$2000 to \$2100

Understanding Domain and Range

Find the range of each function with domain $\{-2, 0, 3.5\}$.

22. $f(x) = -2x^2$ **23.** $g(x) = 10 - x^3$ **24.** $y = 5x - 1$

 # Looking Ahead Vocabulary

25. If you say that a plant has new growth, has the size of the plant changed? What do you think the *growth factor* of the plant describes?

26. In a mathematical expression, an exponent indicates repeated multiplication by the same number. How would you expect a quantity to change when it experiences *exponential growth*?

27. Tooth decay occurs when tooth enamel wears away over time. If *exponential decay* models the change in the number of dentists in the United States over time, do you think the number of dentists in the United States is increasing or decreasing?

Exponential and Radical Functions

Big Ideas

1 Equivalence
Essential Question: How can you represent numbers less than 1 using exponents?

2 Function
Essential Question: What are the characteristics of exponential functions?

© Domains

- Building Functions
- Seeing Structure in Expressions
- Linear, Quadratic, and Exponential Models

Interactive Digital Path

Log in to **pearsonsuccessnet.com** and click on Interactive Digital Path to access the Solve Its and animated Problems.

Chapter Preview

Vocabulary

English/Spanish Vocabulary Audio Online:

English	Spanish
average rate of change, *p. 303*	tasa promedio de cambio
compound interest, *p. 311*	interés compuesto
decay factor, *p. 312*	factor de decremento
exponential decay, *p. 312*	decremento exponencial
exponential function, *p. 291*	función exponencial
exponential growth, *p. 309*	incremento exponencial
geometric sequence, *p. 329*	progression geométrica
growth factor, *p. 309*	factor incremental
piecewise function, *p. 357*	función de fragmentas
square root function, *p. 354*	función de raíz cuadrada

5-1 Zero and Negative Exponents

A.SSE.1 Interpret expressions . . . in terms of its context. Also prepares for **A.SSE.1.a**

Objective   To simplify expressions involving zero and negative exponents

Solve It!   Write your solution to the Solve It in the space below.

The patterns you found in the Solve It illustrate the definitions of zero and negative exponents.

Essential Understanding   You can extend the idea of exponents to include zero and negative exponents.

Consider 3^3, 3^2, and 3^1. Decreasing the exponents by 1 is the same as dividing by 3. If you continue the pattern, 3^0 equals 1 and 3^{-1} equals $\frac{1}{3}$.

take note

Properties   Zero and Negative Exponents

Zero as an Exponent   For every nonzero number a, $a^0 = 1$.

Examples $4^0 = 1$ $(-3)^0 = 1$ $(5.14)^0 = 1$

Negative Exponent   For every nonzero number a and integer n, $a^{-n} = \frac{1}{a^n}$.

Examples $7^{-3} = \frac{1}{7^3}$ $(-5)^{-2} = \frac{1}{(-5)^2}$

Why can't you use 0 as a base with zero exponents? The first property above implies the following pattern.

$3^0 = 1$ $2^0 = 1$ $1^0 = 1$ $0^0 = 1$

However, consider the following pattern.

$0^3 = 0$ $0^2 = 0$ $0^1 = 0$ $0^0 = 0$

It is not possible for 0^0 to equal both 1 and 0. Therefore, 0^0 is undefined.

Why can't you use 0 as a base with a negative exponent? Using 0 as a base with a negative exponent will result in division by zero, which is undefined.

Problem 1 Simplifying Powers

Got It? What is the simplified form of each expression?

a. 4^{-3}

b. $(-5)^0$

Think

Can you use zero as an exponent when the base is a negative number?

c. 3^{-2}

d. 6^{-1}

e. $(-4)^{-2}$

Ⓐ Practice Simplify each expression.

1. $\dfrac{1}{2^0}$

2. 1.5^{-2}

An algebraic expression is in simplest form when powers with a variable base are written with only positive exponents.

 Problem 2 **Simplifying Exponential Expressions**

Got It? What is the simplified form of each expression?

a. x^{-9}

b. $\dfrac{1}{n^{-3}}$

Think
Which part of the expression do you need to rewrite?

c. $4c^{-3}b$

d. $\dfrac{2}{a^{-3}}$

e. $\dfrac{n^{-5}}{m^2}$

A Practice Simplify each expression.

3. $c^{-5}d^7$

4. $\dfrac{7s^0 t^{-5}}{2^{-1}m^2}$

When you evaluate an exponential expression, you can simplify the expression before substituting values for the variables.

Problem 3   **Evaluating an Exponential Expression**

Got It?   What is the value of each expression in parts (a)–(d) for $n = -2$ and $w = 5$?

a. $n^{-4}w^0$

b. $\dfrac{n^{-1}}{w^2}$

c. $\dfrac{n^0}{w^6}$

d. $\dfrac{1}{nw^{-1}}$

 e. **Reasoning** Is it easier to evaluate $n^0 w^0$ for $n = -2$ and $w = 3$ by simplifying first or by substituting first? Explain.

Practice Evaluate each expression for $r = -3$ and $s = 5$.

5. $r^{-4}s^2$

6. $2^{-4}r^3s^{-2}$

Problem 4 **Using an Exponential Expression**

Got It? A population of insects triples every week. The number of insects is modeled by the expression $5400 \cdot 3^w$, where w is the number of weeks after the population was measured. Evaluate the expression for $w = -2$, $w = 0$, and $w = 1$. What does each value of the expression represent in the situation?

 Practice **7. Internet Traffic** The number of visitors to a certain Web site triples every month. The number of visitors is modeled by the expression $8100 \cdot 3^m$, where m is the number of months after the number of visitors was measured. Evaluate the expression for $m = -4$. What does the value of the expression represent in the situation?

STEM **8. Population Growth** A Galápagos cactus finch population increases by half every decade. The number of finches is modeled by the expression $45 \cdot 1.5^d$, where d is the number of decades after the population was measured. Evaluate the expression for $d = -2$, $d = 0$, and $d = 1$. What does each value of the expression represent in the situation?

Lesson Check

Do you know HOW?

Simplify each expression.

9. 2^{-5}

10. m^0

11. $5s^2t^{-1}$

12. $\dfrac{4}{x^{-3}}$

Evaluate each expression for $a = 2$ and $b = -4$.

13. a^3b^{-1}

14. $2a^{-4}b^0$

Do you UNDERSTAND?

15. Vocabulary A positive exponent shows repeated multiplication. What repeated operation does a negative exponent show?

16. Error Analysis A student incorrectly simplified $\frac{x^n}{a^{-n}b^0}$ as shown at the right. Find and correct the student's error.

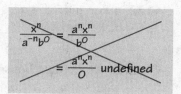

More Practice and Problem-Solving Exercises

B Apply

© **Mental Math** Is the value of each expression positive or negative?

17. -2^2 **18.** $(-2)^2$ **19.** $(-2)^3$ **20.** $(-2)^{-3}$

Write each number as a power of 10 using negative exponents.

21. $\frac{1}{10}$ **22.** $\frac{1}{100}$ **23.** $\frac{1}{1000}$ **24.** $\frac{1}{10,000}$

© **25. a. Patterns** Complete the pattern using powers of 5.

$\frac{1}{5^2} = 5^{\blacksquare}$ $\frac{1}{5^1} = 5^{\blacksquare}$ $\frac{1}{5^0} = 5^{\blacksquare}$ $\frac{1}{5^{-1}} = 5^{\blacksquare}$ $\frac{1}{5^{-2}} = 5^{\blacksquare}$

    b. Write $\frac{1}{5^{-4}}$ using a positive exponent.

    c. Rewrite $\frac{1}{a^{-n}}$ as a power of a.

Rewrite each fraction with all the variables in the numerator.

26. $\frac{a}{b^{-2}}$ **27.** $\frac{4g}{h^3}$ **28.** $\frac{5m^6}{3n}$ **29.** $\frac{8c^5}{11d^4e^{-2}}$

© **30. Think About a Plan** Suppose your drama club's budget doubles every year. This year the budget is \$500. How much was the club's budget 2 yr ago?

- What expression models what the budget of the club will be in 1 yr? In 2 yr? In y years?
- What value of y can you substitute into your expression to find the budget of the club 2 yr ago?

31. Copy and complete the table at the right.

n	3	■	■	$\frac{5}{8}$	■
n^{-1}	■	6	$\frac{1}{7}$	■	0.5

© 32. a. Simplify $a^n \cdot a^{-n}$.

b. **Reasoning** What is the mathematical relationship between a^n and a^{-n}? Explain.

© 33. **Open-Ended** Choose a fraction to use as a value for the variable a. Find the values of a^{-1}, a^2, and a^{-2}.

STEM 34. **Manufacturing** A company is making metal rods with a target diameter of 1.5 mm. A rod is acceptable when its diameter is within 10^{-3} mm of the target diameter. Write an inequality for the acceptable range of diameters.

© 35. **Reasoning** Are $3x^{-2}$ and $3x^2$ reciprocals? Explain.

© Challenge

Simplify each expression.

36. $\left(\dfrac{r^{-7}b^{-8}}{t^{-4}w^1}\right)^0$

37. $(-5)^2 - (0.5)^{-2}$

38. $\dfrac{6}{m^2} + \dfrac{5m^{-2}}{3^{-3}}$

39. $2^3(5^0 - 6m^2)$

40. $\dfrac{2x^{-5}y^3}{n^2} \div \dfrac{r^2y^5}{2n}$

41. $2^{-1} - \dfrac{1}{3^{-2}} + 5\left(\dfrac{1}{2^2}\right)$

42. For what value or values of n is $n^{-3} = \left(\dfrac{1}{n}\right)^5$?

5-2) Exponential Functions

F.IF.4 For a function that models a relationship between two quantities, interpret key features of graphs and tables . . . and sketch graphs showing key features . . . Also **A.REI.11, F.IF.7.e, F.LE.5**

Objective To evaluate and graph exponential functions

Solve It! Write your solution to the Solve It in the space below.

The two plans in the Solve It have different patterns of growth. You can model each type of growth with a different type of function.

Essential Understanding Some functions model an initial amount that is repeatedly multiplied by the same positive number. In the rules for these functions, the independent variable is an exponent.

take note

Key Concept   Exponential Function

Definition

An **exponential function** is a function of the form $y = a \cdot b^x$, where $a \neq 0$, $b > 0$, $b \neq 1$, and x is a real number.

Examples

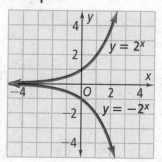

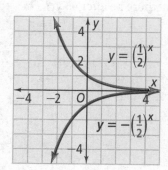

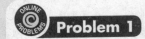

Problem 1 Evaluating an Exponential Function

Got It? An initial population of 20 rabbits triples every half year. The function $f(x) = 20 \cdot 3^x$ gives the population after x half-year periods. How many rabbits will there be after 3 yr?

 Practice

1. **Finance** An investment of $5000 doubles in value every decade. The function $f(x) = 5000 \cdot 2^x$, where x is the number of decades, models the growth of the value of the investment. How much is the investment worth after 30 yr?

2. **Wildlife Management** A population of 75 foxes in a wildlife preserve quadruples in size every 15 yr. The function $y = 75 \cdot 4^x$, where x is the number of 15-yr periods, models the population growth. How many foxes will there be after 45 yr?

Problem 2 Graphing an Exponential Function

Got It? What is the graph of each function?

a. $y = 0.5 \cdot 3^x$

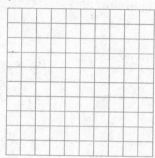

b. $y = -0.5 \cdot 3^x$

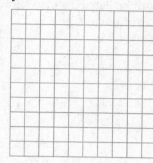

> **Think**
> What are the domain and range of each function?

A Practice Graph each exponential function.

3. $y = -\left(\frac{1}{3}\right)^x$

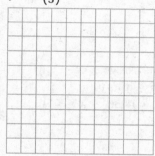

4. $y = \frac{1}{4} \cdot 2^x$

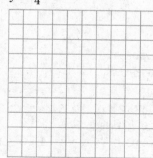

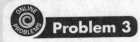

Problem 3   Graphing an Exponential Model

Think

Should you connect the points of the graph?

Got It?   a. You can also zoom out to view a larger area on the map in Problem 3. The function $f(x) = 100 \cdot 4^x$ models the percent of the original area the map shows after zooming out x times. Graph the function.

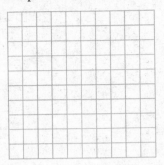

b. Reasoning What is the percent change in area each time you zoom out in part (a)?

Practice   5. **Admissions** A new museum had 7500 visitors this year. The museum curators expect the number of visitors to grow by 5% each year. The function $y = 7500 \cdot 1.05^x$ models the predicted number of visitors each year after x years. Graph the function.

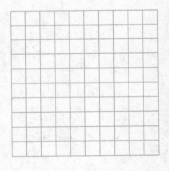

6. **Environment** A solid waste disposal plan proposes to reduce the amount of garbage each person throws out by 2% each year. This year, each person threw out an average of 1500 lb of garbage. The function $y = 1500 \cdot 0.98^x$ models the average amount of garbage each person will throw out each year after x years. Graph the function.

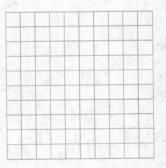

The rules of transformations can help you graph exponential functions.

Problem 4   Graphing an Exponential Model With a Vertical Shift

Got It?   Suppose that the mass of another culture of bacteria is, at any given time, double the mass of the bacteria culture in Problem 4. The total mass, in grams, of this culture and the petri dish can be represented by the function $f(x) = 2 \cdot 2^x + 50$. What is the graph of $f(x) = 2 \cdot 2^x + 50$?

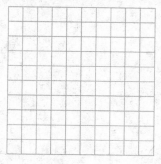

Practice   7. Tracy's normal resting heart rate is about 75 beats per minute (bpm). During a strenuous workout, her heart rate increases 65 beats per minute, up to 140 bpm. When she begins her cool down, her elevated heart rate decreases by about 40% each minute. So Tracy's heart rate, in beats per minute, after x minutes of cooling down, is given by $f(x) = 65(0.6)^x + 75$. What is the graph of $f(x) = 65(0.6)^x + 75$?

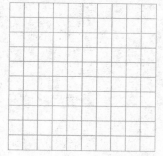

8. James had $25,000 to invest. He deposited $5000 in an account that did not earn any interest but allows him access to the money at any time if he should need it. He also invested $20,000 in an account that paid 5% annual compound interest but had penalties for early withdrawals. The function $f(x) = 20,000(1.05)^x + 5000$ represents how much money James had in these two accounts after x years if he made no other deposits or withdrawals. What is the graph of $f(x) = 20,000(1.05)^x + 5000$?

In the Technology Lab after Lesson 4-1, you solved one-variable linear equations using graphs and a graphing calculator. In the next example, you will write each side of the equation as a function and graph the functions. The x-value where the functions intersect is a solution.

ONLINE PROBLEMS **Problem 5** Solving One-Variable Equations

Got It?   What is the solution or solutions of each equation?

   a. $0.3^x = 5$

Think
What two functions can you graph to find the solution?

   b. $1.25^x = -2x$

   c. $-(2^x) = \frac{3}{4}x - 4$

Practice What is the solution or solutions of each equation?

9. $4^x = \frac{3}{2}x + 5$

10. $x + 3 = 3^x$

Lesson Check

Do you know HOW?

Evaluate each function for the given value.

11. $f(x) = 6 \cdot 2^x$ for $x = 3$

12. $g(w) = 45 \cdot 3^w$ for $w = -2$

Graph each function.

13. $y = 3^x$

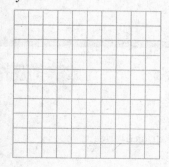

14. $f(x) = 4\left(\frac{1}{2}\right)^x$

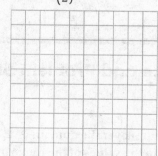

Do you UNDERSTAND?

15. Vocabulary Describe the differences between a linear function and an exponential function.

16. Reasoning Is $y = (-2)^x$ an exponential function? Justify your answer.

17. Error Analysis A student evaluated the function $f(x) = 3 \cdot 4^x$ for $x = -1$ as shown at the right. Describe and correct the student's mistake.

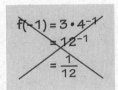

More Practice and Problem-Solving Exercises

 Apply

Evaluate each function over the domain $\{-2, -1, 0, 1, 2, 3\}$. As the values of the domain increase, do the values of the range increase or decrease?

18. $f(x) = 5^x$ **19.** $y = 2.5^x$ **20.** $h(x) = 0.1^x$ **21.** $f(x) = 5 \cdot 4^x$

22. $y = 0.5^x$ **23.** $y = 8^x$ **24.** $g(x) = 4 \cdot 10^x$ **25.** $y = 100 \cdot 0.3^x$

Graph each function.

26. $f(x) = 3^x + 12$ **27.** $f(x) = 2(2)^x - 5$ **28.** $f(x) = 4(1.5)^x + 7$

29. Compare the rule and the function table below. Which function has the greater value when $x = 12$? Explain.

Function 1

$y = 4^x$

Function 2

x	1	2	3	4
y	5	25	125	625

30. You have just read a journal article about a population of fungi that doubles every month. The beginning population was 10. The function $y = 10 \cdot 2^n$ represents the population after n months.

  a. You have a population of 15 of the same fungi. Assuming the journal article gives the correct rate of increase, write the function that represents the population of fungi after n months.

  b. Suppose you find another article that states that the fungi population triples every month. If there are currently 15 fungi in your population, write the function that represents the population after n months.

© **31. Think About a Plan** Hydra are small freshwater animals. They can double in number every two days in a laboratory tank. Suppose one tank has an initial population of 60 hydra. When will there be more than 5000 hydra?
  - How can a table help you identify a pattern?
  - What function models the situation?

32. How does the graph of $f(x) = 5^x + 8$ compare to the graph of $g(x) = 5^x$?

33. How does the graph of $f(x) = 16(0.75)^x - 2$ compare to the graph of $g(x) = 16(0.75)^x$?

© **34. a.** Graph $y = 2^x$, $y = 4^x$, and $y = 0.25^x$ on the same axes.
  b. What point is on all three graphs?
  c. Does the graph of an exponential function of the form $y = b^x$ intersect the x-axis? Explain.
  d. **Reasoning** How does the graph of $y = b^x$ change as the base b increases or decreases?

Which function has the greater value for the given value of x?

35. $y = 4^x$ or $y = x^4$ for $x = 2$

36. $f(x) = 10 \cdot 2x$ or $f(x) = 200 \cdot x^2$ for $x = 7$

37. $y = 3^x$ or $y = x^3$ for $x = 5$

38. $f(x) = 2^x$ or $f(x) = 100x^2$ for $x = 10$

39. Computers A computer valued at $1500 loses 20% of its value each year.
  a. Write a function rule that models the value of the computer.
  b. Find the value of the computer after 3 yr.
  c. In how many years will the value of the computer be less than $500?

© **40. a.** Graph the functions $y = x^2$ and $y = 2^x$ on the same axes.
   b. What do you notice about the graphs for the values of x between 1 and 3?
   c. **Reasoning** How do you think the graph of $y = 8^x$ would compare to the graphs of $y = x^2$ and $y = 2^x$?

© **41. Writing** Find the range of the function $f(x) = 500 \cdot 1^x$ using the domain $\{1, 2, 3, 4, 5\}$. Explain why the definition of *exponential function* states that $b \neq 1$.

ⓒ Challenge

Solve each equation.

42. $2^x = 64$

43. $3^x = \frac{1}{27}$

44. $3 \cdot 2^x = 24$

45. $5 \cdot 2^x - 152 = 8$

46. Suppose $(0, 4)$ and $(2, 36)$ are on the graph of an exponential function.
   a. Use $(0, 4)$ in the general form of an exponential function, $y = a \cdot b^x$, to find the value of the constant a.
   b. Use your answer from part (a) and $(2, 36)$ to find the value of the constant b.
   c. Write a rule for the function.
   d. Evaluate the function for $x = -2$ and $x = 4$.

5-3

Comparing Linear and Exponential Functions

F.LE.1 Distinguish between situations that can be modeled with linear . . . and . . . exponential functions.
Also **F.IF.6, F.LE.1.a, F.LE.3**

Objective To compare properties of linear and exponential functions

Solve It! Write your solution to the Solve It in the space below.

In the Solve It, you compared a linear function and an exponential function. The observations you made for these two functions hold true for linear and exponential functions in general.

Essential Understanding On equal intervals of the domain, *differences* in the values of a linear function are constant, while *ratios* of the values of an exponential function are constant. A quantity growing exponentially will eventually exceed a quantity growing linearly.

Suppose all the *x*-values in a table have a common difference. If all the *y*-values have a common difference, then the table represents a linear function. If all of the *y*-values have a common ratio, then the table represents an exponential function.

Problem 1 Identifying Linear and Exponential Functions

Got it! Does the table or rule represent a linear or an exponential function? Explain.

a.

x	1	2	3	4
y	−1	1	3	5

b. $y = 3 \cdot 6^x$

Think

How can you decide if a table represents a linear or an exponential function?

Determine whether each table represents a linear or exponential function. Explain.

1.

x	1	2	3	4
y	2	8	32	128

2.

x	0	1	2	3
y	6	9	12	15

ONLINE PROBLEMS

Problem 2   Identifying Real-World Linear and Exponential Functions

Got It? Can you model the situation by a *linear function* or an *exponential function*? Explain.

a. Jack pays $30 each month for a gym membership.

Think

How can you us
differences and
ratios to classif
each situation?

b. A culture starts with 1200 bacteria. The number of bacteria in the culture is halved each day.

Practice Tell whether the situation is modeled by a *linear function* or an *exponential function*. Explain.

3. Each shirt costs $15.

4. An initial bacteria population of 5 doubles every hour.

> The **average rate of change** of a function $f(x)$ over the interval $a \leq x \leq b$ is given by
>
> $$\text{average rate of change} = \frac{f(b) - f(a)}{b - a}$$

Problem 3 **Investigating Rates of Change**

Got It? **a. Reasoning** How do the average rates of change for a linear function differ from the average rates of change for an exponential function?

© **b. Reasoning** Use the tables and graphs in Problem 3. How do you know that an increasing exponential function will eventually overtake an increasing linear function?

Graph each function over the domain $0 \leq x \leq 6$. Find the average rate of change for each function over the intervals $0 \leq x \leq 2$, $2 \leq x \leq 4$, and $4 \leq x \leq 6$. Describe what you observe.

5. $f(x) = 2 \cdot 3^x$

6. $f(x) = 4x + 1$

Lesson Check

Do you know HOW?

7. Does the equation $y = 5^x$ represent a linear or an exponential function? Explain.

8. What is the average rate of change for the function $f(x) = 6x + 17$ over the interval $0 \leq x \leq 2$?

Tell whether each situation can be modeled by a linear function or an exponential function. Explain.

9. Ryan's condo fees are $225 each month.

10. The number of customers last month was 30. The number of customers is predicted to double every month.

Do you UNDERSTAND?

11. Vocabulary Given a function, $f(x)$, and the interval $a \leq x \leq b$, what is found using the formula $\frac{f(b) - f(a)}{b - a}$?

© **12. Open-Ended** What is a real-world situation that can be modeled by an exponential function?

© **13. Error Analysis** The function $f(x) = 7 \cdot 2^x$ has an average rate of change of 10.5 over the interval $0 \leq x \leq 2$. Paul said the average rate of change for the function is 28. What is Paul's error? Explain.

More Practice and Problem-Solving Exercises

MATHEMATICAL PRACTICES

Ⓑ **Apply**

© **14. Think About a Plan** The function $f(x) = 2x + 5$ represents the cost of making x bracelets. What is the average rate of change for the function? What does the rate of change mean?
- How can you graph the function on the domain $0 \leq x \leq 6$?
- What is the average rate of change over the intervals $0 \leq x \leq 2$, $2 \leq x \leq 4$, and $4 \leq x \leq 6$?
- What do you observe about the average rate of change?

15. Hummingbirds The function $f(x) = 20 \cdot 1.05^x$ models the hummingbird population after x months. What is the average rate of change of the function over the intervals from $0 \leq x \leq 10$, $10 \leq x \leq 20$, and $20 \leq x \leq 30$? What does each rate of change mean?

16. a. How can you tell when a function is linear given a graph of the function?
   b. Using a rule, how can you tell when a function is linear given an algebraic function rule?
   c. Using a table, how can you tell when a function is linear given a table of input-output pairs?

@ 17. **Error Analysis** Describe and correct the error at the right in determining if the table represents a linear or an exponential function.

x	0	1	2	3
y	−2	−4	−8	−16

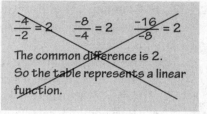

$\dfrac{-4}{-2} = 2$ $\dfrac{-8}{-4} = 2$ $\dfrac{-16}{-8} = 2$

The common difference is 2.
So the table represents a linear function.

18. **Cell Phones** In 2000, there were 500 cell phone users in a city. The number of cell phone users increased by 60% each year after 2000.
   a. Make a table of values to represent this situation.
   b. Is there a common difference or a common ratio? If so, what is the common difference or common ratio?
   c. Is this situation modeled by a linear function or an exponential function? Explain.

19. **Profit** A company was founded in 2004 and made no profit in its first year. Since then, the company made $150,000 more profit each year than it did the previous year.
   a. Make a table of values to represent this situation.
   b. Is there a common difference or a common ratio? What is the common difference or common ratio?
   c. Is this situation modeled by a linear function or an exponential function? Explain.

20. **Water** The table shows the amount of water in a bathtub at different times. Does the table represent a linear or an exponential function? Explain. What does the common difference or common ratio mean?

Number of Minutes, x	0	1	2	3
Number of Gallons, y	70	49	28	7

21. **Sports** It took Brandon 30 seconds to run the 200-meter dash in 2010, 28.2 seconds in 2011, and 26.508 seconds in 2012.
   a. Is there a common difference or a common ratio? What is the common difference or common ratio?
   b. Is this situation modeled by a linear function or an exponential function? Explain.
   c. By what percent does Brandon decrease his time each year?

@ 22. **Reasoning** The slope of a linear function $f(x)$ is k. What is the average rate of change over the interval $-10 \le x \le -8$? Explain how you know.

23. a. Graphing Calculator Graph the functions $y = 2^x$ and $y = x^2$ on the same axes, with x going from 0 to 5 and y going from 0 to 25. On what intervals is $2^x > x^2$?

    b. Use a table to compare values of $f(x) = 2^x$ and $g(x) = x^2$ for $x \geq 4$. Which function is growing faster as x increases? Will $g(x) = x^2$ ever overtake $f(x) = 2^x$? Explain.

    c. Use a graphing calculator to compare $f(x) = 2^x$ and $h(x) = x^3$ for $x \geq 0$. How many points of intersection are there? When is $2^x > x^3$?

    d. Let a be a real number greater than 1, and let n be an integer greater than or equal to 2. Make a conjecture about the difference between a^x and x^n for large values of x.

    e. Find a value of x for which $x > 2$ and $2^x > x^{10}$.

Challenge

24. Half-Life The half-life of a substance is the amount of time it takes for half of the amount of substance to decay. The half-life of a pesticide is 15 years. Initially there are 200 grams of the pesticide. Can this situation be modeled by a linear function or an exponential function? After how many years will there be 50 grams of the pesticide remaining? Explain.

25. Reasoning What is the difference between linear growth and exponential growth in a population over x years? (Use arithmetic terms such as *add*, *subtract, multiply*, and *divide*.)

5-4 Exponential Growth and Decay

F.LE.1.c Recognize situations in which a quantity grows or decays by a constant percent rate . . . Also **A.CED.2, F.BF.1, F.LE.2**

Objective   To model exponential growth and decay

Solve It!   Write your solution to the Solve It in the space below.

In the Solve It, the number of uranium-238 atoms decreases exponentially. In this lesson, you will use exponential functions to model similar situations.

Essential Understanding   An exponential function can model growth or decay of an initial amount.

take note

Key Concept   Exponential Growth

Definitions

Exponential growth can be modeled by the function $y = a \cdot b^x$, where $a > 0$ and $b > 1$. The base b is the **growth factor**, which equals 1 plus the percent rate of change expressed as a decimal.

Graph

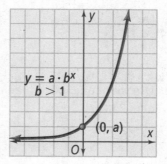

Algebra

$$\underset{\underset{\downarrow}{\text{initial amount (when } x = 0)}}{y = a \cdot b^x} \leftarrow \text{exponent}$$

The base, which is greater than 1, is the growth factor.

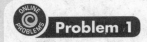

Problem 1 Modeling Exponential Growth

Got It? Suppose that in 1985, there were 285 cell phone subscribers in a small town. The number of subscribers increased by 75% each year after 1985. How many cell phone subscribers were in the small town in 1994?

> **Think**
> How can you use an exponential function to represent the situation?

(A)Practice

1. **College Enrollment** The number of students enrolled at a college is 15,000 and grows 4% each year.

   a. The initial amount a is _____.

   b. The percent rate of change is 4%, so the growth factor b is
   $1 +$ _____ $=$ _____.

   c. To find the number of students enrolled after one year, you calculate $15,000 \cdot$ _____.

   d. Complete the equation $y = \blacksquare \cdot \blacksquare^{\blacksquare}$ to find the number of students enrolled after x years.

   e. Use your equation to predict the number of students enrolled after 25 yr.

2. Population A population of 100 frogs increases at an annual rate of 22%. How many frogs will there be in 5 years?

When a bank pays interest on both the principal *and* the interest an account has already earned, the bank is paying **compound interest**. Compound interest is an example of exponential growth.

You can use the following formula to find the balance of an account that earns compound interest.

$$A = P\left(1 + \frac{r}{n}\right)^{nt}$$

A = the balance

P = the principal (the initial deposit)

r = the annual interest rate (expressed as a decimal)

n = the number of times interest is compounded per year

t = the time in years

Problem 2 Compound Interest

Got It? Suppose that when your friend was born, your friend's parents deposited $2000 in an account paying 4.5% interest compounded monthly. What will the account balance be after 18 yr?

Think

Is the compound interest formula an exponential growth formula?

3. $775 deposit earning 4.25% compounded annually, after 12 yr

4. $3500 deposit earning 6.75% compounded monthly, after 6 months

The function $y = a \cdot b^x$ can model *exponential decay* as well as exponential growth. In both cases, b represents the rate of change. The value of b tells if the equation models exponential growth or decay.

take note

Key Concept Exponential Decay

Definitions

Exponential decay can be modeled by the function $y = a \cdot b^x$, where $a > 0$ and $0 < b < 1$. The base b is the **decay factor**, which equals 1 minus the percent rate of change expressed as a decimal.

Algebra

initial amount (when $x = 0$)
$$\downarrow$$
$$y = a \cdot b^x \leftarrow \textbf{exponent}$$
$$\uparrow$$
The base is the decay factor.

Graph

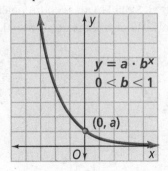

$y = a \cdot b^x$
$0 < b < 1$

$(0, a)$

Got It? **a.** The kilopascal is a unit of measure for atmospheric pressure. The atmospheric pressure at sea level is about 101 kilopascals. For every 1000-m increase in altitude, the pressure decreases about 11.5%. What is the atmospheric pressure at an altitude of 5000 m?

b. **Reasoning** Why do you subtract the percent decrease from 1 to find the decay factor?

 Practice **5.** Identify the initial amount a and the decay factor b in the exponential function $f(x) = 10 \cdot 0.1^x$.

6. Population The population of a city is 45,000 and decreases 2% each year. If the trend continues, what will the population be after 15 yr?

Given a table of values or a graph for an exponential function, you can determine the values of a and b to write an equation $y = a \cdot b^x$ for the function.

Problem 4 Writing Exponential Functions

Got It? What is an exponential function that represents the table or graph?

a.

x	y
−3	512
−2	128
−1	32
0	8
1	2
2	0.5

b.

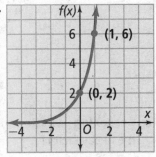

A Practice What is an exponential function that represents the table or graph?

7.

x	y
−2	4
−1	8
0	16
1	32
2	64
3	128

8.

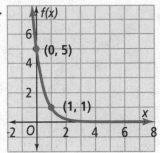

Lesson Check

Do you know HOW?

9. What is the growth factor in the function $y = 34 \cdot 4^x$?

10. What is the initial amount in the function $y = 15 \cdot 3^x$?

11. What is the decay factor in the function $y = 17 \cdot 0.2^x$?

12. A population of fish in a lake decreases 6% annually. What is the decay factor?

13. Suppose your friend's parents invest $20,000 in an account paying 5% interest compounded annually. What will the balance be after 10 yr?

Do you UNDERSTAND?

14. Vocabulary How can you tell if an exponential function models growth or decay?

15. Reasoning How can you simplify the compound interest formula when the interest is compounded annually? Explain.

16. Error Analysis A student deposits $500 into an account that earns 3.5% interest compounded quarterly. Describe and correct the student's error in calculating the account balance after 2 yr.

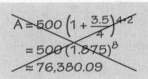

$$A = 500\left(1 + \frac{3.5}{4}\right)^{4 \cdot 2}$$
$$= 500(1.875)^8$$
$$\approx 76{,}380.09$$

More Practice and Problem-Solving Exercises

B Apply

State whether the equation represents *exponential growth*, *exponential decay*, or *neither*.

17. $y = 0.93 \cdot 2^x$ **18.** $y = 2 \cdot 0.68^x$ **19.** $y = 68 \cdot x^2$ **20.** $y = 68 \cdot 0.2^x$

21. What exponential function passes through the points $(0, 10)$ and $(2, 2.5)$?

22. Sports In a single-elimination tournament starting with 128 teams, half of the remaining teams are eliminated in each round.
  a. Make a table, a scatter plot, and a function rule to represent the situation.
  b. Is it possible for 24 teams to remain after a round? Which representation in part (a) made it the easiest to answer the question?
  c. What is the domain of the function? What does the domain represent?
  d. How many teams will be left after 5 rounds?

23. **Car Value** A family buys a car for $20,000. The value of the car decreases about 20% each year. After 6 yr, the family decides to sell the car. Should they sell it for $4000? Explain.

 24. **Think About a Plan** You invest $100 and expect your money to grow 8% each year. About how many years will it take for your investment to double?
   - What function models the growth of your investment?
   - How can you use a table to find the approximate amount of time it takes for your investment to double?
   - How can you use a graph to find the approximate amount of time it takes for your investment to double?

25. **Reasoning** Give an example of an exponential function in the form $y = a \cdot b^x$ that is neither an exponential growth function nor an exponential decay function. Explain your reasoning.

State whether each graph shows an *exponential growth function*, an *exponential decay function*, or *neither*.

26.
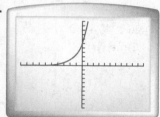

27.
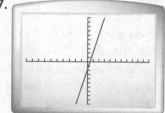

28. Use a table and a scatter plot to answer each question.
   a. You play a game of musical chairs in which 32 players start and you remove 2 chairs in each round. How many rounds will you play before two players are left?
   b. In another game of musical chairs, you take away half of the chairs each time. If the game begins with 32 players, how many rounds will it take to get down to two players?
   c. Will a game where you remove half of the chairs always end more quickly than one in which you take the same number of chairs each time? Give an example.

29. A classmate opens a savings account. The table represents the amount of money in the savings account when she opens it and after several years. What exponential function represents the account balance, b, after t years?

Time in years, t	Balance, b
0	$5000
1	$5250
2	$5512.50
3	$5788.13

30. The graph at the right shows the amount, A, of radioactive material (in milligrams) that remains in a beaker after h hours. What exponential function is shown in the graph?

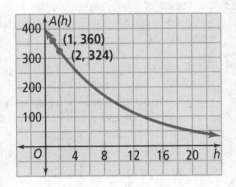

31. Business Suppose you start a lawn-mowing business and make a profit of $400 in the first year. Each year after the first year, your profit increases 5%.
  a. Write a function that models your annual profit.
  b. If you continue your business for 10 yr, what will your *total* profit be?

STEM **32. Medicine** Cesium-137 is a radioisotope used in radiology where levels are measured in millicuries (mci). Use the graph at the right. What is a reasonable estimate of the half-life of cesium-137?

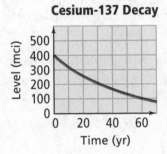

Cesium-137 Decay

 **Challenge**

33. Credit Suppose you use a credit card to buy a new suit for $250. If you do not pay the entire balance after one month, you are charged 1.8% monthly interest on your account balance. Suppose you can make a $30 payment each month.
  a. What is your balance after your first monthly payment?
  b. How much interest are you charged on the remaining balance after your first payment?
  c. What is your balance just before you make your second payment?
  d. What is your balance after your second payment?
  e. How many months will it take for you to pay off the entire bill?
  f. How much interest will you have paid in all?

© 34. Open-Ended Write two exponential growth functions $f(x)$ and $g(x)$ such that $f(x) < g(x)$ for $x < 3$ and $f(x) > g(x)$ for $x > 3$.

Using Properties of Exponents to Transform Functions

A.SSE.3.c Use the properties of exponents to transform . . . exponential functions.

The list below summarizes what you have learned about the laws of exponents. Assume that no denominator is 0, and that m and n are integers.

Product of Powers Property	$a^m \cdot a^n = a^{m+n}$
Power of a Power Property	$\left(a^m\right)^n = a^{mn}$
Power of a Product Property	$(ab)^m = a^m b^m$
Quotient of Powers Property	$\dfrac{a^m}{a^n} = a^{m-n}$
Power of a Quotient Property	$\left(\dfrac{a}{b}\right)^n = \dfrac{a^n}{b^n}$

Example 1

Use the laws of exponents to simplify each expression.

A $x^3 \cdot x^4$

$\begin{aligned} x^3 \cdot x^4 &= x^{3+4} \\ &= x^7 \end{aligned}$ 　　　　Product of Powers Property

　　　　　　　　　　Simplify.

B $(y^3)^{-2}$

$\begin{aligned} (y^3)^{-2} &= y^{3 \cdot (-2)} \\ &= y^{-6} \end{aligned}$ 　　　　Power of a Power Property

　　　　　　　　　　Simplify.

C $(2n \cdot m)^4$

$\begin{aligned} (2n \cdot m)^4 &= 2^4 \cdot n^4 \cdot m^4 \\ &= 16n^4 m^4 \end{aligned}$ 　　　Power of a Product Property

　　　　　　　　　　Simplify.

D $\dfrac{12s^5}{2s^{-2}}$

$\begin{aligned} \dfrac{12s^5}{2s^{-2}} &= 6s^{5-(-2)} \\ &= 6s^{5+2} \\ &= 6s^7 \end{aligned}$ 　　Quotient of Powers Property

　　　　　　　　　Simplify.

E $\left(\dfrac{8c}{3d}\right)^9$

$\left(\dfrac{8c}{3d}\right)^9 = \dfrac{8^9 c^9}{3^9 d^9}$ 　　　　Power of a Quotient Property

You can transform functions using the laws of exponents to reveal information about the function.

Example 2

The interest earned on Rodney's bank account is given by $f(m) = 1.005^m$, where m is the number of months. What is the approximate annual interest rate on Rodney's account?

There are 12 months in one year, so $y = \frac{m}{12}$, or $m = 12y$, where y is the number of years.

$$f(m) = 1.005^m$$

$\quad\quad = 1.005^{12y}$ Substitute $12y$ for m.

$\quad\quad = (1.005^{12})^y$ Power of a Power Property

$\quad\quad \approx 1.062^y$ Simplify.

The annual interest rate on Rodney's bank account is about 6.2%.

Exercises

1. Simplify each expression.

   a. $-3h^5 \cdot 6h^2$

   b. $(-3g \cdot 4h)^3$

   c. $\dfrac{-42s^3t^{-4}u^6}{-6s^5t^{-3}u^{-2}}$

2. Population The population P of deer in a state forest is modeled by the function $P(t) = 200(1.03)^t$, where t is the number of years since 1970.

a. Use the fact that there are 10 years in one decade to find a function that models the deer population in the state forest after d decades.

b. What is the approximate rate of increase per decade of the deer population in the state forest? Explain.

3. Interest The interest I earned after n years by a savings account compounded annually is given by $I = Pr^n$, where P is the principal, and r is the annual interest rate written as a decimal. If the interest is compounded quarterly, the interest earned is given by $I = P\left(\frac{r}{4}\right)^{4n}$. Show that the ratio of the interest earned quarterly to the interest earned annually increases exponentially by showing that the ratio is equal to $\left(\frac{r^3}{256}\right)^n$.

A.CED.1 Create equations and inequalities in one variable and . . . solve problems . . . Also **A.REI.11**

Objective To solve exponential equations

Solve It! Write your solution to the Solve It in the space below.

You can model the situation in the Solve It using the exponential equation $64\left(\frac{1}{2}\right)^x = 1$, or $\left(\frac{1}{2}\right)^x = \frac{1}{64}$. Notice that you can rewrite this equation as $\left(\frac{1}{2}\right)^x = \left(\frac{1}{2}\right)^6$.

Essential Understanding You can solve many exponential equations by writing each side of the equation with the same base.

take note

Key Concept   Solving Exponential Equations With the Same Base

When an exponential equation has the same base on each side of the equation, then the exponents must be equal.

$\qquad$ Let $b > 0$ and $b \neq 1$. Then $b^x = b^y$ if and only if $x = y$.

Problem 1 Solving Exponential Equations With the Same Base

Got It? What is the solution of each exponential equation?

a. $7^x = 343$

Think

How can you rewrite the constant in each equation to help you solve it?

b. $\frac{1}{216} = 6^x$

c. $2^{x+4} = \frac{1}{1,024}$

Practice Solve each exponential equation.

1. $9^x = 729$

2. $5^{x+1} = 125$

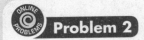

Got It? The function $R(x) = 2^x$ represents the number of regions formed when you fold a tablecloth x times. How many folds do you need to make 128 regions?

 Practice **3. Ecology** The function $f(x) = 6^{x+1}$ models the fly population in a controlled experiment after x days. According to the model, after how many days will there be 1,296 flies?

4. Archaeology The function $F(x) = 3^{x+2}$ models the number of fossils an archaeologist finds after x years. According to the model, after how many years will the archaeologist find 81 fossils?

You can solve an exponential equation by graphing each side of the equation. The solution is the x-coordinate of the point of intersection of the two graphs.

Problem 3 — Solving Exponential Equations by Graphing

Got It? What is the solution of the equation $3 = 9 \cdot 3^{x-2}$? Use a graph.

Think
How can you check your solution?

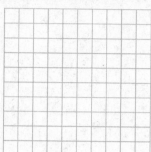

Practice Find the solution of each equation by graphing.

5. $9 = 3^{x-1}$

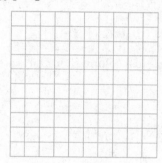

6. $64 = 4^{x+1}$

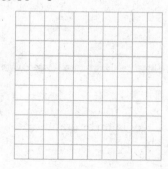

Lesson Check

Do you know HOW?

Solve each exponential equation.

7. $729 = 3^x$

8. $512 = 2^x$

9. $2^x = \frac{1}{8}$

10. $\frac{1}{64} = 4^{x-5}$

11. The function $f(x) = 8^x$ represents the number of bacteria in a colony after x days. After how many days will there be 32,768 bacteria?

Do you UNDERSTAND?

© **12. Reasoning** How do you find a solution of an exponential equation by graphing?

13. Open-Ended In this lesson, you learned that when $b > 0$ and $b \neq 1$, $b^x = b^y$ if and only if $x = y$. Explain this in words.

14. Error Analysis A classmate says that the solution of the equation $7^{x+1} = 343$ is $x = 3$. Explain the classmate's error.

More Practice and Problem-Solving Exercises

Apply

15. Error Analysis Describe and correct the error at the right in determining the solution of the equation.

16. Writing Explain how to solve an exponential equation where each side has the same base.

$$8^{2x} = 2^{x+5}$$
$$2x = x + 5$$
$$x = 5$$

Solve each exponential equation.

17. $7^{2x} = 2401$

18. $3^{-2x+3} = \frac{1}{243}$

19. $\frac{1}{125} = \frac{1}{5^{3x}}$

20. $1024 = 4^{6x-7}$

21. $4096 = 8^x$

22. $\frac{1}{256} = 4^x$

23. Think About a Plan The function $F(x) = 2^{x-1}$ models the number of free throws you made after x weeks. After how many weeks will you make 32 free throws? Use a graph.
- What do you graph to represent the left side of the equation?
- What do you graph to represent the right side of the equation?
- What tells you the solution of the equation?

24. Test Grades The function $T(x) = 3^{x+1}$ models your test grade after studying x hours. How many hours will you have to study to earn an 81 on the test? Use a graph.

© 25. **Open-Ended** Write an exponential equation that has a solution $x = 5$.

26. **Food Drive** The function $C(x) = 2^{3x+2}$ models the number of cans collected for a canned food drive after x days. According to the model, after how many days will there be 131,072 cans?

27. **Photographs** You enlarge a photograph x times. Each time, you increase its size by 300%. If you continue enlarging the photograph in this way, after how many enlargements will the photograph be 243 times the original size?

© **Challenge**

28. **Earnings** Peter earned one cent the first day, two cents the second day, four cents the third day, eight cents the fourth day, and so on. After how many days will Peter earn a total of $327.67?

29. What is the solution of $3^{4-7x} = \dfrac{1}{9^{x-1}}$?

5-6 Geometric Sequences

F.BF.2 Write . . . sequences both recursively and with an explicit formula, use them to model situations, and translate between the two forms. Also **F.IF.3, F.BF.1.a, F.LE.2**

Objective   To write and use recursive formulas for geometric sequences

Solve It!   Write your solution to the Solve It in the space below.

In the Solve It, the sales prices form a *geometric sequence*.

Essential Understanding   In a **geometric sequence**, the ratio of any term to its preceding term is a constant value.

take note

Key Concept   Geometric Sequence

A geometric sequence with a *starting value a* and a *common ratio r* is a sequence of the form

$$a, ar, ar^2, ar^3, \ldots$$

A *recursive definition* for the sequence has two parts:

$a_1 = a$ Initial condition

$a_n = a_{n-1} \cdot r$, for $n \geq 2$ Recursive formula

An *explicit definition* for this sequence is a single formula:

$a_n = a_1 \cdot r^{n-1}$, for $n \geq 1$

Every geometric sequence has a starting value and a common ratio. The starting value and common ratio define a unique geometric sequence.

ONLINE PROBLEMS **Problem 1** **Identifying Geometric Sequences**

Got It? Which of the following are geometric sequences? If the sequence is not geometric, is it arithmetic?

a. 3, 6, 12, 24, 48, . . .

b. 3, 6, 9, 12, 15, . . .

Think

How do you find the common ratio between two consecutive terms?

c. $\frac{1}{3}, \frac{1}{9}, \frac{1}{27}, \frac{1}{81}, \ldots$

d. 4, 7, 11, 16, 22, . . .

Ⓐ Practice Determine whether the sequence is a geometric sequence. Explain.

1. 256, 192, 144, 108, . . .

2. 6, −12, 24, −48, . . .

Any geometric sequence can be written with both an explicit and a recursive formula. The recursive formula is useful for finding the next term in the sequence. The explicit formula is more convenient when finding the nth term.

Problem 2 **Finding Recursive and Explicit Formulas**

Got It? Find the recursive and explicit formulas for each of the following.

a. 2, 4, 8, 16, . . .

Think

What do you need to write recursive and explicit formulas for a geometric sequence?

b. 40, 20, 10, 5, . . .

 Practice **3.** Write the explicit formula for the geometric sequence
686, 98, 14, 2, ...

4. Write the recursive formula for the geometric sequence
192, 128, $85\frac{1}{3}$, $56\frac{8}{9}$, ...

Got It? Write a recursive formula and an explicit formula for each sequence.
Find the 8th term of each sequence.

    a. 14, 84, 504, 3024, . . .

    b. 648, 324, 162, 81, . . .

Practice **5.** A store manager plans to offer discounts on some sweaters according
to this sequence: $48, $36, $27, $20.25, ... Write the explicit and
recursive formulas for the sequence.

STEM **6. Science** When a radioactive substance
decays, measurements of the amount
remaining over constant intervals of
time form a geometric sequence. The
table shows the amount of Fl-18
remaining after different constant
intervals. Write the explicit and recursive formulas for the
geometric sequence formed by the amount of Fl-18 remaining.

Fluorine-18 Remaining				
Time (min)	0	110	220	330
Fl-18 (picograms)	260	130	65	32.5

You can also represent a sequence by using function notation. This allows you to plot the sequence using the points (n, a_n), where n is the term number and a_n is the term.

Problem 4   **Writing Geometric Sequences as Functions**

Got It?   A geometric sequence has an initial value of 2 and a common ratio of 3. Write a function to represent the sequence. Graph the function.

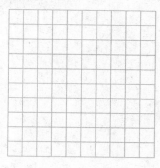

Practice   **7.** A geometric sequence has an initial value of 18 and a common ratio of $\frac{1}{2}$. Write a function to represent this sequence. Graph the function.

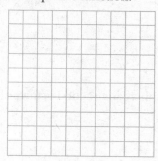

8. Write and graph the function that represents the sequence in the table.

x	1	2	3	4
f(x)	8	16	32	64

Lesson Check

Do you know HOW?

Determine whether each sequence is a geometric sequence. For each geometric sequence, find the common ratio.

9. 3, 9, 27, 81, . . .

10. 200, 50, 12.5, 3.125, . . .

11. 10, 8, 6, 4, . . .

Write the explicit and recursive formulas for each geometric sequence.

12. 5, 20, 80, 320, . . .

13. 4, −8, 16, −32, . . .

14. 162, 108, 72, 48, . . .

15. 3, 6, 12, 24, . . .

Do you UNDERSTAND?

© **16. Error Analysis** A friend says that the recursive formula for the geometric sequence $1, -1, 1, -1, 1, \ldots$ is $a_n = 1 \cdot (-1)^{n-1}$. Explain your friend's error and give the correct recursive formula for the sequence.

© **17. Critical Thinking** Describe the similarities and differences between arithmetic and geometric sequences.

More Practice and Problem-Solving Exercises

MATHEMATICAL PRACTICES

Ⓑ **Apply**

Determine if each sequence is a geometric sequence. If it is, find the common ratio and write the explicit and recursive formulas.

18. $5, 10, 20, 40, \ldots$ **19.** $20, 15, 10, 5, \ldots$ **20.** $3, -9, 27, -81, \ldots$

21. $98, 14, 2, \frac{2}{7}, \ldots$ **22.** $-3, -1, 1, 3, \ldots$ **23.** $200, -100, 50, -25, \ldots$

Identify each sequence as *arithmetic*, *geometric*, or *neither*.

24. $1.5, 4.5, 13.5, 40.5, \ldots$ **25.** $42, 38, 34, 30, \ldots$ **26.** $4, 9, 16, 25, \ldots$

27. $-4, 1, 6, 11, \ldots$ **28.** $1, 2, 3, 5, \ldots$ **29.** $2, 8, 32, 128, \ldots$

© **30. Think About a Plan** Suppose you are rehearsing for a concert. You plan to rehearse the piece you will perform four times the first day and then to double the number of times you rehearse the piece each day until the concert. What are two formulas you can write to describe the sequence of how many times you will rehearse the piece each day?

- How can you write a sequence of numbers to represent this situation?
- Is the sequence arithmetic, geometric, or neither?
- How can you write explicit and recursive formulas for this sequence?

© **31. Open-Ended** Write a geometric sequence. Then write the explicit and recursive formulas for your sequence.

Lesson 5-6   Geometric Sequences   **335**

STEM **32. Science** A certain culture of yeast increases by 50% every three hours. A scientist places 9 grams of the yeast in a culture dish. Write the explicit and recursive formulas for the geometric sequence formed by the growth of the yeast.

Challenge

33. The differences between consecutive terms in a geometric sequence form a new geometric sequence. For instance, when you take the differences between the consecutive terms of the geometric sequence 5, 15, 45, 135, . . . , you get $15 - 5$, $45 - 15$, $135 - 45$, ... The new geometric sequence is 10, 30, 90, ... Compare the two sequences. How are they similar, and how do they differ?

5-7 Combining Functions

F.BF.1.b Combine standard function types . . .

Objective   To add, subtract, multiply, and divide linear and exponential functions

Solve It!   Write your solution to the Solve It in the space below.

You can represent the function $f(x)$ in the Solve It as a difference of two functions.

Essential Understanding   You can perform arithmetic operations on functions just as you do on numbers or algebraic expressions. You can add, subtract, multiply, or divide two functions.

take note

Key Concept   Function Operations

Addition $(f + g)(x) = f(x) + g(x)$

Subtraction $(f - g)(x) = f(x) - g(x)$

Multiplication $(f \cdot g)(x) = f(x) \cdot g(x)$

Division $\left(\dfrac{f}{g}\right)(x) = \dfrac{f(x)}{g(x)}, g(x) \neq 0$

Problem 1 Adding and Subtracting Functions

Think

Is the order in which you apply $f(x)$ and $g(x)$ important?

Got It? $f(x) = 5^x - 4$ and $g(x) = 3x + 8$. What is $(f + g)(x)$? What is $(f + g)(3)$?

Practice Find each sum or difference if $f(x) = 3 \cdot 8^x$ and $g(x) = 2 \cdot 8^x + 1$.

1. a. $(f + g)(x)$

b. $(f + g)(2)$

2. a. $(f - g)(x)$

b. $(f - g)(3)$

Problem 2 Multiplying and Dividing Functions

Got It? $f(x) = 8x + 15$ and $g(x) = 4x$. What is $(f \cdot g)(x)$? What is $(f \cdot g)(-5)$?

Practice Find each product or quotient if $f(x) = 144x - 48$ and $g(x) = 12$.

3. a. $(f \cdot g)(x)$

   b. $(f \cdot g)(-5)$

4. a. $\left(\dfrac{f}{g}\right)(x)$

   b. $\left(\dfrac{f}{g}\right)(3)$

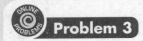

Problem 3   **Operations on Functions in Real Life**

Got It?   **Biology** Scientists conducted a study of the sparrow populations in two cities. The results of the study projected that the population in City C in x years will be modeled by $C(x) = 950 \cdot 1.29^x - 120x$ and the population in City D in x years will be modeled by $D(x) = 500x - 600$. What is a function giving the difference in population of sparrows between City C and City D? Predict what the difference in population will be in 6 years.

> **Think**
>
> Is the order in which you apply $C(x)$ and $D(x)$ important in the difference function?

Practice   **5. Manufacturing** The cost of manufacturing x T-shirts is modeled by the function $T(x) = 5x + 12$ and the cost of manufacturing x sweatshirts is modeled by $S(x) = 15x + 18$. What is a function giving the total cost of manufacturing T-shirts and sweatshirts? Find the total cost of manufacturing 15 T-shirts and 15 sweatshirts.

6. Fundraising The amount of money raised for Cause A in x years will be modeled by $A(x) = 1{,}200 \cdot 5^x$ and the amount of money raised for Cause B in x years will be modeled by $B(x) = 800 \cdot 5^x$. What is a function giving the difference in the amounts raised for Cause A and Cause B? Predict what the difference in the amounts raised will be in 4 years.

Lesson Check

Do you know HOW?

Find each sum, difference, product, or quotient if $f(x) = 15x + 3$ and $g(x) = 3x$.

7. $(f + g)(x)$

8. $(f - g)(x)$

9. $(f \cdot g)(x)$

10. $\left(\dfrac{f}{g}\right)(x)$

Do you UNDERSTAND?

MATHEMATICAL PRACTICES

11. When multiplying powers with the same base, what operation is performed on the exponents?

12. Writing Explain how to add two functions.

© **13. Error Analysis** A classmate says that the product of the functions $f(x) = 6 \cdot 2^x$ and $g(x) = 3 \cdot 2^x$ is $9 \cdot 2^x$. Explain the classmate's error.

More Practice and Problem-Solving Exercises

Ⓑ **Apply**

© **14. Writing** Explain how to find $\left(\frac{f}{g}\right)(5)$ if $f(x) = 2 - 16x$ and $g(x) = 4x$.

© **15. Think About a Plan** The number of food labels collected in School A in x weeks is modeled by $A(x) = 200 \cdot 5^x - 75x$ and the number of food labels collected in School B in x weeks is modeled by $B(x) = 140{,}000x - 79{,}000$. What is a function giving the difference in the number of food labels collected between School A and School B? Use the function to predict the difference in the number of food labels collected between School A and School B in 5 weeks.

- What operation should you use to find the difference in the number of food labels collected between School A and School B?
- How can you predict the difference in the number of food labels collected between School A and School B in 5 weeks?

16. Sporting Goods The cost of producing x baseball gloves is modeled by $C(x) = 20 + 15x$. The function $M(x) = 1.5$ represents the markup factor that the company uses to set the selling price of the baseball gloves. What function gives the total selling price of x baseball gloves? Find the selling price of 9 baseball gloves.

Find the sum or difference if $f(x) = 9 \cdot 2^x + 16x - 6$ and $g(x) = (-8) \cdot 2^x - 17$.

17. $(f + g)(x)$ **18.** $(f - g)(x)$ **19.** $(f + g)(4)$ **20.** $(f - g)(1)$

Find the product or quotient if $f(x) = 9x + 3 - 6^x$ and $g(x) = 3x$.

21. $(f \cdot g)(x)$ **22.** $\left(\frac{f}{g}\right)(x)$ **23.** $(f \cdot g)(3)$ **24.** $\left(\frac{f}{g}\right)(4)$

© **25. Error Analysis** Describe and correct the error at the right in finding the product of two functions.

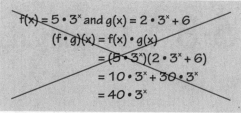

© **Open-Ended** Write exponential functions that have the following characteristics.

26. $(f - g)(x) = 4^x + 3$

27. $(f \cdot g)(x) = 16x + 8$

28. $(f + g)(x) = 5 \cdot 6^x - 1$

29. $\left(\dfrac{f}{g}\right)(x) = 18$

30. Demographics The population in City A in x years is modeled by $A(x) = 5 \cdot 7^x - 275$, the population in City B in x years is modeled by $B(x) = 7^x + 6{,}000x$, and the population in City C in x years is modeled by $C(x) = 3{,}500x - 450$. What is a function giving the total population in Cities A, B, and C? Use the function to predict the total population in Cities A, B, and C in 8 years.

Challenge

31. Manufacturing The number of widgets produced in x days will be modeled by the function $W(x) = 800 + 16x$ and the number of defective widgets in x days will be modeled by $D(x) = 4 + 2x$. Write a function giving the percent of defective widgets. Predict the percent of defective widgets produced in 12 days. Round to the nearest tenth of a percent.

32. Profit The cost of producing x printers is modeled by $C(x) = 300 + 1.2^x$. The function $M(x) = 1.75$ represents the markup factor that the company uses to set the selling price of the printers. What is a function giving the profit earned for selling x printers? Predict the profit from selling 16 printers.

5-8 Simplifying Radicals

A.SSE.1.a Interpret parts of an expression . . . Also **A.SSE.1.b**

Objective To simplify radicals involving products and quotients

Solve It! Write your solution to the Solve It in the space below.

In the Solve It, the maximum height of the mirror is a *radical expression*. A **radical expression**, such as $2\sqrt{3}$ or $\sqrt{x + 3}$, is an expression that contains a radical. A radical expression is simplified if the following statements are true.

- The radicand has no perfect-square factors other than 1.
- The radicand contains no fractions.
- No radicals appear in the denominator of a fraction.

Simplified			**Not Simplified**		
$3\sqrt{5}$	$9\sqrt{x}$	$\dfrac{\sqrt{2}}{4}$	$3\sqrt{12}$	$\sqrt{\dfrac{x}{2}}$	$\dfrac{5}{\sqrt{7}}$

Essential Understanding You can simplify radical expressions using multiplication and division properties of square roots.

take note

Property Multiplication Property of Square Roots

Algebra

For $a \geq 0$ and $b \geq 0$, $\sqrt{ab} = \sqrt{a} \cdot \sqrt{b}$

Example

$\sqrt{48} = \sqrt{16} \cdot \sqrt{3} = 4\sqrt{3}$

You can use the Multiplication Property of Square Roots to simplify radicals by removing perfect-square factors from the radicand.

Problem 1 Removing Perfect-Square Factors

Got It? What is the simplified form of $\sqrt{72}$?

Think

How can you use factoring to help you solve this problem?

Ⓐ**Practice** Simplify each radical expression.

1. $\sqrt{225}$

2. $-4\sqrt{117}$

Sometimes you can simplify radical expressions that contain variables. A variable with an even exponent is a perfect square. A variable with an odd exponent is the product of a perfect square and the variable. For example, $n^3 = n^2 \cdot n$, so $\sqrt{n^3} = \sqrt{n^2 \cdot n}$. In this lesson, assume that all variables in radicands represent nonnegative numbers.

Problem 2 Removing Variable Factors

Got It? What is the simplified form of $-m\sqrt{80m^9}$?

Think

How do you know when a radical expression is in simplified form?

Ⓐ**Practice** Simplify each radical expression.

3. $\sqrt{50t^5}$

4. $-2\sqrt{243y^3}$

You can use the Multiplication Property of Square Roots to write $\sqrt{a} \cdot \sqrt{b} = \sqrt{ab}$.

Problem 3 **Multiplying Two Radical Expressions**

Got it? What is the simplified form of each expression in parts (a)−(c)?

a. $3\sqrt{6} \cdot \sqrt{18}$

b. $\sqrt{2a} \cdot \sqrt{9a^3}$

c. $7\sqrt{5x} \cdot 3\sqrt{20x^5}$

ⓒ d. **Reasoning** In Problem 3, can you simplify the given product by first simplifying $\sqrt{14t^2}$? Explain.

A **Practice** Simplify each product.

5. $10\sqrt{12x^3} \cdot 2\sqrt{6x^3}$

6. $-\frac{1}{3}\sqrt{18c^5} \cdot \left(-6\sqrt{8c^9}\right)$

Problem 4 **Writing a Radical Expression**

Got It? A door's height is four times its width w. What is the maximum length of a painting that fits through the door?

A **Practice** **7. Construction** Students are building rectangular wooden frames for the set of a school play. The height of a frame is 6 times the width w. Each frame has a brace that connects two opposite corners of the frame. What is a simplified expression for the length of a brace?

8. Park A park is shaped like a rectangle with a length 5 times its width w. What is a simplified expression for the distance between opposite corners of the park?

You can simplify some radical expressions using the following property.

Property Division Property of Square Roots

Algebra

For $a \geq 0$ and $b > 0$, $\sqrt{\dfrac{a}{b}} = \dfrac{\sqrt{a}}{\sqrt{b}}$

Example

$\sqrt{\dfrac{36}{49}} = \dfrac{\sqrt{36}}{\sqrt{49}} = \dfrac{6}{7}$

When a radicand has a denominator that is a perfect square, it is easier to apply the Division Property of Square Roots first and then simplify the numerator and denominator of the result. When the denominator of a radicand is not a perfect square, it may be easier to simplify the fraction first.

Problem 5 Simplifying Fractions Within Radicals

Got It? What is the simplified form of each radical expression?

a. $\sqrt{\dfrac{144}{9}}$

b. $\sqrt{\dfrac{36a}{4a^3}}$

c. $\sqrt{\dfrac{25y^3}{z^2}}$

A Practice Simplify each radical expression.

9. $-5\sqrt{\dfrac{162t^3}{2t}}$

10. $11\sqrt{\dfrac{49a^5}{4a^3}}$

When a radicand in a denominator is not a perfect square, you may need to **rationalize the denominator** to remove the radical. To do this, multiply the numerator and denominator by the same radical expression. Choose an expression that makes the radicand in the denominator a perfect square. It may be helpful to start by simplifying the original radical in the denominator.

Problem 6   Rationalizing Denominators

Got It?   What is the simplified form of each radical expression?

a. $\dfrac{\sqrt{2}}{\sqrt{3}}$

b. $\dfrac{\sqrt{5}}{\sqrt{18m}}$

c. $\sqrt{\dfrac{7s}{3}}$

A Practice Simplify each radical expression.

11. $\dfrac{1}{\sqrt{11}}$

12. $\dfrac{8\sqrt{7s}}{\sqrt{28s^3}}$

Lesson Check

Do you know HOW?

Simplify each radical expression.

13. $\sqrt{98}$

14. $\sqrt{16b^5}$

15. $3\sqrt{5m} \cdot 4\sqrt{\frac{1}{5}m^3}$

16. $\sqrt{\frac{15x}{x^3}}$

17. $\frac{\sqrt{5}}{\sqrt{3}}$

18. $\frac{\sqrt{6}}{\sqrt{2n}}$

Do you UNDERSTAND?

19. Vocabulary Is the radical expression in simplified form? Explain.

a. $\dfrac{\sqrt{31}}{3}$

b. $7\sqrt{\dfrac{6}{11}}$

c. $-5\sqrt{175}$

20. Compare and Contrast Simplify $\dfrac{3}{\sqrt{12}}$ two different ways. Which way do you prefer? Explain.

21. Writing Explain how you can tell whether a radical expression is in simplified form.

More Practice and Problem-Solving Exercises

Ⓑ **Apply**

Ⓒ **22. Look for a Pattern** From a viewing height of h feet, the approximate distance d to the horizon, in miles, is given by the equation $d = \sqrt{\frac{3h}{2}}$.

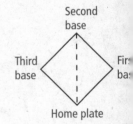

    a. To the nearest mile, what is the distance to the horizon from a height of 150 ft? 225 ft? 300 ft?

    b. How does the distance to the horizon increase as the height increases?

Ⓒ **23. Think About a Plan** A square picture on the front page of a newspaper occupies an area of 24 in.². What is the length of each side of the picture? Write your answer as a radical in simplified form.

    • How can you find the side length of a square if you know the area?

    • What property can you use to write your answer in simplified form?

Explain why each radical expression is or is not in simplified form.

24. $\frac{13x}{\sqrt{4}}$ **25.** $\frac{3}{\sqrt{3}}$ **26.** $-4\sqrt{5}$ **27.** $5\sqrt{30}$

Ⓒ **28. Error Analysis** A student simplified the radical expression at the right. What mistake did the student make? What is the correct answer?

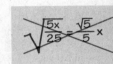

Ⓒ **29. Reasoning** You can simplify radical expressions with negative exponents by first rewriting the expressions using positive exponents. What are the simplified forms of the following radical expressions?

    a. $\frac{\sqrt{3}}{\sqrt{f^{-3}}}$ **b.** $\frac{\sqrt{x^{-3}}}{\sqrt{x}}$ **c.** $\frac{\sqrt{5a^{-2}}}{\sqrt{10a^{-1}}}$ **d.** $\frac{\sqrt{(2m)^{-3}}}{m^{-1}}$

30. Sports The bases in a softball diamond are located at the corners of a 3600-ft² square. How far is a throw from second base to home plate?

Ⓒ **31.** Suppose a and b are positive integers.

    a. Verify that if $a = 18$ and $b = 10$, then $\sqrt{a} \cdot \sqrt{b} = 6\sqrt{5}$.

    b. **Open-Ended** Find two other pairs of positive integers a and b such that $\sqrt{a} \cdot \sqrt{b} = 6\sqrt{5}$.

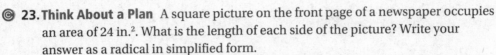

Second base

Third base

First base

Home plate

Simplify each radical expression.

32. $\sqrt{12} \cdot \sqrt{75}$ **33.** $\sqrt{26 \cdot 2}$ **34.** $\dfrac{\sqrt{72}}{\sqrt{64}}$ **35.** $\dfrac{-2}{\sqrt{a^3}}$

36. $\dfrac{\sqrt{180}}{\sqrt{3}}$ **37.** $\dfrac{\sqrt{x^2}}{\sqrt{y^3}}$ **38.** $\dfrac{-3\sqrt{2}}{\sqrt{6}}$ **39.** $\sqrt{8} \cdot \sqrt{10}$

40. $\sqrt{20a^2b^3}$ **41.** $\sqrt{a^3b^5c^3}$ **42.** $\sqrt{\dfrac{3m}{16m^2}}$ **43.** $\dfrac{16a}{\sqrt{6a^3}}$

Ⓖ **44. Open-Ended** What are three numbers whose square roots can be written in the form $a\sqrt{3}$ for some integer value of a?

⟳ Challenge

Simplify each radical expression.

45. $\sqrt{24} \cdot \sqrt{2x} \cdot \sqrt{3x}$ **46.** $2b\left(\sqrt{5b}\right)^2$ **47.** $\sqrt{45a^7} \cdot \sqrt{20a}$

48. Geometry The equation $r = \sqrt{\dfrac{A}{\pi}}$ gives the radius r of a circle with area A. What is the radius of a circle with the given area? Write your answer as a simplified radical and as a decimal rounded to the nearest hundredth.
   a. 50 ft^2 **b.** 32 in.^2 **c.** 10 m^2

49. For a linear equation in standard form $Ax + By = C$, where $A \neq 0$ and $B \neq 0$, the distance d between the x- and y-intercepts is given by $d = \sqrt{\left(\dfrac{C}{A}\right)^2 + \left(\dfrac{C}{B}\right)^2}$. What is the distance between the x- and y-intercepts of the graph of $4x - 3y = 2$?

Radical and Piecewise Functions

F.IF.4 For a function that models a relationship between two quantities, interpret key features of graphs and tables . . . and sketch graphs showing key features . . . Also **F.IF.5, F.IF.6, F.IF.9**

Objective   To understand properties of radical and piecewise functions

Solve It!   Write your solution to the Solve It in the space below.

The Solve It involves a square root function. Square root functions are examples of *radical functions*.

take note

Key Concept   Square Root Functions

A **square root function** is a function containing a square root with the independent variable in the radicand. The parent square root function is $y = \sqrt{x}$.

The table and graph below show the parent square root function.

x	y
0	0
1	1
2	1.4
4	2
9	3

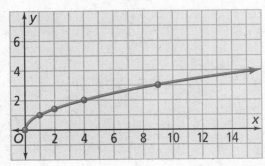

The domain and range of the parent square root function are all nonnegative real numbers.
The *x*- and *y*-intercepts of the parent square root function are both 0.
It is increasing on its entire domain.

Essential Understanding You can graph a radical function by plotting points or by using a transformation of the parent function.

Problem 1 **Graphing a Square Root Function**

Think

What happens when $x < 4$?

Got It? Graph the function $f(x) = \sqrt{x + 4} - 2$. What are the domain and range of the function?

A Practice Graph each square root function.

1. $f(x) = \sqrt{x - 1} - 3$

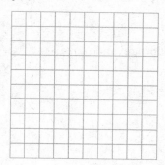

2. $f(x) = \sqrt{x + 5} + 1$

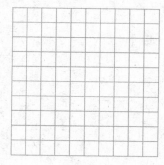

Another kind of radical function is the cube root function.

take note

Key Concept Cube Root Functions

A **cube root function** is a function containing a cube root with the independent variable in the radicand. The parent cube root function is $y = \sqrt[3]{x}$.

The table and graph below show the parent cube root function.

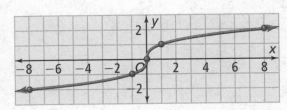

x	y
−8	−2
−1	−1
0	0
1	1
8	2

The domain and range of the parent cube root function are all real numbers. The *x*-and *y*-intercepts of the parent cube root function are both 0. It is increasing on its entire domain.

Problem 2 Graphing a Cube Root Function

Got It? Graph the function $f(x) = \sqrt[3]{x} + 2$. What is the domain and range of the function?

Think

Can you find the cube root of a negative number?

Practice Graph each cube root function.

3. $f(x) = 3\sqrt[3]{x}$

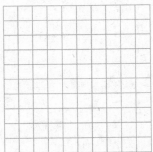

4. $f(x) = \sqrt[3]{x - 2} + 4$

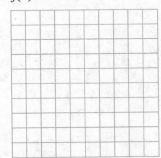

You will learn about other kinds of radical functions in later courses.

A **piecewise function** is a function that has different rules for different parts of its domain.

Essential Understanding You can graph a piecewise function by graphing each part of the function.

Problem 3 Graphing a Piecewise Function

Got It? Graph the function $f(x) = \begin{cases} x - 3, & \text{for } x \geq 2 \\ 3x - 2, & \text{for } x < 2 \end{cases}$.

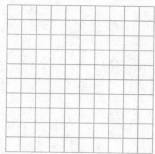

A Practice Graph each piecewise function.

5. $f(x) = \begin{cases} \frac{1}{2}x + 1, & \text{for } x \geq 0 \\ x - 4, & \text{for } x < 0 \end{cases}$

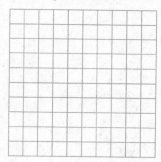

6. $f(x) = \begin{cases} 3x - 5, & \text{for } x > -1 \\ x + 6, & \text{for } x \leq -1 \end{cases}$

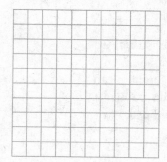

A function you are already familiar with, the absolute value function, can be written as a piecewise function. You can give a piecewise definition of the absolute value function $f(x) = |x|$ by writing $f(x) = \begin{cases} x, & \text{for } x \geq 0 \\ -x, & \text{for } x < 0 \end{cases}$.

Problem 4   Writing a Piecewise Function

Got It?   Write a piecewise definition for the absolute value function $f(x) = |x + 3|$.

Ⓐ Practice   Write a piecewise definition for each absolute value function.

7. $f(x) = |x + 1|$

8. $f(x) = 2|x|$

Another example of a piecewise function is a **step function**. A step function is a function that pairs every number in an interval with a single value. The graph of a step function can look like the steps of a staircase. Each piece of the graph is a horizontal segment with any missing points indicated by open circles.

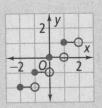

Graphing a Step Function

Got It? Make a graph that models the relationship between the number of
students x that go to the game by bus and the number of buses y that
are needed if each bus holds a maximum of 50 students.

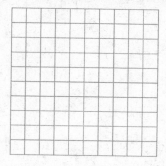

Ⓐ **Practice** 9. **Postage** The table lists postage for letters weighing
as much as 3 oz. You want to mail a letter that weighs
2.7 oz. Graph the step function. How much will you
pay in postage?

First-Class Postage

Weight x	Price y
$0 <$ Weight < 1 oz	$.45
1 oz $\leq$ Weight < 2 oz	$.65
2 oz $\leq$ Weight ≤ 3 oz	$.85

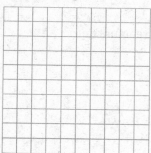

10. **Bicycle Rental** A bicycle rental company charges by the hour, or any
part of the hour. The company charges $10 for the first hour. Each hour,
or part of an hour, after the first hour costs an additional $5. There is a
five-hour maximum for bicycle rentals. Graph the step function. How
much will it cost for a customer to rent a bicycle for $3\frac{3}{4}$ hours?

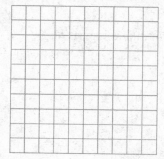

Lesson Check

Do you know HOW?

11. What are the domain and range of the function $f(x) = \sqrt{x - 10}$? Explain.

12. Why can a cube root function have negative output values?

13. How is the function $f(x) = \sqrt[3]{x - 12} + 6$ related to its parent function?

Do you UNDERSTAND?

14. Vocabulary What kind of function has different rules for different parts of its domain?

15. Open-Ended What is a real-world situation that can be modeled by a piecewise function?

16. Error Analysis A classmate said the domain of the function $f(x) = \sqrt[3]{x+8} - 7$ is $x \geq 8$. Explain his error.

More Practice and Problem-Solving Exercises

Apply

17. Think About a Plan The function $v(h) = 8\sqrt{h}$ represents the velocity v in feet per second of an object dropped from height h ft. Graph the function. What are the domain and range of the function?
- How can you make a table to help graph the function?
- How can you use the graph to identify the domain and range of the function?

18. Parking Garage A long-term parking garage at an airport charges $12 for the first day. Each day, or part of a day, after the first day costs an additional $4. There is a maximum of seven days for parking a vehicle in this garage.
 a. Graph a step function for the cost of parking in this garage.
 b. How much will it cost for a customer to park a car for $5\frac{1}{4}$ days?

19. Compare and Contrast Explain how the domain and range of the parent square root function and parent cube root function are different.

20. Error Analysis A classmate said the average rate of change for the parent square root function is constant. Explain why this classmate is incorrect.

21. Triathlon While training for a triathlon, an athlete took a 4-hour bicycle ride, traveling at a constant speed. The piecewise function $f(x) = \begin{cases} 5x, \text{ for } 0 \leq x \leq 2 \\ -5x + 20, \text{ for } 2 < x \leq 4 \end{cases}$ represents the distance the athlete is from his house after x hours.
 a. Graph the function.
 b. What are the domain and range of the function?
 c. What is the average rate of change from 0 to 2 hours? 2 to 4 hours? 0 to 4 hours?

22. Aquarium The function $s(v) = \sqrt[3]{v}$ represents the side length s in feet of a cubic fish aquarium with volume v in cubic feet.

    a. Graph the function.

    b. What are the domain and range of the function?

    c. What domain and range make sense in this situation? Explain.

23. Horizon The function $d(a) = 1.22\sqrt{a}$ represents the approximate distance d in miles a person is from the horizon a feet above the ground.

    a. Graph the function.

    b. What are the domain and range of the function?

24. Collect Calls The cost to receive a collect phone call is $4 for the first minute, or any part of a minute. Each additional minute, or part of a minute costs $2.

    a. Graph the step function.

    b. How much will it cost for a collect phone call that lasts 4 minutes 34 seconds?

ⓒ Challenge

25. You walk to the library, check out a book, and walk back home. The graph at the right represents the distance you are from home in feet after t minutes. Write a piecewise function to represent this situation.

ⓒ 26. Reasoning What is the domain for the function $f(x) = \dfrac{6}{\sqrt{x-7}}$?

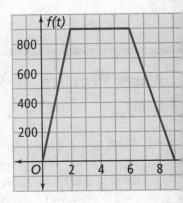

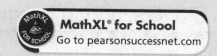

MathXL® for School
Go to pearsonsuccessnet.com

5-1 Zero and Negative Exponents

Quick Review

You can use zero and negative integers as exponents. For every nonzero number a, $a^0 = 1$. For every nonzero number a and any integer n, $a^{-n} = \frac{1}{a^n}$. When you evaluate an exponential expression, you can simplify the expression before substituting values for the variables.

Example

What is the value of $a^2 b^{-4} c^0$ for $a = 3$, $b = 2$, and $c = -5$?

$a^2 b^{-4} c^0 = \frac{a^2 c^0}{b^4}$ Use the definition of negative exponents.

$= \frac{a^2(1)}{b^4}$ Use the definition of a zero exponent.

$= \frac{3^2}{2^4}$ Substitute.

$= \frac{9}{16}$ Simplify.

Exercises

Simplify each expression.

1. 5^0 2. 7^{-2}

3. $\frac{4x^{-2}}{y^{-8}}$ 4. $\frac{1}{p^2 q^{-4} r^0}$

Evaluate each expression for $x = 2$, $y = -3$, and $z = -5$.

5. $x^0 y^2$ 6. $(-x)^{-4} y^2$

7. $x^0 z^0$ 8. $\frac{5x^0}{y^{-2}}$

9. $y^{-2} z^2$ 10. $\frac{2x}{y^2 z^{-1}}$

11. **Reasoning** Is it true that $(-3b)^4 = -12b^4$? Explain why or why not.

5-2 Exponential Functions

Quick Review

An **exponential function** involves repeated multiplication of an initial amount a by the same positive number b. The general form of an exponential function is $y = a \cdot b^x$, where $a \neq 0$, $b > 0$, and $b \neq 1$.

Example

What is the graph of $y = \frac{1}{2} \cdot 5^x$?

Make a table of values. Graph the ordered pairs.

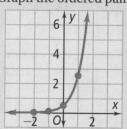

x	y
−2	$\frac{1}{50}$
−1	$\frac{1}{10}$
0	$\frac{1}{2}$
1	$\frac{5}{2}$
2	$\frac{25}{2}$

Exercises

Evaluate each function for the domain {1, 2, 3}.

12. $f(x) = 4^x$ 13. $y = 0.01^x$

14. $y = 40\left(\frac{1}{2}\right)^x$ 15. $f(x) = 3 \cdot 2^x$

Graph each function.

16. $f(x) = 2.5^x$ 17. $y = 0.5(0.5)^x$

18. $f(x) = \frac{1}{2} \cdot 3^x$ 19. $y = 0.1^x$

20. **Biology** A population of 50 bacteria in a laboratory culture doubles every 30 min. The function $p(x) = 50 \cdot 2^x$ models the population, where x is the number of 30-min periods.
    a. How many bacteria will there be after 2 h?
    b. How many bacteria will there be after 1 day?

5-3 Comparing Linear and Exponential Functions

Quick Review

On equal intervals of the domain, *differences* in the values of a linear function are constant, while *ratios* of the values of an exponential function are constant.

The **average rate of change** of a function $f(x)$ over the interval $a \leq x \leq b$ is equal to $\frac{f(b) - f(a)}{b - a}$.

Example

Find the average rate of change for the function $f(x) = 4 \cdot 2^x$ over the intervals $0 \leq x \leq 2$, $2 \leq x \leq 4$, and $4 \leq x \leq 6$. Describe what you observe.

$$\frac{f(2) - f(0)}{2 - 0} = \frac{16 - 4}{2} = 6$$

$$\frac{f(4) - f(2)}{4 - 2} = \frac{64 - 16}{2} = 24$$

$$\frac{f(6) - f(4)}{6 - 4} = \frac{256 - 64}{2} = 96$$

The average rate of change is different over each interval. It increases with each interval. So the rate of change is increasing.

Exercises

Does the table or rule represent a linear or an exponential function? Explain.

21.

x	0	1	2	3
y	−5	−8	−11	−14

22. $y = 7 \cdot 3^x$

Determine whether you can model each situati with a *linear function* or an *exponential functio* Explain.

23. Each car has 4 wheels.

24. A deer population triples every year.

25. **Bacteria** The function $f(x) = 5 \cdot 3^x$ represen the number of bacteria in a container after x weeks. Find the average rate of change for t function over the intervals $0 \leq x \leq 2$, $2 \leq x \leq$ and $4 \leq x \leq 6$. Describe what you observe.

5-4 Exponential Growth and Decay

Quick Review

When $a > 0$ and $b > 1$, the function $y = a \cdot b^x$ models **exponential growth**. The base b is called the **growth factor**. When $a > 0$ and $0 < b < 1$, the function $y = a \cdot b^x$ models **exponential decay**. In this case the base b is called the **decay factor**.

Example

The population of a city is 25,000 and decreases 1% each year. Predict the population after 6 yr.

$y = 25,000 \cdot 0.99^x$ Exponential decay function

$= 25,000 \cdot 0.99^6$ Substitute 6 for x.

$\approx 23,537$ Simplify.

The population will be about 23,537 after 6 yr.

Exercises

Tell whether the function represents *exponenti growth* or *exponential decay*. Identify the grow or decay factor.

26. $y = 5.2 \cdot 3^x$

27. $f(x) = 7 \cdot 0.32^x$

28. $y = 0.15\left(\frac{3}{2}\right)^x$

29. $g(x) = 1.3\left(\frac{1}{4}\right)^x$

30. **Finance** Suppose $2000 is deposited in an account paying 2.5% interest compounded quarterly. What will the account balance be after 12 yr?

31. **Music** A band performs a free concert in a local park. There are 200 people in the crow the start of the concert. The number of peop in the crowd grows 15% every half hour. Ho many people are in the crowd after 3 h? Rou to the nearest person.

5-5 Solving Exponential Equations

Quick Review

You can solve many exponential equations by writing each side of the equation with the same base.

When an exponential equation has the same base on each side of the equation, then the exponents must be equal.

Let $b > 0$ and $b \neq 1$. Then $b^x = b^y$ if and only if $x = y$.

Example

Find the solution of the exponential equation $7^{x+2} = 343$.

$7^{x+2} = 7^3$ Write each side of the equation using the same base.

$x + 2 = 3$ The bases are the same, so the exponents must be equal.

$x = 1$ Subtract 2 from each side.

Exercises

Find the solution of each exponential equation.

32. $1296 = 6^x$

33. $512 = 2^{x-4}$

34. $3^{2x+1} = 243$

35. $4^{-x+2} = \frac{1}{1024}$

36. What is the solution of the equation $27 = 3^{x-2}$? Use a graph.

37. Ornithology The function $B(x) = 5^{x+1}$ models the number of birds that migrate south after x days. According to the model, after how many days will 3125 birds migrate?

5-6 Geometric Sequences

Quick Review

In a geometric sequence the ratio of any term to its preceding term is a constant value.

Examples

Find the common ratio of the geometric sequence.

$$2, \quad 6, \quad 18, \quad 54, \dots$$
$$\times 3 \quad \times 3 \quad \times 3$$

The common ratio of the geometric sequence is 3.

Write a recursive formula to represent the geometric sequence.

$$256, \quad 64, \quad 16, \quad 4, \dots$$
$$\times \frac{1}{4} \quad \times \frac{1}{4} \quad \times \frac{1}{4}$$

$$a_1 = 256; \, a_n = a_{a-1} \cdot \frac{1}{4}$$

Exercises

Find the common ratio of each geometric sequence.

38. $10, 20, 40, 80, \dots$

39. $1, 10, 100, 1000, \dots$

40. $100, 20, 4, 0.8, \dots$

41. $6561, 2187, 729, 243, \dots$

Write a recursive formula to represent each geometric sequence.

42. $20, 60, 180, 540, \dots$

43. $5, 2.5, 1.25, 0.625, \dots$

44. $3, 12, 48, 192, \dots$

45. $10, 1, 0.1, 0.01, \dots$

5-7 Combining Functions

Quick Review

You can add, subtract, multiply, or divide two functions just as you do numbers or algebraic expressions.

To add or subtract functions, combine like terms.

Example

$f(x) = 3 \cdot 2^x$ and $g(x) = 2^x - 7$. What are $(f - g)(x)$ and $(f - g)(5)$?

$$(f - g)(x) = f(x) - g(x)$$
$$= (3 \cdot 2^x) - (2^x - 7)$$
$$= (3 \cdot 2^x - 2^x) - (-7)$$
$$= 2 \cdot 2^x + 7$$
$$(f - g)(5) = 2 \cdot 2^5 + 7$$
$$= 2 \cdot 32 + 7$$
$$= 64 + 7$$
$$= 71$$

Exercises

$f(x) = 9x - 3$ and $g(x) = 3x$. Find the sum, difference, product, or quotient.

46. $(f + g)(x)$

47. $(f - g)(x)$

48. $(f \cdot g)(x)$

49. $\left(\dfrac{f}{g}\right)(x)$

50. **Fish Tank** The number of fish in Tank A in x years will be modeled by $A(x) = 102 \cdot 2^x$ an the number of fish in Tank B in x years will be modeled by $B(x) = 59 \cdot 2^x$. What is a functior giving the difference in the number of fish in Tank A and Tank B? Predict the difference in the number of fish after 7 years.

5-8 Simplifying Radicals

Quick Review

A **radical expression** is simplified if the following statements are true.
- The radicand has no perfect-square factors other than 1.
- The radicand contains no fractions.
- No radicals appear in the denominator of a fraction.

Example

What is the simplified form of $\dfrac{\sqrt{3x}}{\sqrt{2}}$?

$$\dfrac{\sqrt{3x}}{\sqrt{2}} = \dfrac{\sqrt{3x}}{\sqrt{2}} \cdot \dfrac{\sqrt{2}}{\sqrt{2}} \qquad \text{Multiply by } \dfrac{\sqrt{2}}{\sqrt{2}}.$$
$$= \dfrac{\sqrt{6x}}{\sqrt{4}} \qquad \begin{array}{l}\text{Multiply numerators}\\\text{and denominators.}\end{array}$$
$$= \dfrac{\sqrt{6x}}{2} \qquad \text{Simplify.}$$

Exercises

Simplify each radical expression.

51. $3\sqrt{14} \cdot (-2\sqrt{21})$ 52. $\sqrt{8} \cdot \frac{1}{4}\sqrt{6}$

53. $\sqrt{\dfrac{25a^3}{4a}}$ 54. $\dfrac{\sqrt{8s}}{\sqrt{18s^3}}$

55. $-2\sqrt{7x^2} \cdot \frac{1}{3}\sqrt{28x^3}$ 56. $6\sqrt{5t^3} \cdot \sqrt{15t^5}$

57. **Open-Ended** Write three radical expressions that have $4\sqrt{2s}$ as their simplified form. Wha do the three expressions have in common? Explain.

58. **Geometry** The width of a rectangle is s. Its length is $3s$. How long is a diagonal of the rectangle? Express your answer in simplified radical form.

5-9 Radical and Piecewise Functions

Quick Review

You can graph square root and cube root functions by plotting points or using transformations. You can also graph a piecewise function by graphing each part of the function.

Example

Graph the function $f(x) = \sqrt[3]{x + 1} - 2$.

Make a table.   Plot the points on a graph.

x	y
−3	−3.3
−2	−3
−1	−2
0	−1
1	−0.7

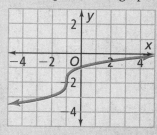

The graph can be obtained by translating the parent function $f(x) = \sqrt[3]{x}$ to the left 1 unit, and down 2 units.

Exercises

Graph each function.

59. $f(x) = \sqrt{x - 2}$

60. $f(x) = \sqrt[3]{x + 1}$

61. $f(x) = \begin{cases} x + 2, & \text{for } x > 4 \\ -x - 3, & \text{for } x \le 4 \end{cases}$

62. Jet Ski Rental A company charges by the hour, or any part of the hour, to rent a jet ski. It costs \$30 for the first hour. Each hour, or part of an hour, after the first hour costs an additional \$10. There is a four-hour maximum for renting a jet ski.

  a. Graph the step function.
  b. How much will it cost for a customer to rent a jet ski for 2.25 hours?

Pull It **All Together**

 ASSESSMEN

Analyzing Sales Data

A company makes two different video game consoles. The company's sales data for each console are shown in the tables below.

PlayBox

Year	Sales (thousands)
2011	12.00
2012	14.60
2013	17.20
2014	19.80

GameStation

Year	Sales (thousands)
2011	15.00
2012	18.00
2013	21.60
2014	25.92

Task Description

Predict the year in which total sales of the two consoles will reach 100,000 units.

a. Determine whether the data in each table represent a linear function, an exponential function, or neither. Justify your answers.

b. Let $x =$ the number of years since 2010.
Write a function, $P(x)$, that models the sales of PlayBox.

c. Write a function, $G(x)$, that models the sales of GameStation.

d. Write a function, $T(x)$, that models total sales of the video game consoles.

e. Write and solve an equation to predict the year when total sales of the two consoles will reach 100,000 units. Explain how you found and interpreted the solution.

Get Ready!

Multiplying and Dividing Real Numbers

Simplify each fraction.

1. $\dfrac{6+4+7+9}{4}$

2. $\dfrac{1.7+4.2+3.1}{3}$

3. $\dfrac{11+16+9+12+7}{5}$

Distributive Property

Simplify each expression.

4. $6(x-7)$

5. $\frac{1}{2}(4x+6)$

6. $-2(5-x)$

7. $0.5(5+4x)$

Comparing Unit Rates

8. Transportation A car traveled 360 km in 6 h. A train traveled 400 km in 8 h. A boat traveled 375 km in 5 h. Which had the fastest average speed?

9. Plants A birch tree grew 2.5 in. in 5 months. A bean plant grew 8 in. in 10 months. A rose bush grew 5 in. in 8 months. Which grew the fastest?

Graphing a Function Rule

Make a table of values for each function rule. Then graph each function.

10. $f(x) = x + 3$

11. $f(x) = -2x$

12. $f(x) = x - 4$

 Looking Ahead Vocabulary

13. On a highway, the *median* is the strip of land that divides the two sides of opposing traffic. How would you expect a *median* to divide a data set?

14. *Percentiles* and *quartiles* are used to rank data divided into equal parts. How many equal parts do you think *quartiles* divide data into? How many equal parts do you think *percentiles* divide data into?

CHAPTER 6

Data Analysis

Big Ideas

1 Data Collection and Analysis
Essential Question How can collecting and analyzing data help you make decisions or predictions?

2 Data Representation
Essential Question How can you make and interpret different representations of data?

3 Modeling
Essential Question How can you make predictions based on a scatter plot?

ⓒ Domains
- Interpreting Categorical and Quantitative Data
- Quantities

Interactive Digital Path

Log in to **pearsonsuccessnet.com** and click on Interactive Digital Path to access the Solve Its and animated Problems.

Chapter Preview

🔊 Vocabulary

English/Spanish Vocabulary Audio Online:

English	Spanish
box-and-whisker plot, *p. 394*	gráfica de cajas
frequency table, *p. 371*	tabla de frecuencias
measure of central tendency, *p. 379*	medida de tendencia ce
outlier, *p. 379*	valor extremo
percentile, *p. 395*	percentil
quartile, *p. 392*	cuartiles
range of a data set, *p. 382*	rango de un conjunto de
scatter plot, *p. 399*	diagrama de puntos
trend line, *p. 401*	línea de tendencia
two-way frequency table, *p. 414*	tabla de frecuencias de entrada

6-1 Frequency and Histograms

S.ID.1 Represent data with plots on the real number line . . . Also **N.Q.1, S.ID.3**

Objective   To make and interpret frequency tables and histograms

Solve It!   Write your solution to the Solve It in the space below.

> **Essential Understanding**   There are many ways to organize and visually display data. Sometimes it is helpful to organize numerical data into intervals.
>
> The **frequency** of an interval is the number of data values in that interval. A **frequency table** groups a set of data values into intervals and shows the frequency for each interval. Intervals in frequency tables do not overlap, do not have any gaps, and are usually of equal size.

Problem 1   Making a Frequency Table

Got It?   What is a frequency table for the data in Problem 1 that uses intervals of 5?

Think

Can there be more than one starting value for the first interval?

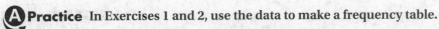

A **Practice** In Exercises 1 and 2, use the data to make a frequency table.

1. marathon times (min): 135 211 220 180 175 161
246 201 192 167 235 208

2. top speeds (mi/h): 108 90 96 150 120 115 135
126 165 155 130 125 100

A **histogram** is a graph that can display data from a frequency table. A histogram has one bar for each interval. The height of each bar shows the frequency of data in the interval it represents. There are no gaps between bars. The bars are usually of equal width.

 **Problem 2** **Making a Histogram**

Got It? The finishing times, in seconds, for a race are shown below. What is a histogram that represents the data?

95 105 83 80 93 98 102 99 82 89 90 82 89

Plan

How can you use a frequency table to help make a histogram?

In Exercises 3 and 4, use the data to make a histogram.

3. restaurant waiting times (min): 20 35 15 25 5 10 40
                                       30 10 50 20 60 10 8

4. points per game: 10 2 13 18 22 20 8 9 12
                        33 10 13 21 18 5 16 17 13

You can describe histograms in terms of their shape. Three types are shown below.

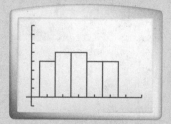

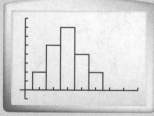

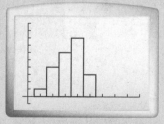

If the bars are roughly the same height, then the histogram is *uniform*.

If a vertical line can divide the histogram into two parts that are close to mirror images, then the histogram is *symmetric*.

If the histogram has one peak that is not in the center, then the histogram is *skewed*.

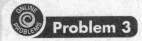
Got It? **a.** The following set of data shows the numbers of dollars Jay spent on lunch over the last two weeks. Make a histogram of the data. Is the histogram *uniform, symmetric,* or *skewed*?

17   1   4   11   14   14   5   16   6   5   9   10   13   9

Ⓒ **b. Reasoning** How much money should Jay plan to bring for lunch next week? Explain your reasoning.

Ⓐ **Practice** Tell whether each histogram is *uniform, symmetric,* or *skewed.*

5.
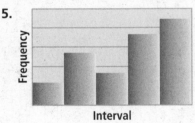

6.
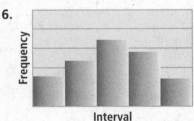

A **cumulative frequency** table shows the number of data values that lie in or below a given interval. For example, if the cumulative frequency for the interval 70–79 is 20, then there are 20 data values less than or equal to 79.

Problem 4 **Making a Cumulative Frequency Table**

Got It? What is a cumulative frequency table that represents the data below?

12 13 15 1 5 7 10 9 2 2 7 11 2 1 0 15

 **Practice** **In Exercises 7 and 8, use the data to make a cumulative frequency table.**

7. heights of buildings (ft): 105 245 300 234 225 156
180 308 250 114 150 285

8. earthquake magnitudes: 2.1 5.4 6.7 3.2 4.5 2.7 2.6
3.1 4.4 8.1 4.1 2.9 2.1

Lesson Check

Do you know HOW?

The data below show battery life, in hours, for different brands of batteries.

    12 9 10 14 10 11 10 18 21 10 14 22

9. Make a frequency table of the data.

10. Make a histogram of the data.

11. Make a cumulative frequency table of the data.

Do you UNDERSTAND?

© **12. Vocabulary** How might a frequency table help a store owner determine the busiest business hours?

© **13. Compare and Contrast** What is the difference between a symmetric histogram and a skewed histogram?

© **14. Writing** How can you use a frequency table of a data set to construct a cumulative frequency table?

More Practice and Problem-Solving Exercises

3 Apply

15. Music The Perpendicular Bisectors' new CD is shown at the right.
  a. Make a cumulative frequency table that represents the lengths of the songs in seconds.
  b. About what percent of the songs are under 4 min? How do you know?

Add It (intro)	1:25
A Fraction of My Love	3:30
Common Denominator	4:14
Always, Sometimes, Never	2:56
Factorial	3:15
Transitive Property	4:20
All You Need Is Math	4:58
SAS	3:51
Frequency	3:32
Subtract It (outro)	1:56

16. Think About a Plan A travel agent conducted a survey to find out how many times people go to the beach each year. The results of the survey are shown in the histogram at the right. About how many people were surveyed?

- What does the height of each bar represent?
- How can you use the bar heights to find the number of people surveyed?

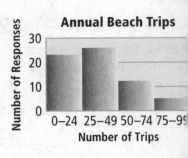

Annual Beach Trips

Use the test scores below.

81 70 73 89 68 79 91 59 77 73 80 75 88 65 82 94 77 67 82

17. What is a histogram of the data that uses intervals of 5?

18. What is a histogram of the data that uses intervals of 10?

19. What is a histogram of the data that uses intervals of 20?

20. Reasoning Which interval size would you use—5, 10, or 20—to make it seem as though there were little variation in the test scores? Explain.

The histogram at the right shows the amounts of money that 50 customers spent in a supermarket.

21. What is the upper limit on the amount of money that any customer spent?

22. Which interval represents the greatest number of customers?

23. How many customers spent less than $20?

24. Writing Summarize the spending of the 50 customers represented in the histogram.

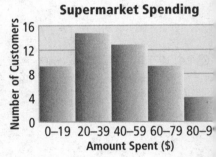

Supermarket Spending

25. Error Analysis A student made the frequency table at the right using the data below. Describe and correct the error.

40 21 28 53 24 48 50 55 42 29 22 52 43 26 44

Interval	Frequency
20–29	6
40–49	5
50–59	4

Challenge

26. Make a histogram for a set of 200 data values. The histogram must have 40% of the values lie in the interval 20–29. The remaining values should be evenly divided among the intervals 0–9, 10–19, 30–39, and 40–49.

27. Copy and complete the cumulative frequency table below.

Interval	Frequency	Cumulative Frequency
0–9	■	6
10–19	■	17
20–29	■	26
30–39	■	35

6-2 Measures of Central Tendency and Dispersion

S.ID.2 Use statistics appropriate to the shape of the data distribution to compare center . . . and spread . . . of two or more different data sets. Also **N.Q.2, S.ID.1, S.ID.3**

Objective To find mean, median, mode, and range

Solve It! Write your solution to the Solve It in the space below.

Essential Understanding You can use different measures to interpret and compare sets of data.

One way to summarize a set of data is to use a *measure of central tendency*. Mean, median, and mode are all **measures of central tendency**.

The measure of central tendency that best describes a data set may depend on whether the data set has an *outlier*. An **outlier** is a data value that is much greater than or less than the other values in the set. Below is a review of mean, median, and mode, and when to use each as the measure of central tendency.

take note

Key Concept Mean, Median, and Mode

Measure

The **mean** equals $\frac{\text{sum of the data values}}{\text{total number of data values}}$. The mean is often referred to as the *average*.

The **median** is the middle value in a data set when the values are arranged in order. For a set containing an even number of data values, the median is the mean of the two middle data values.

The **mode** is the data item that occurs the most times. A data set can have no mode, one mode, or more than one mode.

When to Use

Use mean to describe the middle of a set of data that *does not* have an outlier.

Use median to describe the middle of a set of data that *does* have an outlier.

Use mode when the data are nonnumeric or when choosing the most popular item.

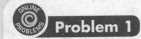

Problem 1 Finding Measures of Central Tendency

Got It? Consider the scores from Problem 1 that do not include the outlier, 189. What are the mean, median, and mode of the scores? Which measure of central tendency best describes the data?

Think

Which measure of central tendency is most affected by an outlier?

Ⓐ Practice Find the mean, median, and mode of each data set. Tell which measure of central tendency best describes the data.

1. weights of books (oz): 12 10 9 15 16 10

2. golf scores: 98 96 98 134 99

You can use an equation to find a value needed to achieve a given average.

Problem 2 Finding a Data Value

Got It? **a.** The grades in Problem 2 were 80, 93, and 91. What grade would you need on your next exam to have an average of 88 on the four exams?

b. Reasoning If 100 is the highest possible score on the fourth exam, is it possible to raise your average to 92? Explain.

 Practice **3.** Find the value of x such that the data set 31.7, 42.8, 26.4, x has a mean of 35.

4. Sales The line plot at the right shows the numbers of weekly sales a salesperson made in the first nine weeks of a ten-week sales period. The salesperson's target is an average of 14 sales each week. How many sales does the salesperson need in the tenth week to meet the target average?

Number of Weekly Sales

		X	X
	X	X	X
X	X	X	X
12	13	14	15

A **measure of dispersion** describes how *dispersed*, or spread out, the values in a data set are. One measure of dispersion is *range*. The **range of a set of data** is the difference between the greatest and least data values.

 **Problem 3** **Finding the Range**

Think

How do the purposes of the range and the mean differ?

Got It? For the same days, the closing prices, in dollars, of Stock C were 7, 4, 3, 6, and 1. The closing prices, in dollars, of Stock D were 24, 15, 2, 10, and 5. What are the range and mean of each set of data? Use your results to compare Stock C with Stock D.

 Practice **5.** Find the range and mean of each data set. Use your results to compare the two data sets.

    Set E: 113 183 479 120 117
    Set F: 145 129 153 135 142

6. Sports Over the past 6 seasons, one baseball player's batting averages were .265, .327, .294, .316, .281, and .318. A second player's batting averages were .304, .285, .312, .291, .303, and .314. What are the range and mean of each player's batting averages? Use your results to compare the players' batting skills.

A **line plot** is a data display in which each mark above a number line corresponds to each data value. Line plots are sometimes called *dot plots* when the mark used to represent each data value is a dot.

Finding Measures of Central Tendency and Ranges

Got It? The list below shows the number of students in each homeroom at Jefferson High School.

21, 22, 19, 20, 23, 21, 20, 24, 20, 19,
20, 21, 21, 23, 21, 22, 19, 21, 19, 20

a. Make a line plot of the data.

b. Find the mean, median, and range of the data.

c. How can you use the line plot to determine whether the mean and median are equal?

Ⓐ Practice **7.** The list below shows the amount of time, in hours, one student spent on the Internet, per day, over a two week period. Make a line plot of the data. Then calculate the mean, median, mode, and range of the data.

3, 1, 4, 3, 2, 3, 2, 5, 6, 1, 3, 1, 3, 5

8. The list below shows ages of students on the math team. Make a line plot of the data. Then calculate the mean, median, mode, and range of the data.

14 14 15 15 16 15 15 16

Problem 5 **Comparing Measures of Central Tendency**

Got It? Use the line plots from Problem 5 together with the results from a third class, shown here.

a. Is the mean for Class C greater than or less than the mean for Class A?

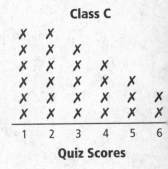

Class C

b. Is the median for Class C greater than or less than the median for Class A?

c. How can you tell which data set has a greater mean by comparing the graphs?

Practice In Exercises 9 and 10, determine which data set has a greater mean and a greater median.

9.

Company A

```
        X   X
        X   X   X   X
    X   X   X   X   X   X
  ─────────────────────────
   50  51  52  53  54  55
```

**Monthly Earnings
(thousands of dollars)**

Company B

```
            X   X   X
            X   X   X
    X   X   X   X   X   X
  ─────────────────────────
   50  51  52  53  54  55
```

**Monthly Earnings
(thousands of dollars)**

10.

Student A

```
                        X
                        X
                    X   X
            X   X   X   X
        X   X   X   X   X
        X   X   X   X   X
    X   X   X   X   X   X
    X   X   X   X   X   X
  ─────────────────────────
   30  31  32  33  34  35
```

Text Messages per Day

Student B

```
        X
        X   X
    X   X   X   X
    X   X   X   X
    X   X   X   X
    X   X   X   X   X
    X   X   X   X   X
    X   X   X   X   X
  ─────────────────────────
   30  31  32  33  34  35
```

Text Messages per Day

Lesson Check

Do you know HOW?

In Exercises 11 and 12, find the mean, median, and mode of each data set. Explain which measure best describes the data.

11. 1 29 33 31 30 33

12. 8.2 9.3 8.5 8.8 9.0

13. A student has gotten the following grades on his tests: 87, 95, 86, and 88. He needs to have an average of 90 to receive an A for the class. What is the minimum grade he must get on the last test in order to have an average of 90?

Do you UNDERSTAND?

14. Vocabulary How do mean, median, and mode describe the central tendency of a data set? Why are three different measures needed?

15. Error Analysis One student said 10 was the range of the data set 2, 10, 8, and 3. Another student said the range was 8. Which student is correct? Explain.

16. Reasoning How is the range of a data set affected by an outlier?

More Practice and Problem-Solving Exercises

B Apply

©17. Reasoning The mean of a data set is 7.8, the mode is 6.6, and the median is 6.8. What is the least possible number of data values in the set? Explain.

EM 18. Manufacturing Two manufacturing plants make sheets of steel for medical instruments. The back-to-back stem-and-leaf plot at the right shows data collected from the two plants.

   a. What are the mean, median, mode, and range of each data set?

   b. Which measure of central tendency best describes each data set? Explain.

   c. How can you use the shape of the back-to-back stem-and-leaf plot to determine which data set has the greater mean? Explain.

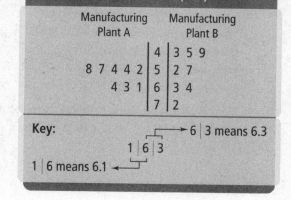

©19. Think About a Plan The diameters of 5 circles are given below. What are the mean, median, mode, and range of the circumferences of the circles?

   6.5 in. 3.2 in. 7.4 in. 6.5 in. 5.8 in.

   • What are the mean, median, mode, and range of the diameters?

   • How do the mean, median, mode, and range change when the data change from diameters to circumferences?

©20. Reasoning How does subtracting the same amount from each value in a data set affect the mean, median, mode, and range? Explain.

©21. Reasoning How does dividing each value in a data set by the same nonzero amount affect the mean, median, mode, and range? Explain.

22. Wildlife Management A wildlife manager measured and tagged twelve adult male crocodiles. The data he collected are at the right. He estimates the crocodiles will grow 0.1 m each year. What will be the mean, median, mode, and range of the crocodiles' lengths after 4 yr?

Crocodile Lengths (m)			
2.4	2.5	2.5	2.3
2.8	2.4	2.3	2.4
2.1	2.2	2.5	2.7

©23. Reasoning A friend tells you to apply for a sales job at a certain company because the salespeople earned an average of $47,500 last year. Last year, 6 salespeople earned $33,000, 3 earned $46,000, 2 earned $42,000, and 1 earned $150,000. Would you apply for the job based on what your friend says? Explain.

Challenge

24. Travel During the first 6 h of a car trip, your average speed is 44 mi/h. During the last 4 h of your trip, your average speed is 50 mi/h. What is your average speed for the whole trip? (*Hint:* First find the total number of miles traveled.)

25. Find the mean, median, mode, and range of the following algebraic expressions: $9x$, $4x$, $11x$, $7x$, $5x$, $4x$. Assume that $x > 0$.

Mean Absolute Deviation

S.ID.2 Use statistics appropriate to the shape of the data distribution to compare . . . spread . . . of two or more different data sets.

The **mean absolute deviation (MAD)** of a data set describes how the values in the data set *deviate*, or differ, from the mean. You can use the MAD to determine how well the mean represents the data. Data sets that have a low MAD are more closely grouped around the mean than data sets with a high MAD.

The MAD can be found by using the formula $\text{MAD} = \dfrac{|x_1 - \bar{x}| + |x_2 - \bar{x}| + \cdots + |x_n - \bar{x}|}{n}$, where $x_1, x_2, \ldots, x_n$ are the data values, $\bar{x}$ is the mean, and n is the number of data values.

Activity

The table shows the numbers of hours worked by two students at part-time jobs over the past 5 weeks.

Hours Spent Working					
Student A	15	20	15	25	20
Student B	10	25	20	30	25

1. Find the mean of each data set.

2. For each data set, subtract the mean from each data value. Then find the absolute value of the difference. Complete the tables.

Student A	
x_i	$|x_i - \bar{x}|$
15	
20	
15	
25	
20	

Student B	
x_i	$|x_i - \bar{x}|$
10	
25	
20	
30	
25	

3. For each data set, find the mean of the absolute values of the differences you found in Exercise 2. This is the mean absolute deviation.

© **4. Writing** Compare the numbers of hours worked by each student. Use the mean absolute deviation in your comparison.

Exercises

Find the mean absolute deviation of each data set. Then compare the data sets.

5.

Average Wait Times (minutes)							
Diner A	11	19	16	8	10	15	13	16
Diner B	5	22	14	13	18	7	9	12

6.

Digital Camera Prices									
Store A	$85	$110	$79	$184	$125	$35	$179	$104	$140	$75
Store B	$49	$35	$122	$65	$110	$80	$52	$96	$77	$115

LESSON LAB

Use With Lesson 6-2

Standard Deviation

S.ID.2 Use statistics appropriate to the shape of the data distribution to compare . . . spread . . . of two or more different data sets.

Statisticians use measures of dispersion to describe how spread out the values in a data set are. One measure of dispersion is *standard deviation*. **Standard deviation** is a measure of how the values in a data set vary, or deviate, from the mean.

Statisticians use several special symbols in the formula for standard deviation.

The Greek letter sigma (σ) represents standard deviation.

x is a value in the data set.
$\bar{x}$ is the mean of the data set.

$$\sigma = \sqrt{\frac{\Sigma(x - \bar{x})^2}{n}}$$

The capital sigma (Σ) represents the sum of a series of numbers.

n is the number of values in the data set.

Example

Find the mean and standard deviation of each data set. Which data set has greater standard deviation?

Step 1 Find the mean, $\bar{x}$.

Step 2 Find the difference between each data value and the mean, $x - \bar{x}$.

Step 3 Square each difference, $(x - \bar{x})^2$.

Step 4 Find the average (mean) of these squares, $\frac{\Sigma(x-\bar{x})^2}{n}$.

Step 5 Take the square root to find the standard deviation, $\sqrt{\frac{\Sigma(x-\bar{x})^2}{n}}$.

Data Set 1				Data Set 2			
x_1	$\bar{x}_1$	$x_1 - \bar{x}_1$	$(x_1 - \bar{x}_1)^2$	x_2	$\bar{x}_2$	$x_2 - \bar{x}_2$	$(x_2 - \bar{x}_2)^2$
12.6	15	−2.4	5.76	13.4	14.5	−1.1	1.21
15.1	15	0.1	0.01	11.7	14.5	−2.8	7.84
11.2	15	−3.8	14.44	18.3	14.5	3.8	14.44
17.9	15	2.9	8.41	14.8	14.5	0.3	0.09
18.2	15	3.2	10.24	14.3	14.5	−0.2	0.04
$\frac{\Sigma(x_1 - \bar{x}_1)^2}{n}$			7.772	$\frac{\Sigma(x_2 - \bar{x}_2)^2}{n}$			4.724
$\sqrt{\frac{\Sigma(x_1 - \bar{x}_1)^2}{n}}$			≈ 2.79	$\sqrt{\frac{\Sigma(x_2 - \bar{x}_2)^2}{n}}$			≈ 2.17

Data set 1 has a greater standard deviation at 2.79.

390   Lesson Lab   Standard Deviation

Exercises

Find the mean and standard deviation of each data set. Round to the nearest hundredth. Which data set has the greater standard deviation?

1. Data set 1: 4, 8, 5, 12, 3, 9, 5, 2

Data set 2: 5, 9, 11, 4, 6, 11, 2, 7

2. Data set 1: 102, 98, 103, 86, 101, 110

Data set 2: 90, 89, 100, 97, 102, 97

3. Data set 1: 8.2, 11.6, 8.7, 10.6, 9.4, 10.1, 9.3

Data set 2: 9.3, 10.2, 8.1, 12.3, 8.7, 9.9, 10.1

4. Data set 1: 32, 40, 35, 28, 42, 32, 44

Data set 2: 40, 38, 51, 39, 46, 40, 52

Box-and-Whisker Plots

S.ID.2 Use statistics appropriate to the shape of the data distribution to compare center . . . and spread . . . of two or more different data sets. Also **N.Q.1, S.ID.1**

Objectives To make and interpret box-and-whisker plots
To find quartiles and percentiles

Solve It! Write your solution to the Solve It in the space below.

In the Solve It, you may have looked at different parts of each data set in order to compare the two data sets.

Essential Understanding Separating data into subsets is a useful way to summarize and compare data sets.

Quartiles are values that divide a data set into four equal parts. The median (or second quartile, Q_2) separates the data into upper and lower halves. The first quartile (Q_1) is the median of the lower half of the data. The third quartile (Q_3) is the median of the upper half of the data. The **interquartile range** is the difference between the third and first quartiles.

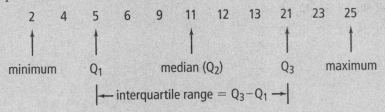

For a set of data that has an odd number of values, you do not include the median in either half when finding the first and third quartiles.

Got It?   What are the minimum, first quartile, median, third quartile, and maximum of each data set?

> **a.** 95   85   75   85   65   60   100   105   75   85   75

Think

How do you arrange the given data to find the required values?

> **b.** 11   19   7   5   21   53

Practice   Find the minimum, first quartile, median, third quartile, and maximum of each data set.

> **1.** 4.5   3.2   6.3   5.2   5   4.8   6   3.9   12

> **2.** 55   53   67   52   50   49   51   52   52

A **box-and-whisker plot** is a graph that summarizes a set of data by displaying it along a number line. It consists of three parts: a box and two whiskers.

Box-and-Whisker Plot

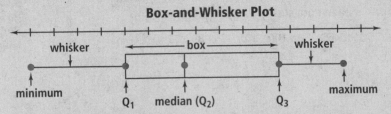

- The left whisker extends from the minimum to the first quartile. It represents about 25% of the data.
- The box extends from the first quartile to the third quartile and has a vertical line through the median. The length of the box represents the interquartile range. It contains about 50% of the data.
- The right whisker extends from the third quartile to the maximum. It represents about 25% of the data.

 **Problem 2** **Making a Box-and-Whisker Plot**

Got It? What box-and-whisker plot represents the following monthly sales, in millions of dollars, of audio devices: 15   4   9   16   10   16   8   14   25   34?

Ⓐ **Practice**   Make a box-and-whisker plot to represent each set of data.

3. weekly museum visitors: 531   469   573   206   374   421   505   489   702

4. camera prices: $280 $220 $224 $70 $410 $90 $30 $120

Problem 3 Interpreting Box-and-Whisker Plots

Got It? Use the box-and-whisker plots from Problem 3. What do the medians tell you about the average monthly rainfalls for Miami and New Orleans?

ⒶPractice **5. Fuel Use** Use the box-and-whisker plots below. What do they tell you about the fuel efficiency for each type of vehicle? Explain.

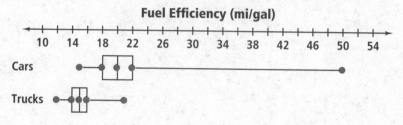

Fuel Efficiency (mi/gal)

Percentiles separate data sets into 100 equal parts. The **percentile rank** of a data value is the percentage of data values that are less than or equal to that value.

Problem 4 Finding a Percentile Rank

Got It? **a.** Of the 25 scores in Problem 4, there are 15 scores less than or equal to 85. What is the percentile rank of 85?

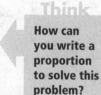

Think

How can you write a proportion to solve this problem?

ⓒb. Reasoning Is it possible to have a percentile rank of 0? Explain.

6. Of 10 test scores, six are less than or equal to 80. What is the percentile rank of a test score of 80?

7. Of 35 judges' scores awarded during a gymnastics event, 28 are less than or equal to 7.5. What is the percentile rank of a score of 7.5?

Lesson Check

Do you know HOW?

Identify the minimum, first quartile, median, third quartile, and maximum of each data set. Then make a box-and-whisker plot of each data set.

8. file sizes (megabytes): 54   100   84   124   188   48   256

9. daily attendance: 29   24   28   32   30   31   26   33

10. In the box-and-whisker plots at the right, which class has the greater interquartile range of arm spans?

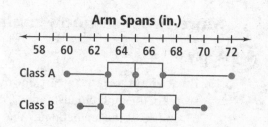

Arm Spans (in.)

Class A

Class B

Do you UNDERSTAND?

MATHEMATICAL
PRACTICES

11. **Vocabulary** Which portion of a box-and-whisker plot represents the interquartile range?

12. Students taking a make-up test receive the following grades: 77, 89, 88, 67, 91, 95, 83, 79, 81, and 65. Which grade has a percentile rank of 70?

13. **Reasoning** About what percent of the data in a data set falls between the minimum value and the third quartile? Explain.

14. **Error Analysis** A test is graded on a scale from 0 to 100. Your friend says that if you score a 78, your percentile rank must be 78. Is your friend correct? Explain.

More Practice and Problem-Solving Exercises

Ⓑ Apply

Ⓒ **15. Think About a Plan** You are one of the finalists at a science fair. The scores of the other finalists are 87, 89, 81, 85, 87, 83, 86, 94, 90, 97, 80, 89, 85, and 88. Write an inequality that represents your possible scores if your percentile rank is 80.
- What percent of the scores must be less than or equal to your score?
- What is the total number of finalists' scores?

Ⓒ **16. Writing** Explain the difference between *range* and *interquartile range*.

17. Basketball The heights of the players on a basketball team are 74 in., 79 in., 71.5 in., 81 in., 73 in., 76 in., 78 in., 71 in., 72 in., and 73.5 in. When the 76-in.-tall player is replaced, the percentile rank of the 73.5-in.-tall player becomes 60. Write an inequality that represents the possible heights of the replacement player.

Ⓒ **18. Open-Ended** Make a data set of 10 numbers that has a median of 22, an interquartile range of 10, and a minimum less than 4.

Ⓒ **19. Reasoning** Must the third quartile of a data set be less than the maximum value? Explain.

STEM 20. Packaging A cereal company is choosing between two devices to package their cereal into bags. The box-and-whisker plots at the right show the weights of the bags packed by each device.
- **a.** Which device produces packages with a more consistent weight? Explain.
- **b.** Which device should be chosen if the manufacturer wants to minimize the number of packages with weights less than 17 oz? More than 17.2 oz? Explain.

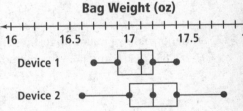

Ⓒ Challenge

Ⓒ **21. Reasoning** Can you find the mean, median, and mode of a data set by looking at a box-and-whisker plot? Explain.

22. Of 100 people that take a test, nine have scores greater than 93. What is the percentile rank of a score of 93?

Scatter Plots and Trend Lines

S.ID.6.c Fit a linear function for a scatter plot . . . Also **S.ID.6, S.ID.6.a, S.ID.7, S.ID.8, S.ID.9**

Objectives To write an equation of a trend line and of a line of best fit
To use a trend line and a line of best fit to make predictions

Solve It! Write your solution to the Solve It in the space below.

In the Solve It, the number of albums downloaded per year and the number of CDs sold per year are related.

Essential Understanding You can determine whether two sets of numerical data are related by graphing them as ordered pairs. If the two sets of data are related, you may be able to use a line to estimate or predict values.

A **scatter plot** is a graph that relates two different sets of data by displaying them as ordered pairs. Most scatter plots are in the first quadrant of the coordinate plane because the data are usually positive numbers.

You can use scatter plots to find trends in data. The scatter plots below show the three types of relationships that two sets of data may have.

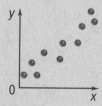 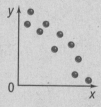 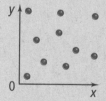

When y tends to increase as x increases, the two sets of data have a **positive correlation**.

When y tends to decrease as x increases, the two sets of data have a **negative correlation**.

When x and y are not related, the two sets of data have **no correlation**.

Got It? **a.** Make a scatter plot of the data in the table below. What type of relationship does the scatter plot show?

Gasoline Purchases								
Dollars Spent	10	11	9	10	13	5	8	4
Gallons Bought	2.5	2.8	2.3	2.6	3.3	1.3	2.2	1.1

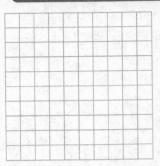

© b. Reasoning Consider the population of a city and the number of letters in the name of the city. Would you expect a *positive correlation,* a *negative correlation,* or *no correlation* between the two sets of data? Explain your reasoning.

For each table in Exercises 1 and 2, make a scatter plot of the data. Describe the type of correlation the scatter plot shows.

1.

Jeans Sales				
Average Price ($)	21	28	36	40
Number Sold	130	112	82	65

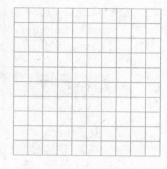

2.

Gasoline Purchases					
Dollars Spent	10	11	9	8	13
Gallons Bought	2.6	3	2.4	2.2	3.5

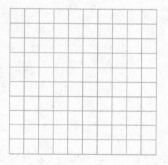

When two sets of data have a positive or negative correlation, you can use a *trend line* to show the correlation more clearly. A **trend line** is a line on a scatter plot, drawn near the points, that shows a correlation.

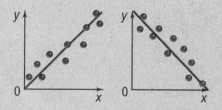

You can use a trend line to estimate a value between two known data values or to predict a value outside the range of known data values. **Interpolation** is estimating a value between two known values. **Extrapolation** is predicting a value outside the range of known values.

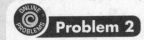

Problem 2 Writing an Equation of a Trend Line

Plan

How do you draw an accurate trend line?

Got It?

a. Make a scatter plot of the data below. Draw a trend line and write its equation. What is the approximate body length of a 7-month-old panda?

Body Length of a Panda								
Age (month)	1	2	3	4	5	6	8	9
Body Length (in.)	8.0	11.75	15.5	16.7	20.1	22.2	26.5	29.0

b. Reasoning Do you think you can use your model to extrapolate the body length of a 3-year-old panda? Explain.

Theme Parks Use the table below for Exercises 3 and 4.

Attendance and Revenue at U.S. Theme Parks									
Year	1990	1992	1994	1996	1998	2000	2002	2004	2006
Attendance (millions)	253	267	267	290	300	317	324	328	335
Revenue (billions of dollars)	5.7	6.5	7.0	7.9	8.7	9.6	9.9	10.8	11.5

SOURCE: International Association of Amusement Parks and Attractions

3. Make a scatter plot of the data pairs (year, attendance). Draw a trend line and write its equation. Estimate the attendance at U.S. theme parks in 2005.

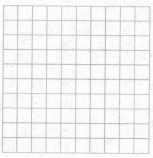

4. Make a scatter plot of the data pairs (year, revenue). Draw a trend line and write its equation. Predict the revenue at U.S. theme parks in 2012.

The trend line that shows the relationship between two sets of data most accurately is called the **line of best fit**. A graphing calculator computes the equation of the line of best fit using a method called linear regression.

The graphing calculator also gives you the **correlation coefficient** r, a number from -1 to 1, that tells you how closely the equation models the data.

$r = -1$ $r = 0$ $r = 1$

strong negative correlation   no correlation   strong positive correlation

The nearer r is to 1 or -1, the more closely the data cluster around the line of best fit. If r is near 1, the data lie close to a line of best fit with positive slope. If r is near -1, the data lie close to a line of best fit with negative slope.

Problem 3   **Finding the Line of Best Fit**

Got It?   **a.** Use the data in Problem 3. Predict the cost of attending in the 2016–2017 academic year.

©**b. Reasoning** What does the slope of the line of best fit in Problem 3 tell you about the rate of change in the cost?

 Practice   **5. Entertainment** Use a graphing calculator to find the equation of the line of best fit for the data in the table. Find the value of the correlation coefficient r to three decimal places. Then predict the number of movie tickets sold in the U.S. in 2014.

Movie Tickets Sold in U.S. by Year									
Year	1998	1999	2000	2001	2002	2003	2004	2005	2006	2007
Tickets Sold (millions)	1289	1311	1340	1339	1406	1421	1470	1415	1472	1470

Source: Motion Picture Association of America

Causation is when a change in one quantity causes a change in a second quantity. A correlation between quantities does not always imply causation.

Problem 4 Identifying Whether Relationships Are Causal

Got It? In the following situations, is there likely to be a correlation? If so, does the correlation reflect a causal relationship? Explain.

    a. the cost of a family's vacation and the size of their house

    b. the time spent exercising and the number of Calories burned

Practice In each situation, tell whether a correlation is likely. If it is, tell whether the correlation reflects a causal relationship. Explain your reasoning.

    6. the amount of time you study for a test and the score you receive

    7. a person's height and the number of letters in the person's name

You have used a graphing calculator to find lines of best fit for linear data. However, sometimes a scatter plot suggests a nonlinear trend for a data set. You can also use a graphing calculator to determine exponential models for nonlinear data.

Problem 5   Analyzing a Nonlinear Trend

Got It? The table shows the value of Denise's car each year since she purchased it. Use a graphing calculator to make a scatter plot for the data. Which is a suitable model for the data, a linear model or an exponential model? Write the model and predict the value of Denise's car after 8 years.

Think

How can a scatter plot show whether a linear or exponential model is better?

Value of Denise's Car					
Age (years), x	1	2	3	4	5
Value (thousands of dollars), y	28.6	18.5	14.1	10.2	8.9

Practice   **8.** The table shows the values of a stock during the first several months after the stock was bought. Use a graphing calculator to make a scatter plot for the data. Which is a suitable model for the data, a linear model or an exponential model? Write the model and predict the value of the stock after 10 months.

Values of a Stock Over Time						
Months, x	1	2	3	4	5	6
Stock Value (in dollars), y	4.10	5.40	7.30	9.93	13.51	17.90

9. The table shows the number of bacteria in a culture at the start of each hour as it is being studied. Use a graphing calculator to make a scatter plot for the data. Which is a suitable model for the data, a linear model or an exponential model? Write the model and predict the number of bacteria after 12 hours.

Bacteria Culture 0819023								
Number of Hours, x	1	2	3	4	5	6	7	8
Number of Bacteria, y	1200	780	510	330	210	140	100	85

Lesson Check

Do you know HOW?

Use the table for Exercises 10–12.

10. Make a scatter plot of the data. What type of relationship does the scatter plot show?

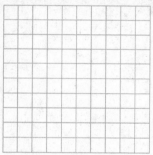

Average Maximum Daily Temperature in January for Northern Latitudes							
Latitude (°N)	35	33	30	25	43	40	39
Temperature (°F)	46	52	67	76	32	37	44

11. Draw a trend line on the scatter plot and write its equation.

12. Predict the average maximum daily temperature in January at a latitude of 50° N.

Do you UNDERSTAND?

© 13. Vocabulary Given a set of data pairs, how would you decide whether to use interpolation or extrapolation to find a certain value?

© 14. Compare and Contrast How are a trend line and the line of best fit for a set of data pairs similar? How are they different?

© 15. Error Analysis Refer to the table at the right. A student says that the data have a negative correlation because as x decreases, y also decreases. What is the student's error?

x	10	7	5	4	1	0
y	1	0	−2	−4	−7	−9

More Practice and Problem-Solving Exercises

MATHEMATICAL
PRACTICES

Ⓑ Apply

© 16. Writing Give two data sets that are correlated but do *not* have a causal relationship.

17. Business During one month at a local deli, the amount of ham sold decreased as the amount of turkey sold increased. Is this an example of *positive correlation, negative correlation,* or *no correlation*?

18. Think About a Plan Students measured the diameters and circumferences of the tops of a variety of cylinders. Below are the data that they collected. Estimate the diameter of a cylinder with circumference 22 cm.

Cylinder Tops										
Diameter (cm)	3	3	5	6	8	8	9.5	10	10	12
Circumference (cm)	9.3	9.5	16	18.8	25	25.6	29.5	31.5	30.9	39.5

- How can you use a scatter plot to find an equation of a trend line?
- How can you use the equation of the trend line to make an estimate?

19. The table represents the population of Covetown at different times since it was founded in 1980.

Population of Covetown						
Year	1980	1990	2000	2005	2010	2012
Population	8400	17,300	35,900	51,100	73,500	85,200

- **a.** Let x represent the number of years since 1980 so that $x = 0$ represents 1980. Let y represent the population of Covetown in thousands of people. Using these definitions, rewrite the values in the table. Explain why doing so will make it easier to find a best-fitting model for the data.
- **b.** Make a scatter plot of the data. Do the data appear to be linear or exponential?
- **c.** Write an equation of the best-fitting line or best-fitting curve. What is the correlation coefficient? Does your equation appear to be a good fit for the data set?
- **d.** According to your equation, what was the population of Covetown in 1995 and what will the population be in 2025? Which estimate do you think is likely to be more accurate? Explain.

20. U.S. Population Use the data below.

Estimated Population of the United States (thousands)							
Year	2000	2001	2002	2003	2004	2005	2006
Male	138,482	140,079	141,592	142,937	144,467	145,973	147,512
Female	143,734	145,147	146,533	147,858	149,170	150,533	151,886

SOURCE: U.S. Census Bureau

- **a.** Make a scatter plot of the data pairs (male population, female population).
- **b.** Draw a trend line and write its equation.
- **c.** Use your equation to predict the U.S. female population if the U.S. male population increases to 150,000,000.
- **d.** **Reasoning** Consider a scatter plot of the data pairs (year, male population). Would it be reasonable to use this scatter plot to predict the U.S. male population in 2035? Explain your reasoning.

21. a. Graphing Calculator Use a graphing calculator to find the equation of the line of best fit for the data below. Let $x = 8$ represent 1998, $x = 9$ represent 1999, and so on.

U.S. Computer and Video Game Unit Sales									
Year	1998	1999	2000	2001	2002	2003	2004	2005	2006	2007
Unit Sales (millions)	152.4	184.5	196.3	210.3	225.8	240.9	249.5	229.5	241.6	267.9

Source: The NPD Group/Retail Tracking Service

b. What is the slope of the line of best fit? What does the slope mean in terms of the number of computer and video game units sold?

c. What is the y-intercept of the line of best fit? What does the y-intercept mean in terms of the number of computer and video game units sold?

Challenge

22. a. Make a scatter plot of the data below. Then find the equation of the line of best fit. Draw the line of best fit on your scatter plot.

Car Stopping Distances								
Speed (mi/h)	10	15	20	25	30	35	40	45
Stopping Distance (ft)	27	44	63	85	109	136	164	196

b. Use your equation to predict the stopping distance at 90 mi/h.

c. Reasoning The actual stopping distance at 90 mi/h is close to 584 ft. Why do you think this distance is not close to your prediction?

d. Suppose you plot (90, 584) on your scatter plot. What effect would it have on the slope and y-intercept of the line of best fit you found in part (a)?

Using Residuals

S.ID.6.b . . . Assess the fit of a function by . . . analyzing residuals.

In Lesson 6-4, you learned how to assess the line of best fit by using the correlation coefficient r. In this activity you will learn how to determine whether the best linear function is a good fit for the data. As you learn different types of functions in future chapters, residual plots will help you analyze the fit of other models.

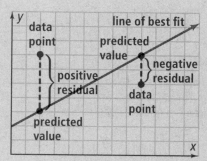

A **residual** is the difference between the y-value of a data point and the corresponding y-value of a model for the data set.

You can find a residual by calculating $y - \hat{y}$, where y represents the y-value of the data set and $\hat{y}$ represents the corresponding y-value predicted from the model.

Activity

The linear function $\hat{y} = 2.3x + 33.4$ models the data shown below.

Mean Heights of Boys Ages 5 to 13

Age (yr)	5	6	7	8	9	10	11	12	13
Height (in.)	44.5	46.9	49.7	52.2	54.4	55.7	58.5	60.9	63.1

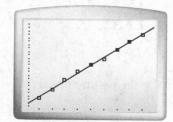

1. Complete the table below to calculate the residuals.

Age (x)	Height (y)	Predicted value $\hat{y} = 2.3x + 33.4$	Residual $y - \hat{y}$
5	44.5	2.3(5) + 33.4 = 44.9	44.5 − 44.9 = −0.4
6			
7			
8			
9			
10			
11			
12			
13			

You can plot each of the points $(x, y - \hat{y})$ on a coordinate plane, and analyze the residual plot to assess whether the function is a good fit for the data. For a good fit, the points appear to have no pattern.

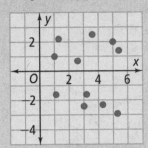

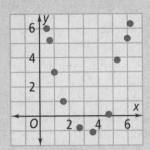

There is no apparent pattern in the residual plot. This indicates that the model function is a good fit for the data.

The points in the residual plot form a pattern. This indicates that the model function is not a good fit for the data.

2. Plot the points $(x, y - \hat{y})$ from the table in Exercise 1 on a coordinate plane.

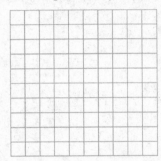

3. Do the points appear to form a pattern?

Ⓒ **4. Writing** Explain how you can use the residual plot to determine whether the model function is a good fit for the data.

Exercises

5. You model two data sets using linear models. The resulting residual plots are shown at the right. Which residual plot indicates that the linear model is a good fit for the data? Justify your answer.

Plot A

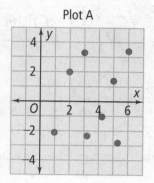

Plot B

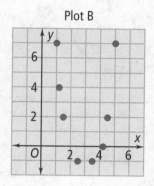

6. Use a graphing calculator to determine the line of best fit for the data set below. Then use a residual plot to determine whether the line of best fit is a good model. Explain.

Latitude and Temperature in Selected Cities

City	Latitude (°N)	Mean High Temperature in April (°F)
Lagos, Nigeria	6	89
San Juan, Puerto Rico	18	84
Kolkata, India	23	97
Cairo, Egypt	30	83
Tokyo, Japan	35	63
Rome, Italy	42	68
Belgrade, Serbia	45	45
London, England	52	56
Copenhagen, Denmark	56	50
Moscow, Russia	56	47

6-5 Two-Way Frequency Tables

S.ID.5 Summarize categorical data for two categories in two-way frequency tables. Interpret relative frequencies in the context of the data . . . Recognize possible associations and trends in the data.

Objective To use two-way frequency tables to summarize, interpret, and analyze trends in data

 Solve It! Write your solution to the Solve It in the space below.

In the Solve It, you used a *two-way frequency* table to draw a conclusion about categorical data. Categorical data are data that fall into categories, such as boy or girl. A **two-way frequency table** is a table in which frequencies correspond to two variables. One variable is used to categorize rows, and a second variable is used to categorize columns. Two-way frequency tables have at least two rows and two columns. An entry in the body of the table is a **joint frequency**. An entry in the Total row or Total column is a **marginal frequency**.

	Bicycle Status		
Gender	Own a Bicycle	Do Not Own a Bicycle	Total
Boys	16	4	20
Girls	18	12	30
Total	34	16	50

grand total

joint frequency

Essential Understanding Two-way frequency tables are a convenient way to show categorical data. You can use two-way frequency tables to analyze categorical data.

Got It? A survey asked 170 freshmen and sophomores whether they preferred Math or English. Of the 87 freshmen, 36 said that they preferred Math. Of the 83 sophomores, 27 said that they preferred English. Make a two-way frequency table for the data.

Think

How can you check if your table is reasonable?

 Practice   **1. News** A survey asked 295 males and females whether they preferred reading about the news from a newspaper or on the Internet. Of the 138 males, 97 said that they preferred the Internet. Of the 157 females, 32 said that they preferred a newspaper. Make a two-way frequency table for the data.

2. Foreign Language A survey asked 152 juniors and seniors whether they preferred Spanish or French. Of the 68 juniors, 34 said that they preferred Spanish. Of the 84 seniors, 47 said that they preferred Spanish. Make a two-way frequency table for the data.

The **relative frequency** of a category, such as girls who own a bicycle, is the ratio of the frequency of the category to the total frequency. So the relative frequency of girls who own a bicycle in the Solve It is $\frac{18}{30} = 0.6$.

You find a **joint relative frequency** by dividing a frequency that is not in the Total row or the Total column by the grand total.

You find a **marginal relative frequency** by dividing a row total or a column total by the grand total.

A **two-way relative frequency table** displays both joint relative frequencies and marginal relative frequencies.

Bicycle Status			
Gender	Own a Bicycle	Do Not Own a Bicycle	Total
Boys	$\frac{16}{50} = 0.32$	$\frac{4}{50} = 0.08$	$\frac{20}{50} = 0.4$
Girls	$\frac{18}{50} = 0.36$	$\frac{12}{50} = 0.24$	$\frac{30}{50} = 0.6$
Total	$\frac{34}{50} = 0.68$	$\frac{16}{50} = 0.32$	$\frac{50}{50} = 1$

marginal relative frequency

joint relative frequency

Problem 2 Making and Interpreting a Two-Way Relative Frequency Table

Got It?   Use the table in Problem 2.

a. What is the joint relative frequency of women who saw Movie B?

b. What is the marginal relative frequency of people who saw Movie A?

3. Use the data from Exercise 1.

    a. Make a two-way relative frequency table for the data.

    b. What is the joint relative frequency of females who preferred the Internet?

    c. What is the marginal relative frequency of people who preferred a newspaper?

4. Use the data from Exercise 2.

    a. Make a two-way relative frequency table for the data.

    b. What is the joint relative frequency of juniors who preferred French?

    c. What is the marginal relative frequency of seniors?

You can find **conditional relative frequency** by dividing a joint frequency by that frequency's row total or column total.

Problem 3   **Calculating Conditional Relative Frequency**

Got It?   Use the table in Problem 3. Round to the nearest hundredth.

  a. What is the conditional relative frequency that a person surveyed opposed the bond issue, given that the person was between 18 and 25?

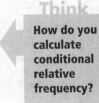

Think

How do you calculate conditional relative frequency?

  b. What is the conditional relative frequency that a person surveyed opposed the bond issue, given that the person was between 26 and 64?

  c. What is the conditional relative frequency that a person surveyed opposed the bond issue, given that the person was 65 or older?

  d. Reasoning What conclusion can you draw based on the conditional relative frequencies you found in parts (a)–(c)?

5. **Baseball** The table shows statistics about a baseball team and the number of times players reached base for different positions in the batting order.

Position in Lineup			
	1–3	4–6	7–9
Reach Base	9	6	2
Out	3	4	7

   a. What is the conditional relative frequency that a player batting in the 1st, 2nd, or 3rd position reached base?

   b. What is the conditional relative frequency that a player batting in the 4th, 5th, or 6th position reached base?

   c. What is the conditional relative frequency that a player batting in the 7th, 8th, or 9th position reached base?

6. Surveys The table shows the results of a survey about 8th grade boys and girls and the number of times they packed their lunch each week.

Number of Times Packing Lunch Each Week		
Gender	0–2	3–5
Boy	23	89
Girl	62	71

a. What is the conditional relative frequency that a person surveyed packed a lunch 0–2 times each week, given that the person was a boy?

b. What is the conditional relative frequency that a person surveyed packed a lunch 0–2 times each week, given that the person was a girl?

ⓒ c. **Reasoning** What conclusion can you draw based on the conditional relative frequencies you found in parts (a)–(b)?

Lesson Check

Do you know HOW?

The table shows the numbers of freshman boys and girls who play and do not play a sport.

Sport Status			
Gender	Play a Sport	Do Not Play a Sport	Total
Boy	58	62	120
Girl	26	94	120
Total	84	156	240

7. What is the marginal frequency of freshmen who played a sport?

8. What is the marginal frequency of freshmen who were girls?

9. What is the joint relative frequency of the girls who played a sport?

10. What is the joint relative frequency of the boys who did not play a sport?

Do you UNDERSTAND?

11. Vocabulary Which type of frequency is found by dividing a joint frequency by that frequency's row total or column total?

12. Compare and Contrast What is the difference between joint frequency and marginal frequency?

13. Writing How can you make a two-way relative frequency table from a two-way frequency table?

14. Reasoning Explain why the grand total of a two-way relative frequency table is always equal to 1.

More Practice and Problem-Solving Exercises

B Apply

ⓒ 15. Think About a Plan A survey asked 615 males and females whether they had a television in their bedroom. Of the 375 males, 298 said they had a television in their bedroom. Of the 240 females, 162 said they did not have a television in their bedroom. What is the joint relative frequency of females who had a television in their bedroom? What is the marginal relative frequency of people who did not have a television in their bedroom?

- How can you show the information?
- How can you find the missing information?
- How do you find the joint relative frequencies and marginal relative frequencies?

16. Text Message Plans A survey asked 1,162 males and females whether they had a 500 text messages per month plan or an unlimited text message plan. Of the 541 females, 108 said they had a 500 text messages per month plan. There were 196 people who said they had a 500 text messages per month plan. What is the joint relative frequency of males who had an unlimited text message plan? What is the marginal relative frequency of people who had an unlimited text message plan?

ⓒ 17. Writing Use the information from Exercise 16. Explain how to find the conditional relative frequency that a person surveyed was a female, given they had an unlimited text message plan.

ⓒ 18. Error Analysis Your friend surveyed people about their hair color. Of the 315 males, 75 had black hair, 130 had brown hair, and 12 had red hair. Of the 509 females, 286 had brown hair and 151 had blond hair. There were 122 males and females that had black hair. Your friend made the two-way frequency table below. Describe and correct his error.

Hair Color					
Gender	Black	Brown	Blond	Red	Total
Male	75	130	98	12	315
Female	47	286	151	22	509
Total	122	416	249	34	824

© **19. Movies** McKenzie surveyed 800 students and adults who attended two different movies, one shown at 7:00 and one shown at 9:00. There was a total of 465 adults that attended either the 7:00 movie or the 9:00 movie. Of the 330 people that went to the 7:00 movie, 120 were adults.
  a. Make a two-way frequency table.
  b. What is the conditional relative frequency that a person surveyed was a student, given that the person went to the 9:00 movie?
  c. What is the conditional relative frequency that a person surveyed was an adult, given that the person went to the 9:00 movie?
  d. **Reasoning** What conclusion can you draw based on the conditional relative frequencies you found in parts (b)–(c)?

© **20. Reasoning** Explain how to draw a conclusion based on conditional relative frequencies.

© **Challenge**

21. Shirt Color A survey asked 16 boys and 14 girls about their shirt color. There were 8 boys with a blue shirt, 6 girls with a red shirt, and 6 girls with a white shirt. There were a total of 9 boys and girls with a red shirt.
  a. Make a two-way frequency table.
  b. Make a two-way relative frequency table.
  c. What is the joint relative frequency of a boy wearing a red shirt?
  d. What is the joint relative frequency of a girl wearing a blue shirt?
  e. What is the marginal relative frequency of a person wearing a white shirt?
  f. What is the conditional relative frequency that a person surveyed was a boy, given that the person wore a blue shirt? Red shirt? White shirt?
© g. **Reasoning** What conclusions can you draw based on the conditional relative frequencies you found in part (f)?

6-1 Frequency and Histograms

Quick Review

A **histogram** displays data in intervals, showing the frequency of values in each interval.

Example

Below are the prices of the television models sold at an electronics store. What is a histogram of the data?

$1399 $1349 $999 $2149 $149 $279
$449 $379 $1379 $799 $3199 $1099
$499 $899 $949 $1799 $1699 $3499

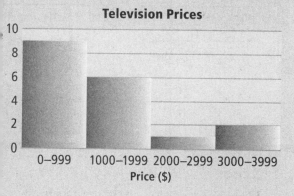

Television Prices

Exercises

Use the data to make a histogram.

1. customers: 141 128 132 141 152 169 121
   133 131 156 142 136 135 144 135 153

2. workout times (min): 41 29 46 39 37 44 33
   51 42 30

Tell whether each histogram is *uniform*, *symmetric*, or *skewed*.

3.

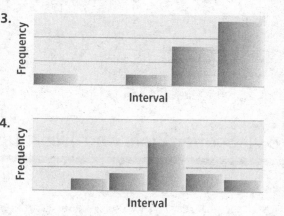

4.

6-2 Measures of Central Tendency and Dispersion

Quick Review

The **mean** of a data set equals $\frac{\text{sum of the data values}}{\text{total number of data values}}$.
The **median** is the middle value in the data set when the values are arranged in order. The **mode** is the data item that occurs the most times.

Example

What are the mean, median, and mode of the data?

5.6, 7.9, 7.0, 5.9, 7.8, 6.2, 6.4, 5.2, and 5.6

Mean:

$$\frac{5.6 + 7.9 + 7.0 + 5.9 + 7.8 + 6.2 + 6.4 + 5.2 + 5.6}{9} = 6.4$$

5.2 5.6 5.6 5.9 6.2 6.4 7.0 7.8 7.9   Order the data.

Median: 6.2   6.2 is the middle value.

Mode: 5.6   5.6 occurs most often.

Exercises

5. Find the mean, median, mode, and range of the points scored by a football team.: 23 31 26
   27 25 28 23 23 25 29 29 29 25 22 30

6. **Cats** A veterinarian examines 9 cats. The weights of the cats are 13.4 lb, 13.1 lb, 10.4 lb, 6.8 lb, 11.4 lb, 10.8 lb, 13.4 lb, 11.3 lb, and 9.3 lb. Find the mean, median, and mode of the data. Which measure of central tendency best describes the data?

7. **Basketball** A basketball player scores 22, 19, 25, and 17 points in four games. How many points does the basketball player need to score in the fifth game to average 22 points scored per game?

6-3 Box-and-Whisker Plots

Quick Review

A **box-and-whisker plot** organizes data values into four groups using the minimum value, the first quartile, the median, the third quartile, and the maximum value.

Example

What box-and-whisker plot represents the test scores below?

62 57 78 69 85 43 94 82 61 90 83 51 67 88 55

Arrange the data in order from least to greatest.

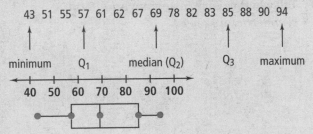

43 51 55 57 61 62 67 69 78 82 83 85 88 90 94

minimum   Q$_1$ median (Q$_2$)   Q$_3$ maximum

40 50 60 70 80 90 100

Exercises

Make a box-and-whisker plot of each data set.

8. movie lengths (min):

   125 117 174 131 142 108 188 162 155 16
   129 133 147 175 150

9. dog weights (lb):

   23 15 88 34 33 49 52 67 42 71 28

10. book lengths (pages):

    178 223 198 376 284 156 245 202 315 26

11. Which box-and-whisker plot represents the da
    set with the greater interquartile range? Explai

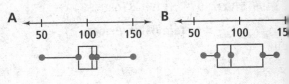

A   50   100   150   B   50   100   15

6-4 Scatter Plots and Trend Lines

Quick Review

A **scatter plot** displays two sets of data as ordered pairs. A **trend line** for a scatter plot shows the correlation between the two sets of data. The most accurate trend line is the **line of best fit**. To estimate or predict values on a scatter plot, you can use **interpolation** or **extrapolation**.

Example

Estimate the length of the kudzu vine in Week 3.

Kudzu Vine Growth

When $w = 3$, $\ell \approx 10$. So in Week 3, the length of the kudzu vine was about 10 ft.

Predict the length of the kudzu vine in Week 11.

$\ell = 3.5w$ Use the equation of the trend line.

$\ell = 3.5(11)$ Substitute 11 for w.

$\ell = 38.5$ Simplify.

The length of the vine in Week 11 will be about 38.5 ft.

Length (ft), ℓ

30

20

$\ell = 3.5w$

10

0

2 4 6 8 10

Week, w

Exercises

12. **a.** Make a scatter plot of the data below.

Heights and Arm Spans					
Height (m)	1.5	1.8	1.7	2.0	1.7	2.1
Arm Span (m)	1.4	1.7	1.7	1.9	1.6	2.0

b. Write an equation of a reasonable trend line or use a graphing calculator to find the equation of the line of best fit.

c. Estimate the arm span of someone who is 1.6 m tall.

d. Predict the arm span of someone who i 2.2 m tall.

Quick Review

A **two-way frequency table** is a table in which frequencies correspond to two variables. An entry in the body of a table is a **joint frequency**. An entry in the Total row or Total column is a **marginal frequency**. The **relative frequency** of a category is the ratio of the frequency of the category to the total frequency.

You find a **joint relative frequency** by dividing a frequency that is not in the Total row or Total column by the grand total. You find a **marginal relative frequency** by dividing a row total or a column total by the grand total. A **two-way relative frequency table** displays both joint and marginal relative frequencies.

You can find **conditional relative frequency** by dividing a joint frequency by that frequency's row or column total.

Example

What is the joint relative frequency of boys whose favorite sport is basketball?

	Favorite Sport		
ender	Basketball	Soccer	Total
oys	52	34	86
irls	29	45	74
otal	81	79	160

Use the table to find the cell that represents boys **and** basketball. This is the numerator. The denominator is the grand total.

The joint relative frequency of boys whose favorite sport is basketball is $\frac{52}{160} = 0.325 \approx 0.33$.

Exercises

A survey asked 59 men and 62 women about a ballot proposition in an upcoming election. In the survey, there were 18 men who intend to vote No on the proposition and 32 women who intend to vote Yes.

13. Make a two-way frequency table.

14. Make a two-way relative frequency table.

15. What is the joint relative frequency of a man intending to vote Yes on the proposition?

16. What is the joint relative frequency of a woman intending to vote No on the proposition?

17. What is the marginal relative frequency of a person intending to vote Yes on the proposition?

18. What is the conditional relative frequency that a person surveyed is a man, given that the person intended to vote No on the proposition?

19. What is the conditional relative frequency that a person surveyed is a man, given that the person intended to vote Yes on the proposition?

20. What conclusion can you draw based on the conditional relative frequencies you found?

Pull It **All Together**

 ASSESSME

Choosing a Location for a Tournament

Luis is the director of a youth baseball league. He needs to find a location for the league's championship tournament in June. The ideal location should be warm, with as little rain as possible. Luis has narrowed down the choices to two cities: Oakville and Fairview.

For each city, Luis collects data on the average June temperature and the June rainfall. The data are shown in the tables.

Oakville Climate										
Year	2004	2005	2006	2007	2008	2009	2010	2011	2012	2013
Avg. June Temp. (°F)	68	79	72	71	72	75	75	78	77	75
June Rainfall (in.)	2.8	5.1	3.4	3.1	3.6	4.1	3.4	4.9	4.5	4.0

Fairview Climate										
Year	2004	2005	2006	2007	2008	2009	2010	2011	2012	2013
Avg. June Temp. (°F)	67	75	60	73	68	72	61	69	71	71
June Rainfall (in.)	2.5	1.3	3.0	1.5	1.9	1.8	3.3	2.0	2.4	2.0

Task Description

Decide whether the tournament should be held in Oakville or Fairview, and justify your decision.

- How can measures of center, measures of dispersion, and/or data displays help you compare the temperatures in the two cities and the rainfall in the two cities?

- What can you learn from making a scatter plot of each city's data?

Get Ready!

Squaring Numbers

Simplify.

1. 3^2 **2.** 4^2 **3.** 11^2

Simplifying Expressions

Simplify each expression. Use 3.14 for π.

4. $2 \cdot 7.5 + 2 \cdot 11$ **5.** $\pi(5)^2$ **6.** $\sqrt{5^2 + 12^2}$

Evaluating Expressions

Evaluate the following expressions for $a = 4$ and $b = -2$.

7. $\dfrac{a+b}{2}$ **8.** $\dfrac{a-7}{3-b}$ **9.** $\sqrt{(7-a)^2 + (2-b)^2}$

Finding Absolute Value

Simplify each absolute value expression.

10. $|-8|$ **11.** $|2-6|$ **12.** $|-5-(-8)|$

Solving Equations

Algebra Solve each equation.

13. $2x + 7 = 13$ **14.** $5x - 12 = 2x + 6$ **15.** $2(x+3) - 1 = 7x$

Looking Ahead Vocabulary

16. Artists often use long streaks to show *rays* of light coming from the sun. A *ray* is also a geometric figure. What do you think the properties of a *ray* are?

17. You and your friend work with each other. In other words, you and your friend are *co*-workers. What might the term *collinear* mean in geometry?

Tools of Geometry

Big Ideas

1 Visualization
Essential Question How can you represent a three-dimensional figure with a two-dimensional drawing?

2 Reasoning
Essential Question What are the building blocks of geometry?

3 Measurement
Essential Question How can you describe the attributes of a segment or angle?

Ⓒ Domains

• Congruence

Chapter Preview

Interactive Digital Path

Log in to **pearsonsuccessnet.com** and click on Interactive Digital Path to access the Solve Its and animated Problems.

 ## Vocabulary

English/Spanish Vocabulary Audio Online:

English	Spanish
angle bisector, *p. 471*	bisectriz de un ángulo
congruent segments, *p. 453*	segmentos congruentes
isometric drawing, *p. 433*	dibujo isométrico
linear pair, *p. 469*	par lineal
net, *p. 431*	plantilla
orthographic drawing, *p. 435*	dibujo ortográfico
postulate, *p. 444*	postulado
segment bisector, *p. 454*	bisectriz de un segmen
supplementary angles, *p. 467*	ángulos suplementario
vertical angles, *p. 466*	ángulos verticales

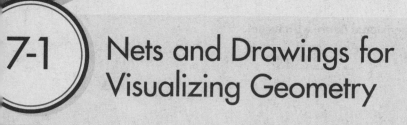

7-1

Nets and Drawings for Visualizing Geometry

Prepares for **G.CO.1** Know precise definitions of angle, circle, perpendicular line, parallel line, and line segment . . .

Objective To make nets and drawings of three-dimensional figures

Solve It! Write your solution to the Solve It in the space below.

In the Solve It, you had to "see" the projection of one side of an object onto a flat surface. Visualizing figures is a key skill that you will develop in geometry.

Essential Understanding You can represent a three-dimensional object with a two-dimensional figure using special drawing techniques.

A **net** is a two-dimensional diagram that you can fold to form a three-dimensional figure. A net shows all of the surfaces of a figure in one view.

Problem 1 Identifying a Solid From a Net

Got It? The net in Problem 1 folds into the cube shown at the right. Which letters will be on the top and right side of the cube?

Practice Match each three-dimensional figure with its net.

1.

2.

3.

A.

B.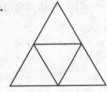

C.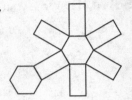

Packaging designers use nets to design boxes and other containers like the box in Problem 2.

 Problem 2 **Drawing a Net From a Solid**

Think
How can you see the net?

Got It?　**a.** What is a net for the figure below? Label the net with its dimensions.

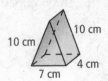

ⓒ **b. Reasoning** Is there another possible net for the figure in part (a)? If so, draw it.

Practice Draw a net for each figure. Label the net with its dimensions.

4.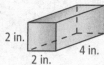

2 in.
2 in.
4 in.

5.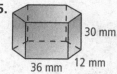

30 mm
36 mm
12 mm

An **isometric drawing** shows a corner view of a three-dimensional figure. It allows you to see the top, front, and side of the figure. You can draw an isometric drawing on isometric dot paper. The simple drawing of a file cabinet at the right is an isometric drawing.

A net shows a three-dimensional figure as a folded-out flat surface. An isometric drawing shows a three-dimensional figure using slanted lines to represent depth.

Front   Right

Problem 3 **Isometric Drawing**

Got It? What is an isometric drawing of this cube structure?

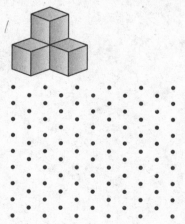

6.

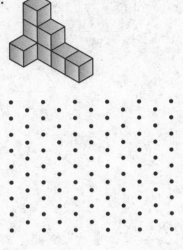

7.

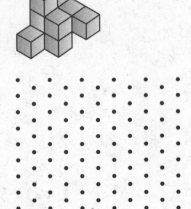

An **orthographic drawing** is another way to represent a three-dimensional figure. An orthographic drawing shows three separate views: a top view, a front view, and a right-side view.

Although an orthographic drawing may take more time to analyze, it provides unique information about the shape of a structure.

Problem 4 **Orthographic Drawing**

Got It? What is the orthographic drawing for this isometric drawing?

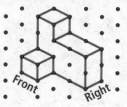

Plan

How can you determine the top, front, and right-side views?

Practice For each isometric drawing in Exercises 8 and 9, make an orthographic drawing. Assume there are no hidden cubes.

8.
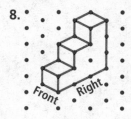

9.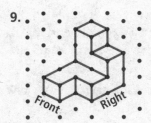

Front   Right

 ## Lesson Check

Do you know HOW?

10. What is a net for the figure below? Label the net with its dimensions.

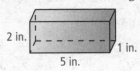

2 in.

5 in.

1 in.

11. What is an isometric drawing of the cube structure?

12. What is the orthographic drawing of the isometric drawing at the right? Assume there are no hidden cubes.

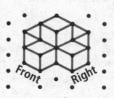

13. Vocabulary Tell whether each drawing is *isometric*, *orthographic*, a *net*, or *none*.

a.

b.
Top

Front   Right

c.
Front   Right

d.

14. Compare and Contrast What are the differences and similarities between an isometric drawing and an orthographic drawing? Explain.

More Practice and Problem-Solving Exercises

B Apply

15. Multiple Representations There are eight different nets for the solid shown at the right. Draw as many of them as you can. (*Hint*: Two nets are the same if you can rotate or flip one to match the other.)

16. a. Open-Ended Make an isometric drawing of a structure that you can build using 8 cubes.
   b. Make an orthographic drawing of this structure.

17. Think About a Plan Draw a net of the can at the right.
  - What shape are the top and bottom of the can?
  - If you uncurl the body of the can, what shape do you get?

18. History In 1525, German printmaker Albrecht Dürer first used the word *net* to describe a printed pattern that folds up into a three-dimensional shape. Why do you think he chose to use the word *net*?

EM **Manufacturing** Match the package with its net.

19.

20.

21.

A.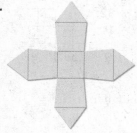

B.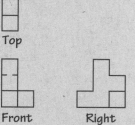

C.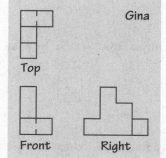

22. Error Analysis Miquela and Gina drew orthographic drawings for the cube structure at the right. Who is correct?

Miquela

Top
Front
Right

Gina

Top
Front
Right

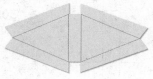
Front   Right

Make an orthographic drawing for each isometric drawing.

23.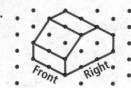
Front   Right

24.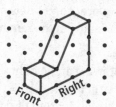
Front   Right

25.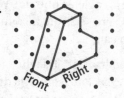
Front   Right

26. **Fort** Use the diagram of the fort at the right.
   a. Make an isometric drawing of the fort.
   b. Make an orthographic drawing of the fort.

STEM 27. **Aerial Photography** Another perspective in aerial photography is the "bird's-eye view," which shows an object from directly overhead. What type of drawing that you have studied in this lesson is a bird's-eye view?

ⓒ 28. **Writing** Photographs of buildings are typically not taken from a bird's-eye view. Describe a situation in which you would want a photo showing a bird's-eye view.

ⓒ **Visualization** Think about how each net can be folded to form a cube. What is the number of the face that will be opposite Face 1?

29. 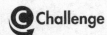   30.   31. 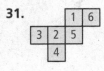   32.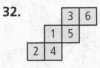

ⓒ 33. **Multiple Representations** There are 11 different nets for a cube. Four of them are shown above.
   a. Draw the other seven nets.
   b. **Writing** Suppose you want to make 100 cubes for an art project. Which of the 11 nets would you use? Explain why.

Ⓒ **Challenge**

34. The net at the right folds into a cube. Sketch the cube so that its front face is shaded as shown below.

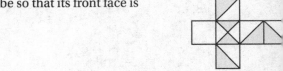

35. **Architecture** What does a net of the staircase shown look like? Draw the net. (*Hint*: Visualize stretching the stairs out flat.)

36. A hexomino is a two-dimensional figure formed with six squares. Each square shares at least one side with another square. The 11 nets of a cube that you found in Exercise 33 are hexominoes. Draw as many of the remaining 24 hexominoes as you can.

ⓒ 37. **Visualization** Use the orthographic drawing at the right.
   a. Make an isometric drawing of the structure.
   b. Make an isometric drawing of the structure from part (a) after it has been turned on its base 90° counterclockwise.
   c. Make an orthographic drawing of the structure from part (b).
   d. Turn the structure from part (a) 180°. Repeat parts (b) and (c).

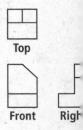

Top

Front   Righ

7-2 Points, Lines, and Planes

G.CO.1 Know precise definitions of . . . and line segment . . . based on the undefined notions of point, line, . . .

Objective To understand basic terms and postulates of geometry

Solve It! Write your solution to the Solve It in the space below.

In this lesson, you will learn basic geometric facts to help you justify your answer to the Solve It.

Essential Understanding Geometry is a mathematical system built on accepted facts, basic terms, and definitions.

In geometry, some words such as *point, line*, and *plane* are undefined. Undefined terms are the basic ideas that you can use to build the definitions of all other figures in geometry. Although you cannot define undefined terms, it is important to have a general description of their meanings.

take note

Key Concept   Undefined Terms

Term Description	How to Name It	Diagram
A **point** indicates a location and has no size.	You can represent a point by a dot and name it by a capital letter, such as *A*.	*A* •
A **line** is represented by a straight path that extends in two opposite directions without end and has no thickness. A line contains infinitely many points.	You can name a line by any two points on the line, such as $\overleftrightarrow{AB}$ (read "line AB") or $\overleftrightarrow{BA}$, or by a single lowercase letter, such as line ℓ.	*ℓ*, *B*, *A*
A **plane** is represented by a flat surface that extends without end and has no thickness. A plane contains infinitely many lines.	You can name a plane by a capital letter, such as plane *P*, or by at least three points in the plane that do not all lie on the same line, such as plane *ABC*.	*P*, *A B C*

Points that lie on the same line are **collinear points**. Points and lines that lie in the same plane are **coplanar**. All the points of a line are coplanar.

Problem 1   **Naming Points, Lines, and Planes**

Got It?   **a.** What are two other ways to name $\overleftrightarrow{RS}$?

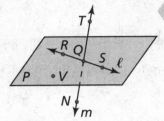

Think

Why can figures have more than one name?

b. What are two more ways to name plane P?

c. What are the names of three other collinear points?

d. What are two points that are *not* coplanar with points R, S, and V?

Practice   Use the figure at the right for Exercises 1 and 2.

1. Name three collinear points.

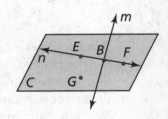

2. Name four coplanar points.

The terms *point, line,* and *plane* are not defined because their definitions would require terms that also need defining. You can, however, use undefined terms to define other terms. A geometric figure is a set of points. **Space** is the set of all points in three dimensions. Similarly, the definitions for *segment* and *ray* are based on points and lines.

Key Concept Defined Terms

Definition	How to Name It	Diagram
A **segment** is part of a line that consists of two endpoints and all points between them.	You can name a segment by its two endpoints, such as $\overline{AB}$ (read "segment *AB*") or $\overline{BA}$.	A ——— B
A **ray** is part of a line that consists of one endpoint and all the points of the line on one side of the endpoint.	You can name a ray by its endpoint and another point on the ray, such as $\overrightarrow{AB}$ (read "ray *AB*"). The order of points indicates the ray's direction.	A ———→ B
Opposite rays are two rays that share the same endpoint and form a line.	You can name opposite rays by their shared endpoint and any other point on each ray, such as $\overrightarrow{CA}$ and $\overrightarrow{CB}$.	←— A C B —→

Problem 2   Naming Segments and Rays

Got It? **Reasoning** $\overrightarrow{EF}$ and $\overrightarrow{FE}$ form a line. Are they opposite rays? Explain.

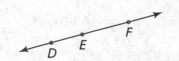

Think

How do you know if two rays are opposite rays?

 Practice Use the figure at the right for Exercises 3 and 4.

3. What are all the segments you can name in the figure?

4. What are all the rays you can name in the figure?

A **postulate** or **axiom** is an accepted statement of fact. Postulates, like undefined terms, are basic building blocks of the logical system in geometry. You will use logical reasoning to prove general concepts in this book.

You have used some of the following geometry postulates in algebra. For example, you used Postulate 1 when you graphed equations such as $y = 2x + 8$. You graphed two points and drew the line through the points.

take note
Postulate 1

Through any two points there is exactly one line.

Line t passes through points A and B. Line t is the only line that passes through both points.

When you have two or more geometric figures, their **intersection** is the set of points the figures have in common.

In algebra, one way to solve a system of two equations is to graph them. The graphs of the two lines $y = -2x + 8$ and $y = 3x - 7$ intersect in a single point, $(3, 2)$. So the solution is $(3, 2)$. This illustrates Postulate 2.

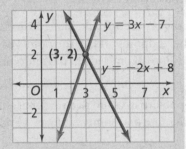

take note
Postulate 2

If two distinct lines intersect, then they intersect in exactly one point.

$\overleftrightarrow{AE}$ and $\overleftrightarrow{DB}$ intersect in point C.

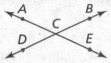

There is a similar postulate about the intersection of planes.

take note
Postulate 3

If two distinct planes intersect, then they intersect in exactly one line.

Plane RST and plane WST intersect in $\overleftrightarrow{ST}$.

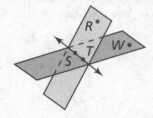

When you know two points that two planes have in common, Postulates 1 and 3 tell you that the line through those points is the intersection of the planes.

Problem 3 Finding the Intersection of Two Planes

Got It? **a.** What are the names of two planes that intersect in $\overleftrightarrow{BF}$?

b. Reasoning Why do you only need to find two common points to name the intersection of two distinct planes?

Practice Use the figure at the right for Exercises 5 and 6.

5. Name the intersection of planes QRS and RSW.

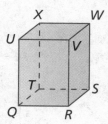

6. Name two planes that intersect in $\overleftrightarrow{QU}$.

When you name a plane from a figure like the box in Problem 3, list the corner points in consecutive order. For example, plane $ADCB$ and plane $ABCD$ are also names for the plane on the top of the box. Plane $ACBD$ is not.

Photographers use three-legged tripods to make sure that a camera is steady. The feet of the tripod all touch the floor at the same time. You can think of the feet as points and the floor as a plane. As long as the feet do not all lie in one line, they will lie in exactly one plane.

This illustrates Postulate 4.

take note

Postulate 4

Through any three noncollinear points there is exactly one plane.

Points Q, R, and S are noncollinear. Plane P is the only plane that contains them.

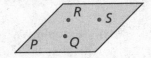

Problem 4   Using Postulate 4

Got It?   **a.** What plane contains points L, M, and N? Shade the plane in the figure below.

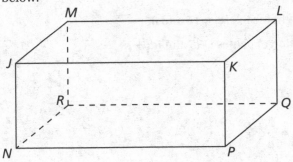

© **b. Reasoning** What is the name of a line that is coplanar with $\overleftrightarrow{JK}$ and $\overleftrightarrow{KL}$?

Practice Shade the plane that contains the given points.

7. *R, V, W*

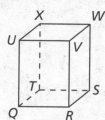

8. *U, V, W*

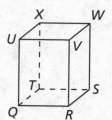

Lesson Check

Do you know HOW?

Use the figure at the right.

9. What are two other names for $\overleftrightarrow{XY}$?

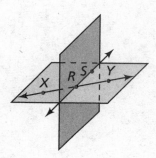

10. What are the opposite rays?

11. What is the intersection of the two planes?

Do you UNDERSTAND?

Ⓒ **12. Vocabulary** A segment has endpoints R and S. What are two names for the segment?

13. Are $\overrightarrow{AB}$ and $\overrightarrow{BA}$ the same ray? Explain.

Ⓒ **14. Reasoning** Why do you use two arrowheads when drawing or naming a line such as $\overleftrightarrow{EF}$?

Ⓒ **15. Compare and Contrast** How is naming a ray similar to naming a line? How is it different?

 Apply

Postulate 4 states that any three noncollinear points lie in exactly one plane. Find the plane that contains the first three points listed. Then determine whether the fourth point is in that plane. Write *coplanar* or *noncoplanar* to describe the points.

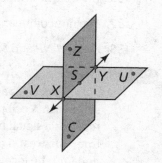

16. *Z, S, Y, C*

17. *S, U, V, Y*

18. *X, Y, Z, U*

19. *X, S, V, U*

20. *X, Z, S, V*

21. *S, V, C, Y*

If possible, draw a figure to fit each description. Otherwise, write *not possible*.

22. four points that are collinear

23. two points that are noncollinear

24. three points that are noncollinear

25. three points that are noncoplanar

© 26. Open-Ended Draw a figure with points *B, C, D, E, F,* and *G* that shows $\overleftrightarrow{CD}$, $\overleftrightarrow{BG}$, and $\overleftrightarrow{EF}$, with one of the points on all three lines.

© 27. Think About a Plan Your friend drew the diagram at the right to prove to you that two planes can intersect in exactly one point. Describe your friend's error.
   • How do you describe a plane?
   • What does it mean for two planes to intersect each other?
   • Can you define an endpoint of a plane?

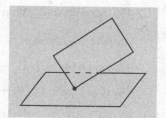

© 28. Reasoning If one ray contains another ray, are they the same ray? Explain.

For Exercises 29–34, determine whether each statement is *always, sometimes,* or *never* true.

29. $\overleftrightarrow{TQ}$ and $\overleftrightarrow{QT}$ are the same line.

30. $\overrightarrow{JK}$ and $\overrightarrow{JL}$ are the same ray.

31. Intersecting lines are coplanar.

32. Four points are coplanar.

33. A plane containing two points of a line contains the entire line.

34. Two distinct lines intersect in more than one point.

© 35. Use the diagram at the right. How many planes contain each line and point?
   a. $\overleftrightarrow{EF}$ and point *G*
   b. $\overleftrightarrow{PH}$ and point *E*
   c. $\overleftrightarrow{FG}$ and point *P*
   d. $\overleftrightarrow{EP}$ and point *G*
   e. Reasoning What do you think is true of a line and a point not on the line? Explain. (*Hint:* Use two of the postulates you learned in this lesson.)

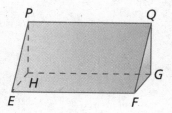

In Exercises 36–38, sketch a figure for the given information. Then state the postulate that your figure illustrates.

36. $\overleftrightarrow{AB}$ and $\overleftrightarrow{EF}$ intersect in point C.

37. The noncollinear points A, B, and C are all contained in plane N.

38. Planes LNP and MVK intersect in $\overleftrightarrow{NM}$.

STEM **39. Telecommunications** A cell phone tower at point A receives a cell phone signal from the southeast. A cell phone tower at point B receives a signal from the same cell phone from due west. Trace the diagram at the right and find the location of the cell phone. Describe how Postulates 1 and 2 help you locate the phone.

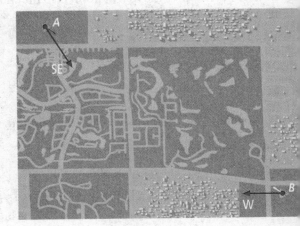

40. Estimation You can represent the hands on a clock at 6:00 as opposite rays. Estimate the other 11 times on a clock that you can represent as opposite rays.

41. Open-Ended What are some basic words in English that are difficult to define?

Coordinate Geometry Graph the points and state whether they are collinear.

42. $(1, 1), (4, 4), (-3, -3)$ **43.** $(2, 4), (4, 6), (0, 2)$

44. $(0, 0), (-5, 1), (6, -2)$ **45.** $(0, 0), (8, 10), (4, 6)$

46. $(0, 0), (0, 3), (0, -10)$ **47.** $(-2, -6), (1, -2), (4, 1)$

ⒸChallenge

48. How many planes contain the same three collinear points? Explain.

49. How many planes contain a given line? Explain.

50. a. Writing Suppose two points are in plane P. Explain why the line containing the points is also in plane P.
    b. Reasoning Suppose two lines intersect. How many planes do you think contain both lines? Use the diagram at the right and your answer to part (a) to explain your answer.

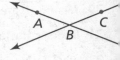

Measuring Segments

G.CO.1 Know precise definitions . . . based on the undefined notions of point, line, distance along a line, and distance around a circular arc. Also **G.GPE.6**

Objective To find and compare lengths of segments

Solve It! Write your solution to the Solve It in the space below.

In the Solve It, you measured the length of an object indirectly.

Essential Understanding You can use number operations to find and compare the lengths of segments.

take note

Postulate 5   Ruler Postulate

Every point on a line can be paired with a real number. This makes a one-to-one correspondence between the points on the line and the real numbers. The real number that corresponds to a point is called the **coordinate** of the point.

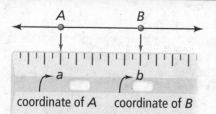

The Ruler Postulate allows you to measure lengths of segments using a given unit and to find distances between points on a number line. Consider $\overleftrightarrow{AB}$ at the right. The **distance** between points A and B is the absolute value of the difference of their coordinates, or $|a - b|$. This value is also AB, or the length of $\overline{AB}$.

$$AB = |a - b|$$

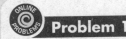 **Problem 1** **Measuring Segment Lengths**

Got It? What are *UV* and *SV* on the number line below?

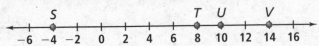

S   T U   V
—6 —4 —2   0   2   4   6   8 10 12 14 16

Practice **Find the length of each segment.**

1. $\overline{BD}$ 2. $\overline{CE}$

A B   C D   E
—8 —6   1 3   7

 Postulate 6 **Segment Addition Postulate**

If three points *A*, *B*, and *C* are collinear and *B* is between
A and *C*, then $AB + BC = AC$.

|←— AB —→|←——— BC ———→|
A   B   C
|←——————— AC ———————→|

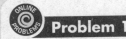 **Problem 2** **Using the Segment Addition Postulate**

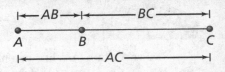

Got It? In the diagram, $JL = 120$. What are *JK* and *KL*?

4x + 6   7x + 15
J   K   L

A Practice Use the number line at the right for Exercises 3 and 4.

R — S — T

3. If $RS = 15$ and $ST = 9$, then what is RT?

4. If $ST = 15$ and $RT = 40$, then what is RS?

When numerical expressions have the same value, you say that they are equal (=). Similarly, if two segments have the same length, then the segments are **congruent** (≅) **segments**.

This means that if $AB = CD$, then $\overline{AB} \cong \overline{CD}$. You can also say that if $\overline{AB} \cong \overline{CD}$, then $AB = CD$.

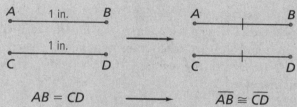

$AB = CD$ ⟶ $\overline{AB} \cong \overline{CD}$

As illustrated above, you can mark segments alike to show that they are congruent. If there is more than one set of congruent segments, you can indicate each set with the same number of marks.

Problem 3 **Comparing Segment Lengths**

Got It? **a.** Is $\overline{AB}$ congruent to $\overline{DE}$?

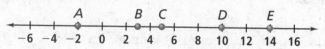

Plan

How do you know if two segments are congruent?

© **b. Reasoning** To find AC, suppose you subtract -2 from 5. Do you get the same result as subtracting 5 from -2? Why?

Ⓐ **Practice** Use the number line below for Exercises 5 and 6. Tell whether the segments are congruent.

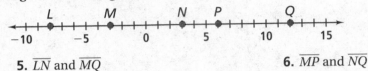

5. $\overline{LN}$ and $\overline{MQ}$ **6.** $\overline{MP}$ and $\overline{NQ}$

The **midpoint** of a segment is a point that divides the segment into two congruent segments. A point, line, ray, or other segment that intersects a segment at its midpoint is said to *bisect* the segment. That point, line, ray, or segment is called a **segment bisector**.

B is the midpoint of $\overline{AC}$.

ℓ is a segment bisector of $\overline{AC}$.

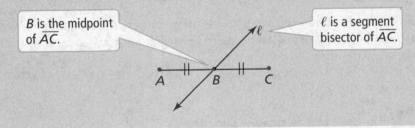

Problem 4 **Using the Midpoint**

Got It?   **a. Reasoning** In Problem 4, is it necessary to substitute 8 for x in the expression for QR in order to find QR? Explain.

b. *U* is the midpoint of $\overline{TV}$. What are *TU*, *UV*, and *TV*?

T   U   V

7. Algebra *A* is the midpoint of $\overline{XY}$.

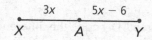

X   A   Y

a. Find *XA*.

b. Find *AY* and *XY*.

Lesson Check

Do you know HOW?

Name each of the following.

     A   B   C   D   E   F   G

−4 −3 −2 −1   0   1   2   3   4

8. The point on $\overrightarrow{DA}$ that is 2 units from *D*

9. Two points that are 3 units from *D*

10. The coordinate of the midpoint of $\overline{AG}$

11. A segment congruent to $\overline{AC}$

© **12. Vocabulary** Name two segment bisectors of $\overline{PR}$.

© **13. Compare and Contrast** Describe the difference between saying that two segments are *congruent* and saying that two segments have *equal length*. When would you use each phrase?

© **14. Error Analysis** You and your friend live 5 mi apart. He says that it is 5 mi from his house to your house and −5 mi from your house to his house. What is the error in his argument?

More Practice and Problem-Solving Exercises

 Apply

On a number line, the coordinates of *X*, *Y*, *Z*, and *W* are −7, −3, 1, and 5, respectively. Find the lengths of the two segments. Then tell whether they are congruent.

15. $\overline{XY}$ and $\overline{ZW}$ **16.** $\overline{ZX}$ and $\overline{WY}$ **17.** $\overline{YZ}$ and $\overline{XW}$

Suppose the coordinate of *A* is 0, *AR* = 5, and *AT* = 7. What are the possible coordinates of the midpoint of the given segment?

18. $\overline{AR}$ **19.** $\overline{AT}$ **20.** $\overline{RT}$

21. Suppose point *E* has a coordinate of 3 and *EG* = 5. What are the possible coordinates of point *G*?

Visualization Without using your ruler, sketch a segment with the given length. Use your ruler to see how well your sketch approximates the length provided.

22. 3 cm   **23.** 3 in.   **24.** 6 in.   **25.** 10 cm   **26.** 65 mm

27. Think About a Plan The numbers labeled on the map of Florida are mile markers. Assume that Route 10 between Quincy and Jacksonville is straight.

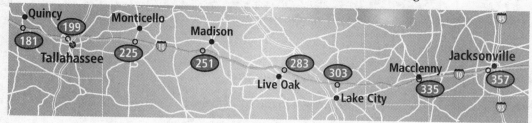

Suppose you drive at an average speed of 55 mi/h. How long will it take to get from Live Oak to Jacksonville?
- How can you use mile markers to find distances between points?
- How do average speed, distance, and time all relate to each other?

28. On a number line, A is at -2 and B is at 4. What is the coordinate of C, which is $\frac{2}{3}$ of the way from A to B?

Error Analysis Use the highway sign for Exercises 29 and 30.

29. A driver reads the highway sign and says, "It's 145 miles from Mitchell to Watertown." What error did the driver make? Explain.

30. Your friend reads the highway sign and says, "It's 71 miles to Watertown." Is your friend correct? Explain.

Algebra Use the diagram at the right for Exercises 31 and 32.

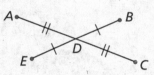

31. If $AD = 12$ and $AC = 4y - 36$, find the value of y. Then find AC and DC.

32. If $ED = x + 4$ and $DB = 3x - 8$, find ED, DB, and EB.

33. Writing Suppose you know PQ and QR. Can you use the Segment Addition Postulate to find PR? Explain.

Challenge

34. C is the midpoint of $\overline{AB}$, D is the midpoint of $\overline{AC}$, E is the midpoint of $\overline{AD}$, F is the midpoint of $\overline{ED}$, G is the midpoint of $\overline{EF}$, and H is the midpoint of $\overline{DB}$. If $DC = 16$, what is GH?

35. a. Algebra Use the diagram at the right. What algebraic expression represents GK?
b. If $GK = 30$, what are GH and JK?

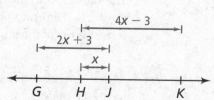

G.CO.1 Know precise definitions of angle, circle, perpendicular line, parallel line . . . based on the undefined notions of point, line, distance along a line . . .

Objective   To find and compare the measures of angles

Solve It!   Write your solution to the Solve It in the space below.

In this lesson, you will learn to describe and measure angles like the ones in the Solve It.

Essential Understanding You can use number operations to find and compare the measures of angles.

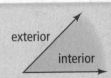

take note

Key Concept   Angle

Definition	**How to Name It**	**Diagram**
An **angle** is formed by two rays with the same endpoint.	You can name an angle by	
	• its vertex, $\angle A$	
	• a point on each ray and the vertex, $\angle BAC$ or $\angle CAB$	The sides of the angle are $\overrightarrow{AB}$ and $\overrightarrow{AC}$. The vertex is A.
The **rays** are the sides of the angle. The endpoint is the **vertex** of the angle.	• a number, $\angle 1$	

When you name angles using three points, the vertex must go in the middle.

The *interior* of an angle is the region containing all of the points between the two sides of the angle. The *exterior* of an angle is the region containing all of the points outside of the angle.

Got It?   **a.** What are two other names for ∠*KML*?

ⓒ **b. Reasoning** Would it be correct to name any of the angles ∠*M*? Explain.

Ⓐ **Practice**   Name each shaded angle in three different ways.

1.

2.

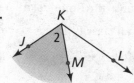

One way to measure the size of an angle is in degrees. To indicate the measure of an angle, write a lowercase *m* in front of the angle symbol. In the diagram, the measure of ∠*A* is 62. You write this as *m*∠*A* = 62. In this book, you will work only with degree measures.

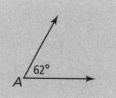

A **circle** is the set of all points in a plane that are a given distance from a given point. A circle has 360°, so 1 degree is $\frac{1}{360}$ of a circle. A protractor forms half a circle and measures angles from 0° to 180°.

take note

Postulate 7 Protractor Postulate

Consider $\overrightarrow{OB}$ and a point A on one side of $\overrightarrow{OB}$. Every ray of the form $\overrightarrow{OA}$ can be paired one-to-one with a real number from 0 to 180.

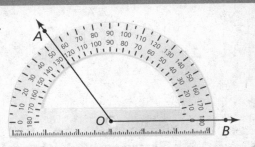

The Protractor Postulate allows you to find the measure of an angle. Consider the diagram below. The **measure** of $\angle COD$ is the absolute value of the difference of the real numbers paired with $\overrightarrow{OC}$ and $\overrightarrow{OD}$. That is, if $\overrightarrow{OC}$ corresponds with c, and $\overrightarrow{OD}$ corresponds with d, then $m\angle COD = |c - d|$.

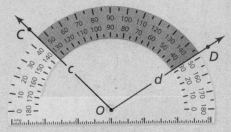

Notice that the Protractor Postulate and the calculation of an angle measure are very similar to the Ruler Postulate and the calculation of a segment length.

You can classify angles according to their measures.

take note

Key Concept Types of Angles

acute angle	right angle	obtuse angle	straight angle
$0 < x < 90$	$x = 90$	$90 < x < 180$	$x = 180$

The symbol ⌐ in the diagram above indicates a right angle.

Problem 2 Measuring and Classifying Angles

Got It? Use the figure in Problem 2. What are the measures of ∠*LKH*, ∠*HKN*, and ∠*MKH*? Classify each angle as *acute*, *right*, *obtuse*, or *straight*.

Think

How do you know whether to use the outer or inner scale on the protractor?

A Practice Use the diagram below. Find the measure of each angle. Then classify the angle as *acute*, *right*, *obtuse*, or *straight*.

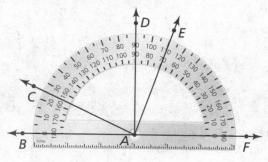

3. ∠*DAF*   4. ∠*BAC*   5. ∠*DAE*

Angles with the same measure are **congruent angles**. This means that if $m\angle A = m\angle B$, then $\angle A \cong \angle B$. You can also say that if $\angle A \cong \angle B$, then $m\angle A = m\angle B$.

You can mark angles with arcs to show that they are congruent. If there is more than one set of congruent angles, each set is marked with the same number of arcs.

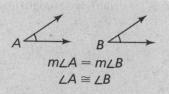

$m\angle A = m\angle B$
$\angle A \cong \angle B$

Problem 3 Using Congruent Angles

Got It? Use the figure in Problem 3. If $m\angle ABC = 49$, what is $m\angle DEF$?

Practice Use the diagram at the right. Complete each statement.

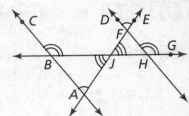

6. If $m\angle EFD = 75$, then $m\angle JAB =$ _____.

7. If $m\angle GHF = 130$, then $m\angle JBC =$ _____.

The Angle Addition Postulate is similar to the Segment Addition Postulate.

take note

Postulate 8   Angle Addition Postulate

If point B is in the interior of $\angle AOC$,
then $m\angle AOB + m\angle BOC = m\angle AOC$.

 Problem 4   Using the Angle Addition Postulate

Got It? $\angle DEF$ is a straight angle. What are $m\angle DEC$ and $m\angle CEF$?

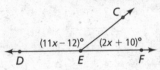

Plan

How can you use the expressions in the diagram?

 Practice   **8.** If $m\angle ABD = 79$, what are $m\angle ABC$ and $m\angle DBC$?

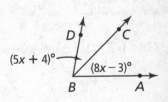

9. ∠*RQT* is a straight angle. What are *m*∠*RQS* and *m*∠*TQS*?

(6*x* + 20)°   (2*x* + 4)°
T   *Q*   *R*

Lesson Check

Do you know HOW?

Use the diagram for Exercises 10–12.

10. What are two other names for ∠1?

11. Algebra If *m*∠*ABD* = 85, what is an expression to represent *m*∠*ABC*?

12. Classify ∠*ABC*.

© **13. Vocabulary** How many sides can two congruent angles share? Explain.

© **14. Error Analysis** Your classmate concludes from the diagram at the right that $\angle JKL \cong \angle LKM$. Is your classmate correct? Explain.

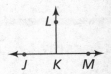

More Practice and Problem-Solving Exercises

Ⓑ **Apply**

Use a protractor. Measure and classify each angle.

15.

16.

17.

18.

© **19. Think About a Plan** A pair of earrings has dark-colored wedges that are all the same size. One earring has a 25° light-colored wedge. The other has a 14° light-colored wedge. Find the angle measure of a dark-colored wedge.
 • How do the angle measures of the earrings relate?
 • How can you use algebra to solve the problem?

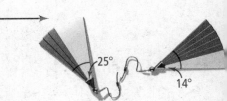

Algebra Use the diagram at the right for Exercises 20 and 21. Solve for x. Find the angle measures to check your work.

20. $m\angle AOB = 4x - 2$, $m\angle BOC = 5x + 10$, $m\angle COD = 2x + 14$

21. $m\angle AOB = 28$, $m\angle BOC = 3x - 2$, $m\angle AOD = 6x$

22. If $m\angle MQV = 90$, which expression can you use to find $m\angle VQP$?

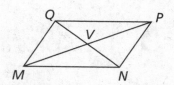

A $m\angle MQP - 90$

C $m\angle MQP + 90$

B $90 - m\angle MQV$

D $90 + m\angle VQP$

23. Literature According to legend, King Arthur and his knights sat around the Round Table to discuss matters of the kingdom. The photo shows a round table on display at Winchester Castle, in England. From the center of the table, each section has the same degree measure. If King Arthur occupied two of these sections, what is the total degree measure of his section?

Challenge

Time Find the angle measure of the hands of a clock at each time.

24. 6:00

25. 7:00

26. 11:00

27. 4:40

28. 5:20

29. 2:15

© 30. Open-Ended Sketch a right angle with vertex V. Name it $\angle 1$. Then sketch a 135° angle that shares a side with $\angle 1$. Name it $\angle PVB$. Is there more than one way to sketch $\angle PVB$? If so, sketch all the different possibilities. (*Hint:* Two angles are the same if you can rotate or flip one to match the other.)

© 31. Technology Your classmate constructs an angle. Then he constructs a ray from the vertex of the angle to a point in the interior of the angle. He measures all the angles formed. Then he moves the interior ray as shown below. What postulate do the two pictures support?

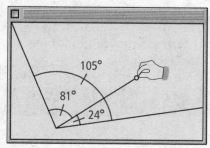

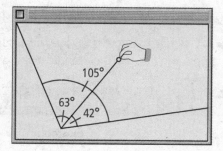

7-5 Exploring Angle Pairs

G.CO.1 Know precise definitions of angle . . .

Objective   To identify special angle pairs and use their relationships to find angle measures

Solve It!   Write your solution to the Solve It in the space below.

In this lesson, you will learn how to describe different kinds of angle pairs.

Essential Understanding   Special angle pairs can help you identify geometric relationships. You can use these angle pairs to find angle measures.

take note

Key Concept   Types of Angle Pairs

Definition	Example
Adjacent angles are two coplanar angles with a common side, a common vertex, and no common interior points.	∠1 and ∠2, ∠3 and ∠4
Vertical angles are two angles whose sides are opposite rays.	∠1 and ∠2, ∠3 and ∠4

Key Concept   Types of Angle Pairs

Definition	Example	

Complementary angles are two angles whose measures have a sum of 90. Each angle is called the *complement* of the other.

∠1 and ∠2, ∠A and ∠B

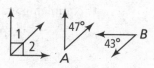

Supplementary angles are two angles whose measures have a sum of 180. Each angle is called the *supplement* of the other.

∠3 and ∠4, ∠B and ∠C

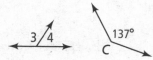

Problem 1   Identifying Angle Pairs

Got It?   Use the diagram at the right. Is the statement true? Explain.

a. ∠AFE and ∠CFD are vertical angles.

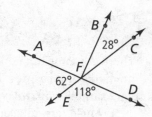

b. ∠BFC and ∠DFE are supplementary.

c. ∠BFD and ∠AFB are adjacent angles.

> **Think**
> What conditions must be met for two angles to be adjacent angles?

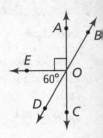

A **Practice** Name an angle or angles in the diagram described
by each of the following. Use the figure at the right.

1. complementary to ∠EOD

2. a pair of vertical angles

Concept Summary Finding Information From a Diagram

There are some relationships you can assume to be true from a diagram that has
no marks or measures. There are other relationships you cannot assume directly.
For example, you *can* conclude the following from an unmarked diagram.
- Angles are adjacent.
- Angles are adjacent and supplementary.
- Angles are vertical angles.

You *cannot* conclude the following from an unmarked diagram.
- Angles or segments are congruent.
- An angle is a right angle.
- Angles are complementary.

Problem 2 Making Conclusions From a Diagram

Got It? Can you make each conclusion from the information in the diagram?
Explain.

a. $\overline{TW} \cong \overline{WV}$

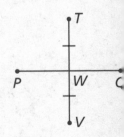

b. $\overline{PW} \cong \overline{WQ}$

c. $\angle TWQ$ is a right angle.

d. $\overline{TV}$ bisects $\overline{PQ}$.

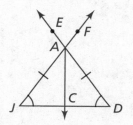

A **Practice** For Exercises 3 and 4, can you make each conclusion from the information in the diagram? Explain.

3. $\angle J \cong \angle D$

4. C is the midpoint of $\overline{JD}$.

A **linear pair** is a pair of adjacent angles whose noncommon sides are opposite rays. The angles of a linear pair form a straight angle.

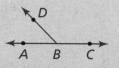

take note

Postulate 9   Linear Pair Postulate

If two angles form a linear pair, then they are supplementary.

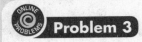
Got It? a. **Reasoning** How can you check your results in Problem 3?

b. ∠ADB and ∠BDC are a linear pair. m∠ADB = 3x + 14 and
m∠BDC = 5x − 2. What are m∠ADB and m∠BDC?

 Practice 5. Name two pairs of angles that form a linear pair in the
diagram at the right.

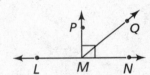

6. ∠EFG and ∠GFH are a linear pair, m∠EFG = 2n + 21, and
m∠GFH = 4n + 15. What are m∠EFG and m∠GFH?

An **angle bisector** is a ray that divides an angle into two congruent angles. Its endpoint is at the angle vertex. Within the ray, a segment with the same endpoint is also an angle bisector. The ray or segment bisects the angle. In the diagram, $\overrightarrow{AY}$ is the angle bisector of $\angle XAZ$, so $\angle XAY \cong \angle YAZ$.

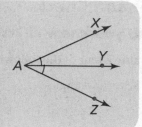

Problem 4 **Using an Angle Bisector to Find Angle Measures**

Got It? $\overrightarrow{KM}$ bisects $\angle JKL$. If $m\angle JKL = 72$, what is $m\angle JKM$?

Plan

How can a diagram help you visualize the given information?

A **Practice**   **7. Algebra** In the diagram, $\overrightarrow{GH}$ bisects $\angle FGI$.

  a. Solve for x and find $m\angle FGH$.

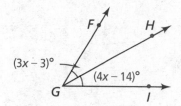

  b. Find $m\angle HGI$.

  c. Find $m\angle FGI$.

Lesson Check

Do you know HOW?

Name a pair of the following types of angle pairs.

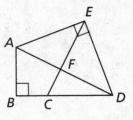

8. vertical angles

9. complementary angles

10. linear pair

11. $\overrightarrow{PB}$ bisects $\angle RPT$ so that $m\angle RPB = x + 2$ and $m\angle TPB = 2x - 6$. What is $m\angle RPT$?

Do you UNDERSTAND?

© **12. Vocabulary** How does the term *linear pair* describe how the angle pair looks?

13. Error Analysis Your friend calculated the value of x below. What is her error?

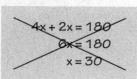

~~$4x + 2x = 180$~~
~~$6x = 180$~~
~~$x = 30$~~

$2x°$

$4x°$

More Practice and Problem-Solving Exercises

3 Apply

Algebra $\overrightarrow{BD}$ bisects $\angle ABC$. Solve for x and find $m\angle ABC$.

14. $m\angle ABD = 5x$, $m\angle DBC = 3x + 10$

15. $m\angle ABC = 4x - 12$, $m\angle ABD = 24$

16. $m\angle ABD = 4x - 16$, $m\angle CBD = 2x + 6$

17. $m\angle ABD = 3x + 20$, $m\angle CBD = 6x - 16$

Algebra In exercises 18 and 19, find the measure of each angle in the angle pair described.

18. Think About a Plan The measure of one angle is twice the measure of its supplement.
- How many angles are there? What is their relationship?
- How can you use algebra, such as using the variable x, to help you?

19. The measure of one angle is 20 less than the measure of its complement.

In the diagram at the right, $m\angle ACB = 65$. Find each of the following.

20. $m\angle ACD$ **21.** $m\angle BCD$

22. $m\angle ECD$ **23.** $m\angle ACE$

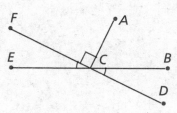

24. Algebra $\angle RQS$ and $\angle TQS$ are a linear pair where $m\angle RQS = 2x + 4$ and $m\angle TQS = 6x + 20$.
- **a.** Solve for x.
- **b.** Find $m\angle RQS$ and $m\angle TQS$.
- **c.** Show how you can check your answer.

25. Writing In the diagram at the right, are ∠1 and ∠2 adjacent? Justify your reasoning.

26. Reasoning When $\overrightarrow{BX}$ bisects ∠ABC, ∠ABX ≅ ∠CBX. One student claims there is always a related equation $m\angle ABX = \frac{1}{2}m\angle ABC$. Another student claims the related equation is $2m\angle ABX = m\angle ABC$. Who is correct? Explain.

STEM **27. Optics** A beam of light and a mirror can be used to study the behavior of light. Light that strikes the mirror is reflected so that the angle of reflection and the angle of incidence are congruent. In the diagram, ∠ABC has a measure of 41.

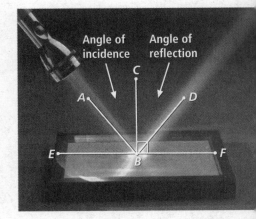

Angle of incidence   Angle of reflection

   a. Name the angle of reflection and find its measure.
   b. Find $m\angle ABD$.
   c. Find $m\angle ABE$ and $m\angle DBF$.

28. Reasoning Describe all situations where vertical angles are also supplementary.

Challenge

Name all of the angle(s) in the diagram described by the following.

29. supplementary to ∠JQM

30. adjacent and congruent to ∠KMQ

31. a linear pair with ∠LMQ

32. complementary to ∠NMR

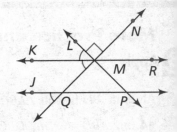

33. Coordinate Geometry The x- and y-axes of the coordinate plane form four right angles. The interior of each of the right angles is a quadrant of the coordinate plane. What is the equation for the line that contains the angle bisector of Quadrants I and III?

34. $\overrightarrow{XC}$ bisects ∠AXB, $\overrightarrow{XD}$ bisects ∠AXC, $\overrightarrow{XE}$ bisects ∠AXD, $\overrightarrow{XF}$ bisects ∠EXD, $\overrightarrow{XG}$ bisects ∠EXF, and $\overrightarrow{XH}$ bisects ∠DXB. If $m\angle DXC = 16$, find $m\angle GXH$.

 **7-6**

Midpoint and Distance in the Coordinate Plane

Prepares for **G.GPE.7** Use coordinates to compute perimeters . . . and areas . . . Also prepares for **G.CO.10**, prepares for **G.GPE.4**

Objectives To find the midpoint of a segment
To find the distance between two points in the coordinate plane

Solve It! Write your solution to the Solve It in the space below.

In this lesson, you will learn how to find midpoints and distance on a grid like the one in the Solve It.

Essential Understanding You can use formulas to find the midpoint and length of any segment in the coordinate plane.

take note

Key Concept   Midpoint Formulas

Description	Formula	Diagram
On a Number Line The coordinate of the midpoint is the *average* or *mean* of the coordinates of the endpoints.	The coordinate of the midpoint M of $\overline{AB}$ is $\frac{a+b}{2}$.	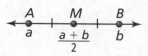
In the Coordinate Plane The coordinates of the midpoint are the average of the x-coordinates and the average of the y-coordinates of the endpoints.	Given $\overline{AB}$ where $A(x_1, y_1)$ and $B(x_2, y_2)$, the coordinates of the midpoint of $\overline{AB}$ are $M\left(\frac{x_1 + x_2}{2}, \frac{y_1 + y_2}{2}\right)$.	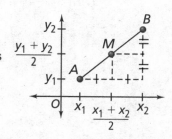

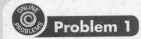

Problem 1 Finding the Midpoint

Plan

How do you decide which midpoint formula to use?

Got It? **a.** $\overline{JK}$ has endpoints at -12 and 4 on a number line. What is the coordinate of its midpoint?

b. What is the midpoint of $\overline{RS}$ with endpoints $R(5, -10)$ and $S(3, 6)$?

Ⓐ Practice Find the coordinates of the midpoint of $\overline{HX}$.

1. $H(7, 10), X(5, -8)$

2. $H\left(5\frac{1}{2}, -4\frac{3}{4}\right), X\left(2\frac{1}{4}, -1\frac{1}{4}\right)$

When you know the midpoint and an endpoint of a segment, you can use the Midpoint Formula to find the other endpoint.

Problem 2 **Finding an Endpoint**

Got It? The midpoint of $\overline{AB}$ has coordinates $(4, -9)$. Endpoint A has coordinates $(-3, -5)$. What are the coordinates of B?

Ⓐ Practice The coordinates of point T are given. The midpoint of $\overline{ST}$ is $(5, -8)$. Find the coordinates of point S.

3. $T(1, 12)$

4. $T(4.5, -2.5)$

In Lesson 7-3, you learned how to find the distance between two points on a number line. To find the distance between two points in a coordinate plane, you can use the Distance Formula.

take note

Key Concept **Distance Formula**

The distance between two points $A(x_1, y_1)$ and $B(x_2, y_2)$ is

$$d = \sqrt{(x_2 - x_1)^2 + (y_2 - y_1)^2}$$

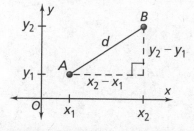

The Distance Formula is based on the *Pythagorean Theorem*. When you use the Distance Formula, you are really finding the length of a side of a right triangle.

$$a^2 + b^2 = c^2$$

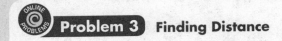

Got It?   **a.** $\overline{SR}$ has endpoints $S(-2, 14)$ and $R(3, -1)$. What is SR to the nearest tenth?

© **b. Reasoning** In Problem 3, suppose you let $V(4, -3)$ be (x_1, y_1) and $U(-7, 5)$ be (x_2, y_2). Do you get the same result? Why?

Ⓐ **Practice**   Find the distance between each pair of points. If necessary, round to the nearest tenth.

5. $R(0, 5)$, $S(12, 3)$

6. $X(-3, -4)$, $Y(5, 5)$

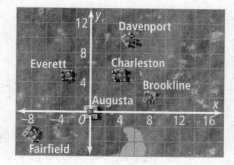

Problem 4 Finding Distance

Got It? Use the figure in Problem 4. How far do you travel from Platform *D* to Platform *E*?

> **Think**
>
> How can a right triangle involving points *D* and *E* help you?

Ⓐ Practice **Maps** For Exercises 7 and 8, use the map at the right. Find the distance between the cities to the nearest tenth.

7. Brookline and Charleston

8. Everett and Fairfield

Lesson Check

Do you know HOW?

9. $\overline{RS}$ has endpoints $R(2, 4)$ and $S(-1, 7)$. What are the coordinates of its midpoint *M*?

10. The midpoint of $\overline{BC}$ is $(5, -2)$. One endpoint is $B(3, 4)$. What are the coordinates of endpoint C?

11. What is the distance between points $K(-9, 8)$ and $L(-6, 0)$?

Do you UNDERSTAND?

12. Reasoning How does the Distance Formula ensure that the distance between two different points is positive?

13. Error Analysis Your friend calculates the distance between points $Q(1, 5)$ and $R(3, 8)$. What is his error?

$$d = \sqrt{(1-8)^2 + (5-3)^2}$$
$$= \sqrt{(-7)^2 + 2^2}$$
$$= \sqrt{49+4}$$
$$= \sqrt{53} \approx 7.3$$

More Practice and Problem-Solving Exercises

Apply

Find (a) PQ to the nearest tenth and (b) the coordinates of the midpoint of $\overline{PQ}$.

14. $P(3, 2), Q(6, 6)$ **15.** $P(0, -2), Q(3, 3)$ **16.** $P(-4, -2), Q(1, 3)$

17. $P(-5, 2), Q(0, 4)$ **18.** $P(-3, -1), Q(5, -7)$ **19.** $P(-5, -3), Q(-3, -5)$

20. $P(-4, -5), Q(-1, 1)$ **21.** $P(2, 3), Q(4, -2)$ **22.** $P(4, 2), Q(3, 0)$

23. Think About a Plan An airplane at $T(80, 20)$ needs to fly to both $U(20, 60)$ and $V(110, 85)$. What is the shortest possible distance for the trip? Explain.
   - What type of information do you need to find the shortest distance?
   - How can you use a diagram to help you?

24. Reasoning The midpoint of $\overline{TS}$ is the origin. Point T is located in Quadrant II. What Quadrant contains point S? Explain.

25. Do you use the Midpoint Formula or the Distance Formula to find the following?
   a. Given points K and P, find the distance from K to the midpoint of $\overline{KP}$.
   b. Given point K and the midpoint of $\overline{KP}$, find KP.

For each graph, find (a) AB to the nearest tenth and (b) the coordinates of the midpoint of $\overline{AB}$.

26.

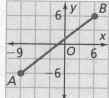

27.

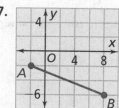

28.

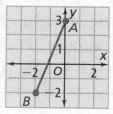

29. Coordinate Geometry Graph the points $A(2, 1)$, $B(6, -1)$, $C(8, 7)$, and $D(4, 9)$. Draw parallelogram $ABCD$, and diagonals $\overline{AC}$ and $\overline{BD}$.
   a. Find the midpoints of $\overline{AC}$ and $\overline{BD}$.
   b. What appears to be true about the diagonals of a parallelogram?

Travel The units of the subway map at the right are in miles. Suppose the routes between stations are straight. Find the distance you would travel between each pair of stations to the nearest tenth of a mile.

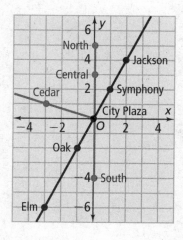

30. Oak Station and Jackson Station

31. Central Station and South Station

32. Elm Station and Symphony Station

33. Cedar Station and City Plaza Station

34. Maple Station is located 6 mi west and 2 mi north of City Plaza. What is the distance between Cedar Station and Maple Station?

35. Open-Ended Point $H(2, 2)$ is the midpoint of many segments.
   a. Find the coordinates of the endpoints of four noncollinear segments that have point H as their midpoint.
   b. You know that a segment with midpoint H has length 8. How many possible noncollinear segments match this description? Explain.

C Challenge

36. Points $P(-4, 6)$, $Q(2, 4)$, and R are collinear. One of the points is the midpoint of the segment formed by the other two points.
   a. What are the possible coordinates of R?
   b. Reasoning $RQ = \sqrt{160}$. Does this information affect your answer to part (a)? Explain.

Geometry in 3 Dimensions You can use three coordinates (x, y, z) to locate points in three dimensions.

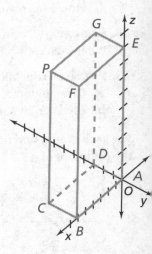

37. Point P has coordinates $(6, -3, 9)$ as shown at the right. Give the coordinates of points A, B, C, D, E, F, and G.

Distance in 3 Dimensions In a three-dimensional coordinate system, you can find the distance between two points (x_1, y_1, z_1) and (x_2, y_2, z_2) with this extension of the Distance Formula.

$$d = \sqrt{(x_2 - x_1)^2 + (y_2 - y_1)^2 + (z_2 - z_1)^2}$$

Find the distance between each pair of points to the nearest tenth.

38. $P(2, 3, 4)$, $Q(-2, 4, 9)$

39. $T(0, 12, 15)$, $V(-8, 20, 12)$

Quadrilaterals and Other Polygons

Prepares for **G.CO.3** Given a . . . polygon, describe the rotations and reflections that carry it onto itself. Also prepares for **G.GPE.7**

A **polygon** is a closed plane figure formed by three or more segments. A **quadrilateral** is a polygon with four sides. The table below shows several different types of quadrilaterals. Matching arrowheads on segments indicate parallel sides.

Definition	Example
A **parallelogram** is a quadrilateral with both pairs of opposite sides parallel.	
A **trapezoid** is a quadrilateral with exactly one pair of parallel sides, called the *bases*. The nonparallel sides are called the *legs* of the trapezoid.	
An **isosceles trapezoid** is a trapezoid with legs that are congruent.	
A **kite** is a quadrilateral with two pairs of consecutive sides congruent and no opposite sides congruent.	
A **rhombus** is a parallelogram with four congruent sides.	
A **rectangle** is a parallelogram with four right angles.	
A **square** is a parallelogram with four congruent sides and four right angles.	

Example 1

Determine the most precise name for each quadrilateral.

A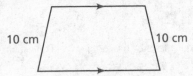

10 cm   10 cm

This quadrilateral is an isosceles trapezoid because it has one pair of parallel sides and one pair of opposite sides congruent.

B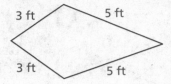

3 ft   5 ft

3 ft   5 ft

This quadrilateral is a kite because it has two pairs of consecutive sides congruent, and opposite sides are not congruent.

A polygon can be classified by its number of sides, as shown in the table below. A **regular polygon** is a polygon whose sides are all congruent and whose angles are all congruent.

Number of Sides	Name of Polygon	Number of Sides	Name of Polygon
3	triangle	7	heptagon
4	quadrilateral	8	octagon
5	pentagon	9	nonagon
6	hexagon	10	decagon

Example 2

Classify each polygon by its number of sides and by its angles.

A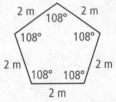

2 m   108°   2 m
108°   108°
2 m   2 m
108°   108°
2 m

B

A This polygon has 5 sides, so it is a pentagon. Its sides are congruent and its angles are congruent, so it is a regular pentagon.

B This polygon has 8 sides, so it is an octagon. Neither its sides nor its angles are congruent, so it is not a regular octagon.

You can also classify a polygon as concave or convex, using the diagonals of the polygon. A **diagonal** is a segment that connects two nonconsecutive vertices.

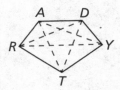

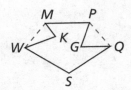

A **convex polygon** has no diagonal with points outside the polygon.

A **concave polygon** has at least one diagonal with points outside the polygon.

In this textbook, a polygon is convex unless otherwise stated.

Example 3

Tell whether the hexagon is *convex* or *concave*.

No diagonal of the hexagon contains points outside the hexagon. The hexagon is convex.

Exercises

The diagram shows the hierarchy of quadrilaterals. The arrows indicate a more specific classification. Fill in the blanks to complete the diagram.

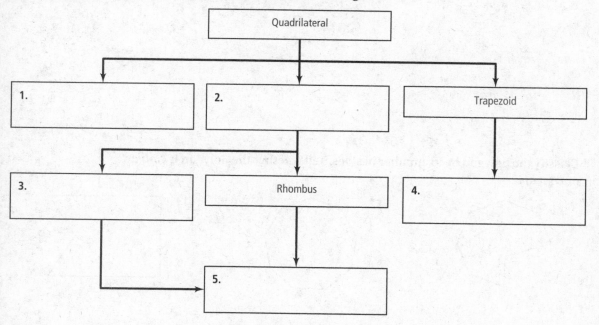

Determine the most precise name for each quadrilateral.

6.

7.

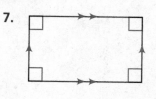

© **8. Reasoning** Use the diagram on the previous page to determine whether a square is *sometimes*, *always*, or *never* a rhombus.

Classify each polygon by its number of sides and its angles.

9.

10.

Classify the polygon by its number of sides. Tell whether the polygon is *convex* or *concave*.

11.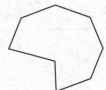

12.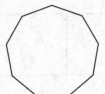

13.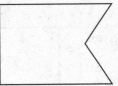

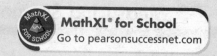

7-1 Nets and Drawings for Visualizing Geometry

Quick Review

A **net** is a two-dimensional pattern that you can fold to form a three-dimensional figure. A net shows all surfaces of a figure in one view.

An **isometric drawing** shows a corner view of a three-dimensional object. It allows you to see the top, front, and side of the object in one view.

An **orthographic drawing** shows three separate views of a three-dimensional object: a top view, a front view, and a right-side view.

Example

Draw a net for the solid at the right.

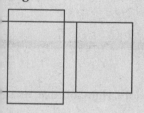

Exercises

1. The net below is for a number cube. What are the three sums of the numbers on opposite surfaces of the cube?

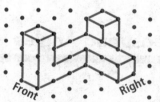

2. Make an orthographic drawing for the isometric drawing below. Assume there are no hidden cubes.

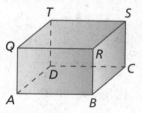

7-2 Points, Lines, and Planes

Quick Review

A **point** indicates a location and has no size.

A **line** is represented by a straight path that extends in two opposite directions without end and has no thickness.

A **plane** is represented by a flat surface that extends without end and has no thickness.

Points that lie on the same line are **collinear points**.

Points and lines in the same plane are **coplanar**.

Segments and **rays** are parts of lines.

Example

Name all the segments and rays in the figure.

Segments: $\overline{AB}$, $\overline{AC}$, $\overline{BC}$, and $\overline{BD}$

Rays: $\overrightarrow{BA}$, $\overrightarrow{CA}$ or $\overrightarrow{CB}$, $\overrightarrow{AC}$
or $\overrightarrow{AB}$, $\overrightarrow{BC}$, and $\overrightarrow{BD}$

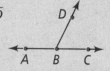

Exercises

Use the figure below for Exercises 3–5.

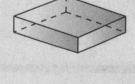

3. Name two intersecting lines.

4. Name the intersection of planes *QRBA* and *TSRQ*.

5. Name three noncollinear points.

Determine whether the statement is *true* or *false*. Explain your reasoning.

6. Two points are always collinear.

7. $\overrightarrow{LM}$ and $\overrightarrow{ML}$ are the same ray.

7-3 Measuring Segments

Quick Review

The **distance** between two points is the length of the segment connecting those points. Segments with the same length are **congruent segments**. A **midpoint** of a segment divides the segment into two congruent segments.

Example

Are $\overline{AB}$ and $\overline{CD}$ congruent?

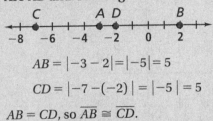

$$AB = |-3 - 2| = |-5| = 5$$

$$CD = |-7 - (-2)| = |-5| = 5$$

$AB = CD$, so $\overline{AB} \cong \overline{CD}$.

Exercises

For Exercises 8 and 9, use the number line below

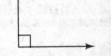

8. Find two possible coordinates of Q such that $PQ = 5$.

9. Find the coordinate of the midpoint of $\overline{PH}$.

10. Find the value of m.

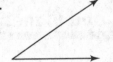

11. If $XZ = 50$, what are XY and YZ?

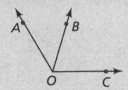

7-4 Measuring Angles

Quick Review

Two rays with the same endpoint form an **angle**. The endpoint is the **vertex** of the angle. You can classify angles as acute, right, obtuse, or straight. Angles with the same measure are **congruent angles**.

Example

If $m\angle AOB = 47$ and $m\angle BOC = 73$, find $m\angle AOC$.

$$m\angle AOC = m\angle AOB + m\angle BOC = 47 + 73 = 120$$

Exercises

Classify each angle as acute, right, obtuse, or straight.

12.

13.

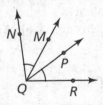

Use the diagram below for Exercises 14 and 15.

14. If $m\angle MQR = 61$ and $m\angle MQP = 25$, find $m\angle PQR$.

15. If $m\angle NQM = 2x + 8$ and $m\angle PQR = x + 22$, find the value of x.

7-5 Exploring Angle Pairs

Quick Review

Some pairs of angles have special names.

Adjacent angles: coplanar angles with a common side, a common vertex, and no common interior points

Vertical angles: sides are opposite rays

Complementary angles: measures have a sum of 90

Supplementary angles: measures have a sum of 180

Linear pair: adjacent angles with noncommon sides as opposite rays

Angles of a linear pair are supplementary.

Example

Are ∠ACE and ∠BCD vertical angles? Explain.

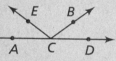

No. They have only one set of sides with opposite rays.

Exercises

Name a pair of each of the following.

16. complementary angles

17. supplementary angles

18. vertical angles

19. linear pair

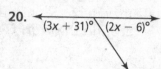

Find the value of x.

20.

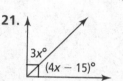

21.

$3x°$
$(4x − 15)°$

7-6 Midpoint and Distance in the Coordinate Plane

Quick Review

You can find the coordinates of the midpoint M of $\overline{AB}$ with endpoints $A(x_1, y_1)$ and $B(x_2, y_2)$ using the **Midpoint Formula**.

$$M\left(\frac{x_1 + x_2}{2}, \frac{y_1 + y_2}{2}\right)$$

You can find the distance d between two points $A(x_1, y_1)$ and $B(x_2, y_2)$ using the **Distance Formula**.

$$d = \sqrt{(x_2 − x_1)^2 + (y_2 − y_1)^2}$$

Example

$\overline{GH}$ has endpoints $G(−11, 6)$ and $H(3, 4)$. What are the coordinates of its midpoint M?

x-coordinate $= \dfrac{−11 + 3}{2} = −4$

y-coordinate $= \dfrac{6 + 4}{2} = 5$

The coordinates of the midpoint of $\overline{GH}$ are $M(−4, 5)$.

Exercises

Find the distance between the points to the nearest tenth.

22. $A(−1, 5), B(0, 4)$

23. $C(−1, −1), D(6, 2)$

24. $E(−7, 0), F(5, 8)$

$\overline{AB}$ has endpoints $A(−3, 2)$ and $B(3, −2)$.

25. Find the coordinates of the midpoint of $\overline{AB}$.

26. Find AB to the nearest tenth.

M is the midpoint of $\overline{JK}$. Find the coordinates of K.

27. $J(−8, 4), M(−1, 1)$

28. $J(9, −5), M(5, −2)$

29. $J(0, 11), M(−3, 2)$

Pull It All Together

Solving a Riddle

While browsing in an antique store, Cameron found a sheet of paper that came from an old book of riddles. The page is shown below.

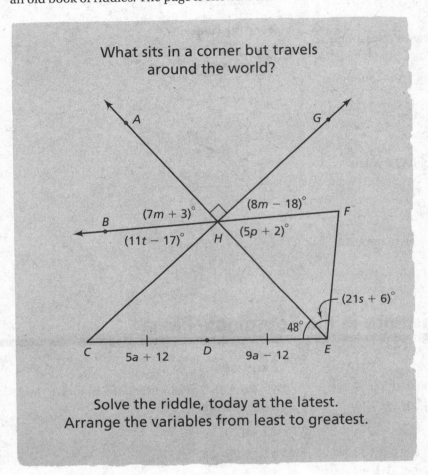

What sits in a corner but travels around the world?

Solve the riddle, today at the latest.
Arrange the variables from least to greatest.

Task Description

Find the answer to the riddle.

- What segment and angle relationships are shown in the figure? How can you use these to write equations?

- Which variables can you solve for immediately, and which ones depend upon knowing the values of other variables?

ostulates and Theorems

stulates

ulate 1
gh any two points there is exactly one line.

ulate 2
distinct lines intersect, then they intersect ctly one point.

ulate 3
distinct planes intersect, then they ect in exactly one line.

ulate 4
gh any three noncollinear points there is y on plane.

ulate 5
Postulate

point on a line can be paired with a real er. This makes a one-to-one correspondence en the points on the line and the real ers.

ulate 6
nt Addition Postulate

e points A, B, and C are collinear and B is en A and C, then $AB + BC = AC$.

ulate 7
ctor Postulate

er $\overrightarrow{OB}$ and a point A on one side of $\overrightarrow{OB}$. ay of the form $\overrightarrow{OA}$ can be paired one to th a real number from 0 to 180.

late 8
Addition Postulate

t B is in the interior of $\angle AOC$, then $B + m\angle BOC = m\angle AOC$.

late 9
Pair Postulate

angles form a linear pair, then they are mentary.

late 10
ddition Postulate

a of a region is the sum of the area of its rlapping parts.

late 11
ide Interior Angles Postulate

sversal intersects two parallel lines, then de interior angles are supplementary.

Postulate 12
Parallel Postulate
Through a point not on a line, there is one and only one line parallel to the given line.

Postulate 13
Perpendicular Postulate
Through a point not on a line, there is one and only one line perpendicular to the given line.

Postulate 14
Side-Side-Side (SSS) Postulate
If three sides of one triangle are congruent to the three sides of another triangle, then the two triangles are congruent.

Postulate 15
Side-Angle-Side (SAS) Postulate
If two sides and the included angle of one triangle are congruent to two sides and the included angle of another triangle, then the two triangles are congruent.

Postulate 16
Angle-Side-Angle (ASA) Postulate
If two angles and the included side of one triangle are congruent to two angles and the included side of another triangle, then the two triangles are congruent.

Theorems

Theorem 1
Vertical Angles Theorem
Vertical angles are congruent.

Theorem 2
Congruent Supplements Theorem
If two angles are supplements of the same angle (or of two congruent angles), then the two angles are congruent.

Theorem 3
Congruent Complements Theorem
If two angles are complements of the same angle (or of two congruent angles), then the two angles are congruent.

Theorem 4
All right angles are congruent.

Theorem 5
If two angles are congruent and supplementary, then each is a right angle.

Theorem 6
Alternate Interior Angles Theorem
If a transversal intersects two parallel lines, the alternate interior angles are congruent.

Theorem 7
Corresponding Angles Theorem
If a transversal intersects two parallel lines, then corresponding angles are congruent.

Theorem 8
Alternate Exterior Angles Theorem
If a transversal intersects two parallel lines, then alternate exterior angles are congruent.

Theorem 9
Converse of the Corresponding Angles Theorem
If two lines and a transversal form corresponding angles that are congruent, then the two lines are parallel.

Theorem 10
Converse of the Alternate Interior Angles Theorem
If two lines and a transversal form alternate interior angles that are congruent, then the two lines are parallel.

Theorem 11
Converse of the Same-Side Interior Angles Postulate
If two lines and a transversal form same-side interior angles that are congruent, then the two lines are parallel.

Theorem 12
Converse of the Alternate Exterior Angles Theorem
If two lines and a transversal form alternate exterior angles that are congruent, then the two lines are parallel.

Theorem 13
If two lines are parallel to the same line, then they are parallel to each other.

Theorem 14
In a plane, if two lines are perpendicular to the same line, then they are parallel to each other.

Theorem 15
Perpendicular Transversal Theorem
In a plane, if a line is perpendicular to one of two parallel lines, then it is perpendicular to the other.

Theorem 16
Triangle Angle-Sum Theorem
The sum of the measures of the angles of a triangle is 180.

Theorem 17
Triangle Exterior Angle Theorem
The measure of each exterior angle of a tria equals the sum of the measure of its two re interior angles.

Corollary
The measure of an exterior angle of a tria is greater than the measure of each of its remote interior angles.

Theorem 18
Third Angles Theorem
If two angles of one triangle are congruent two angles of another triangle, than the thi angles are congruent.

Theorem 19
Angle-Angle-Side (AAS) Theorem
If two angles and a nonincluded side of one triangle are congruent to two angles and a nonincluded side of another triangle, then two triangles are congruent.

Theorem 20
Isosceles Triangle Theorem
If two sides of a triangle are congruent, the angles opposite those sides are congruent.

Corollary
If a triangle is equilateral, then the triang equiangular.

Theorem 21
Converse of the Isosceles Triangle Theorem
If two angles of a triangle are congruent, t the sides opposite the angles are congruen

Corollary
If a triangle is equiangular, then it is equilateral.

Theorem 22
If a line bisects the vertex angle of an isosc triangle, then the line is also the perpendic bisector of the base.

Theorem 23
Hypotenuse-Leg (HL) Theorem
If the hypotenuse and a leg of one right tr are congruent to the hypotenuse and a leg another right triangle, then the triangles a congruent.

Theorem 24
Triangle Midsegment Theorem
If a line segment joins the midpoints of tw of a triangle, then the segment is parallel third side and is half as long.

orem 25

ndicular Bisector Theorem
oint is on the perpendicular bisector of a
egment, then it is equidistant from the
oints of the segment.

orem 26

erse of the Perpendicular Bisector Theorem
oint is equidistant from the endpoints of a
egment, then it is on the perpendicular
or of the segment.

rem 27

Bisector Theorem
oint is on the bisector of an angle, then the
is equidistant from the sides of the angle.

rem 28

rse of the Angle Bisector Theorem
oint in the interior of an angle is
stant from the sides of the angle, then the
is on the angle bisector

rem 29

rrency of Perpendicular Bisectors Theorem
erpendicular bisectors of the sides of a
le are concurrent at a point equidistant
he vertices.

rem 30

rrency of Angle Bisectors Theorem
sectors of the angles of a triangle are
rent at a point equidistant from the sides
triangle.

rem 31

rrency of Medians Theorem
edians of a triangle are concurrent at a
hat is two-thirds the distance from each
to the midpoint of the opposite side.

rem 32

rrency of Altitudes Theorem
es that contain the altitudes of a triangle
ncurrent.

rem 33

sides of a triangle are not congruent, then
ger angle lies opposite the longer side.

em 34

angles of a triangle are not congruent,
e longer side lies opposite the larger angle.

em 35

e Inequality Theorem
n of the lengths of any two sides of a
e is greater than the length of the third

Theorem 36

The Hinge Theorem (SAS Inequality Theorem)
If two sides of one triangle are congruent to two
sides of another triangle and the included angles
are not congruent, then the longer third side is
opposite the larger included angle.

Theorem 37

Converse of the Hinge Theorem (SSS Inequality)
If two sides of one triangle are congruent to two
sides of another triangle and the third sides are
not congruent, then the larger included angle is
opposite the longer third side.

Theorem 38

Polygon Angle-Sum Theorem
The sum of the measures of the angles of an
n-gon is $(n - 2)180$.

> **Corollary**
> The measure of each angle of a regular
> n-gon is $\frac{(n - 2)180}{n}$.

Theorem 39

The sum of the measures of the exterior angles
of a polygon, one at each vertex, is 360.

Theorem 40

If a quadrilateral is a parallelogram, then its
opposite sides are congruent.

Theorem 41

If a quadrilateral is a parallelogram, then its
consecutive angles are supplementary.

Theorem 42

If a quadrilateral is a parallelogram, then its
opposite angles are congruent.

Theorem 43

If a quadrilateral is a parallelogram, then its
diagonals bisect each other.

Theorem 44

If three (or more) parallel lines cut off congruent
segments on one transversal, then they cut off
congruent segments on every transversal.

Theorem 45

If both pairs of opposite sides of a quadrilateral
are congruent, then the quadrilateral is a
parallelogram.

Theorem 46

If an angle of a quadrilateral is supplementary to
both of its consecutive angles, then the
quadrilateral is a parallelogram.

Theorem 47
If both pairs of opposite angles of a quadrilateral are congruent, then the quadrilateral is a parallelogram.

Theorem 48
If the diagonals of a quadrilateral bisect each other, then the quadrilateral is a parallelogram.

Theorem 49
If one pair of opposite sides of a quadrilateral is both congruent and parallel, then the quadrilateral is a parallelogram.

Theorem 50
If a parallelogram is a rhombus, then its diagonals are perpendicular.

Theorem 51
If a parallelogram is a rhombus, then each diagonal bisects a pair of opposite angles.

Theorem 52
If a parallelogram is a rectangle, then its diagonals are congruent.

Theorem 53
If the diagonals of a parallelogram are perpendicular, then the parallelogram is a rhombus.

Theorem 54
If one diagonal of a parallelogram bisects a of opposite angles, then the parallelogram i rhombus.

Theorem 55
If the diagonals of a parallelogram are congruent, then the parallelogram is a recta

Theorem 56
If a quadrilateral is an isosceles trapezoid, th each pair of base angles is congruent.

Theorem 57
If a quadrilateral is an isosceles trapezoid, th its diagonals are congruent.

Theorem 58
Trapezoid Midsegment Theorem
If a quadrilateral is a trapezoid, then

(1) the midsegment is parallel to the bas and

(2) the length of the midsegment is half sum of the lengths of the bases.

Theorem 59
If a quadrilateral is a kite, then its diagonal perpendicular.

lute value function (p. 219)   A function with
aped graph that opens up or down. The
t function for the family of absolute value
ions is $y = |x|$.

Función de valor absoluto (p. 219)   Función cuya
gráfica forma una V que se abre hacia arriba o
hacia abajo. La función madre de la familia de
funciones de valor absoluto es $y = |x|$.

Example

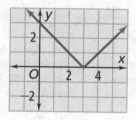

acy (p. 49)   Accuracy is the degree of how
a measurement is to the true value of the
urement.

Exactitud (p. 49)   La exactitud es el grado de lo
cerca que una medición está del valor verdadero
de la cantidad que se mide.

Angle (p. 460)   An acute angle is an angle
 measure is between 0 and 90.

Ángulo agudo (p. 460)   Un ángulo agudo es un
ángulo que mide entre 0 y 90 grados.

Example

17°

ent angles (p. 466)   Adjacent angles are two
ar angles that have a common side and a
on vertex but no common interior points.

Ángulos adyacentes (p. 466)   Los ángulos
adyacentes son dos ángulos coplanarios que tienen
un lado común y el mismo vértice, pero no tienen
puntos interiores comunes.

Example

$\angle 1$ and $\angle 2$ are
adjacent.

$\angle 3$ and $\angle 4$ are
not adjacent.

ate interior (exterior) angles (p. 655)
ate interior (exterior) angles are nonadjacent
r (exterior) angles that lie on opposite sides
transversal.

Ángulos alternos internos (externos) (p. 655)   Los
ángulos alternos internos (externos) son ángulos
internos (externos) no adyacentes situados en lados
opuestos de la transversal.

Example

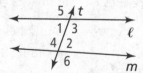

$\angle 1$ and $\angle 2$ are alternate interior angles,
as are $\angle 3$ and $\angle 4$. $\angle 5$ and $\angle 6$ are
alternate exterior angles.

English

Altitude (p. 559) *See* **parallelogram; trapezoid.**

Altitude of a triangle (p. 813) An altitude of a triangle is the perpendicular segment from a vertex to the line containing the side opposite that vertex.

Example

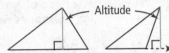

Angle (p. 458) An angle is formed by two rays with the same endpoint. The rays are the *sides* of the angle and the common endpoint is the *vertex* of the angle.

Example

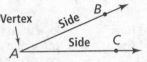

This angle could be named ∠A, ∠BAC, or ∠CAB.

Angle bisector (p. 471) An angle bisector is a ray that divides an angle into two congruent angles.

Example

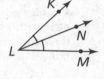

$\vec{LN}$ bisects ∠KLM.
∠KLN ≅ ∠NLM.

Angle of rotation (p. 515) *See* **rotation.**

Area (p. 545) The area of a plane figure is the number of square units enclosed by the figure.

Example

 The area of the rectangle is 12 square units, or 12 units².

Arithmetic sequence (p. 148) A number sequence formed by adding a fixed number to each previous term to find the next term. The fixed number is called the common difference.

Example 4, 7, 10, 13, … is an arithmetic sequence.

Spanish

Altura (p. 559) *Ver* **parallelogram; trapezoid.**

Altura de un triángulo (p. 813) Una altura de triángulo es el segmento perpendicular que va desde un vértice hasta la recta que contiene el opuesto a ese vértice.

Ángulo (p. 458) Un ángulo está formado por semirrectas que convergen en un mismo extre Las semirrectas son los *lados* del ángulo y los extremos en común son el *vértice*.

Bisectriz de un ángulo (p. 471) La bisectriz d ángulo es una semirrecta que divide al ángulo dos ángulos congruentes.

Ángulo de rotación (p. 515) *Ver* **rotation.**

Área (p. 545) El área de una figura plana es cantidad de unidades cuadradas que contiene figura.

Progresión aritmética (p. 148) En una progr aritmética la diferencia entre términos consecutivos es un número constante. El núm constante se llama la diferencia común.

liary line (p. 687) An auxiliary line is a line
is added to a diagram to help explain
ionships in proofs.

Línea auxiliar (p. 687) Una línea auxiliar es
aquella que se le agrega a un diagrama para
explicar la relación entre pruebas.

Example

Auxiliary line

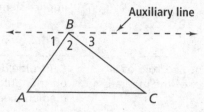

age rate of change (p. 303) The average rate
ange of a function over the interval $a \le x \le b$
ual to $\frac{f(b) - f(a)}{b - a}$.

Tasa media de cambio (p. 303) La tasa media de
cambio de una función sobre el intervalo $a \le x \le b$
es igual a $\frac{f(b) - f(a)}{b - a}$.

Example The average rate of change of the
function $f(x) = x^2 - 2x + 2$ over
the interval $1 \le x \le 4$ is
$\frac{f(4) - f(1)}{4 - 1} = \frac{9}{3} = 3$

m (p. 444) *See* **postulate.**

Axioma (p. 444) *Ver* **postulate.**

 B

s) *See* **isosceles triangle; parallelogram;**
zoid; triangle.

Base(s) *Ver* **isosceles triangle; parallelogram;**
trapezoid; triangle.

angles *See* **trapezoid; isosceles triangle.**

Ángulos de base *Ver* **trapezoid; isosceles triangle.**

ditional (p. 614) A biconditional statement
combination of a conditional statement and
nverse. A biconditional contains the words "if
nly if."

Bicondicional (p. 614) Un enunciado bicondicional
es la combinación de un enunciado condicional y
su recíproco. El enunciado bicondicional incluye las
palabras "si y solo si".

Example This biconditional statement is
true: Two angles are congruent *if*
and only if they have the same
measure.

nd-whisker plot (p. 394) A graph that
arizes data along a number line. The left
er extends from the minimum to the first
ile. The box extends from the first quartile to
ird quartile and has a vertical line through
edian. The right whisker extends from the
quartile to the maximum.

Gráfica de cajas (p. 394) Gráfica que resume los
datos a lo largo de una recta numérica. El brazo
izquierdo se extiende desde el valor mínimo del
primer cuartil. La caja se extiende desde el primer
cuartil hasta el tercer cuartil y tiene una línea
vertical que atraviesa la mediana. El brazo derecho
se extiende desde el tercer cuartil hasta el valor
máximo.

Example

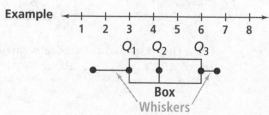

English

C

Causation (p. 405) When a change in one quantity causes a change in a second quantity. A correlation between quantities does not always imply causation.

Center (p. 515) *See* **rotation.**

Centroid of a triangle (p. 811) The centroid of a triangle is the point of concurrency of the medians of the triangle.

Spanish

Causalidad (p. 405) Cuando un cambio en un cantidad causa un cambio en una segunda cantidad. Una correlación entre las cantidades implica siempre la causalidad.

Centro (p. 515) *Ver* **rotation.**

Centroide de un triángulo (p. 811) El centroi un triángulo es el punto de intersección de su medianas.

Example *P* is the centroid of △*ABC*.

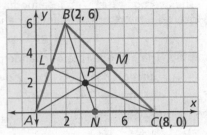

Circle (p. 460) A circle is the set of all points in a plane that are given distance, the *radius*, from a given point, the *center*.

Circle (p. 460) Un círculo es el conjunto de los puntos de un plano situados a una distanc dada, el *radio*, de un punto dado, el *centro*.

Circumcenter of a triangle (p. 803) The circumcenter of a triangle is the point of concurrency of the perpendicular bisectors of the sides of the triangle.

Circuncentro de un triángulo (p. 803) El circuncentro de un triángulo es el punto de intersección de las bisectrices perpendiculares los lados del triángulo.

Example

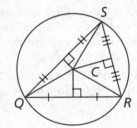

$QC = SC = RC$

C is the circumcenter.

Circumscribed about (p. 803) A circle is circumscribed about a polygon if the vertices of the polygon are on the circle. A polygon is circumscribed about a circle if all the sides of the polygon are tangent to the circle.

Circunscritoa (p. 803) Un círculo está circuns a un polígono si los vértices del polígono está el círculo. Un polígono está circunscrito a un c si todos los lados del polígono son tangentes círculo.

Example

⊙*G* is circumscribed about *ABCD*.

△*XYZ* is circumscribed about ⊙*P*.

icient (p. 6) The numerical factor when a
has a variable.

Coeficiente (p. 6) Factor numérico de un término que contiene una variable.

Example In the expression $2x + 3y + 16$, 2 and 3 are coefficients.

---

ear points (p. 442) Collinear points lie on
me line.

Puntos colineales (p. 442) Los puntos colineales son los que están sobre la misma recta.

Example

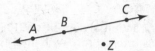

Points A, B, and C are collinear, but points A, B, and Z are noncollinear.

---

non difference (p. 148) The difference
en consecutive terms of an arithmetic
nce.

Diferencia común (p. 148) La diferencia común es la diferencia entre los términos consecutivos de una progresión aritmética.

Example The common difference is 3 in the arithmetic sequence 4, 7, 10, 13, …

---

ass (p. 591) A compass is a geometric tool
o draw circles and parts of circles, called arcs.

Compás (p. 591) El compás es un instrumento usado para dibujar círculos y partes de círculos, llamados arcos.

---

lementary angles (p. 467) Two angles are
ementary angles if the sum of their
res is 90.

Ángulos complementarios (p. 467) Dos ángulos son complementarios si la suma de sus medidas es igual a 90 grados.

Example

$\angle HKI$ and $\angle IKJ$ are complementary angles, as are $\angle HKI$ and $\angle EFG$.

---

osition of transformations (p. 500) A
osition of two transformations is a
ormation in which a second transformation is
med on the image of a first transformation.

Composición de transformaciones (p. 500) Una composición de dos transformaciones es una transformación en la cual una segunda transformación se realiza a partir de la imagen de la primera.

Example

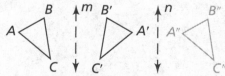

If you reflect $\triangle ABC$ across line m to get $\triangle A'B'C'$ and then reflect $\triangle A'B'C'$ across line n to get $\triangle A''B''C''$, you perform a composition of transformations.

Visual Glossary

Compound inequality (p. 70) Two inequalities that are joined by *and* or *or*.

Desigualdade compuesta (p. 70) Dos desigualdades que están enlazadas por medio una *y* o una *o*.

> **Example** $5 < x$ and $x < 10$
> $14 < x$ or $x \leq -3$

Compound interest (p. 311) Interest paid on both the principal and the interest that has already been paid.

Interés compuesto (p. 311) Interés calculado tanto sobre el capital como sobre los intereses pagados.

> **Example** For an initial deposit of $1000 at a 6% interest rate with interest compounded quarterly, the function $y = 1000\left(\frac{0.06}{4}\right)^x$ gives the account balance y after x years.

Conclusion (p. 607) The conclusion is the part of an *if-then* statement (conditional) that follows *then*.

Conclusión (p. 607) La conclusión es lo que s a la palabra entonces en un enunciado (condicional), si ..., entonces. ...

> **Example** In the statement, 'If it rains, then I will go outside,' the conclusion is 'I will go outside.'

Concurrent lines (p. 803) Concurrent lines are three or more lines that meet in one point. The point at which they meet is the *point of concurrency*.

Rectas concurrentes (p. 803) Las rectas concurrentes son tres o más rectas que se une un punto. El punto en que se unen es el *punt concurrencia*.

> **Example**
>
>
> Point *E* is the point of concurrency of the bisectors of the angles of $\triangle ABC$. The bisectors are concurrent.

Conditional (p. 607) A conditional is an *if-then* statement.

Condicional (p. 607) Un enunciado condicio del tipo *si* ..., *entonces*. ...

> **Example** *If* you act politely, *then* you will earn respect.

glish

Spanish

itional relative frequency (p. 418) Conditional
ve frequency is the quotient of a joint
ency in a two-way frequency table and the
inal frequency of the row or column in which
int frequency appears.

Frecuencia relativa condicionada (p. 418)
Frecuencia relativa condicionada es el cociente de
una frecuencia conjunta en una tabla de
frecuencias de doble entrada y la frecuencia
marginal de la fila o columna en la que la
frecuencia conjunta aparece.

Example

	Male	Female	Totals
Juniors	3	4	7
Seniors	3	2	5
Totals	6	6	12

The conditional relative frequency
that a student is female given
that she is a senior is $\frac{2}{5}$.

uence transformation (p. 774) *See* isometry.

Transformación de congruencia (p. 774)
Ver isometry.

uent angles (p. 461) Congruent angles are
s that have the same measure.

Ángulos congruentes (p. 461) Los ángulos
congruentes son ángulos que tienen la misma
medida.

Example

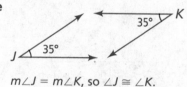

$m\angle J = m\angle K$, so $\angle J \cong \angle K$.

uent polygons (p. 709) Congruent polygons
lygons that have corresponding sides
uent and corresponding angles congruent.

Polígonos congruentes (p. 709) Los polígonos
congruentes son polígonos cuyos lados
correspondientes son congruentes y cuyos ángulos
correspondientes son congruentes.

Example

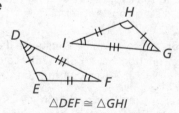

$\triangle DEF \cong \triangle GHI$

uent segments (p. 453) Congruent
nts are segments that have the same length.

Segmentos congruentes (p. 453) Los segmentos
congruentes son segmentos que tienen la misma
longitud.

Example

2 cm ... 2 cm

$\overline{AB} \cong \overline{CD}$

Visual **Glossary**

English

Spanish

Conjecture (p. 600) A conjecture is a conclusion reached by using inductive reasoning.

Conjecture (p. 600) A conjecture is a conclusi reached by using inductive reasoning.

Example As you walk down the street, you see many people holding unopened umbrellas. You make the conjecture that the forecast must call for rain.

Consecutive angles (p. 859) Consecutive angles of a polygon share a common side.

Ángulos consecutivos (p. 859) Los ángulos consecutivos de un polígono tienen un lado común.

Example

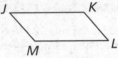

In □JKLM, ∠J and ∠M are consecutive angles, as are ∠J and ∠K. ∠J and ∠L are *not* consecutive.

Consistent system (p. 233) A system of equations that has at least one solution is consistent.

Sistema consistente (p. 233) Un sistema de ecuaciones que tiene por lo menos una soluci consistente.

Example

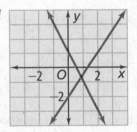

Constant (p. 6) A term that has no variable factor.

Constante (p. 6) Término que tiene un valor

Example In the expression $4x + 13y + 17$, 17 is a constant term.

Constant of variation for direct variation (p. 176) The nonzero constant k in the function $y = kx$.

Constante de variación en variaciones directa (p. 176) La constante k cuyo valor no es cero la función $y = kx$.

Example For the direct variation $y = 24x$, 24 is the constant of variation.

.truction (p. 591) A construction is a metric figure made with only a straightedge compass.

Construcción (p. 591) Una construcción es una figura geométrica trazada solamente con una regla sin graduación y un compás.

Example

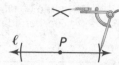

The diagram shows the construction (in progress) of a line perpendicular to a line ℓ through a point P on ℓ.

inuous graph (p. 119) A graph that is oken.

Gráfica continua (p. 119) Una gráfica continua es una gráfica ininterrumpida.

Example

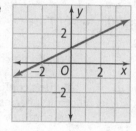

rapositive (p. 610) The contrapositive of the tional "if p, then q" is the conditional "if not en not p." A conditional and its contrapositive vs have the same truth value.

Contrapositivo (p. 610) El contrapositivo del condicional "si p, entonces q" es el condicional "si no q, entonces no p". Un condicional y su contrapositivo siempre tienen el mismo valor verdadero.

Example **Conditional:** If a figure is a triangle, then it is a polygon.
Contrapositive: If a figure is not a polygon, then it is not a triangle.

erse (p. 610) The statement obtained by sing the hypothesis and conclusion of a tional.

Expresión recíproca (p. 610) Enunciado que se obtiene al intercambiar la hipótesis y la conclusión de una situación condicional.

Example The converse of "If I was born in Houston, then I am a Texan" would be "If I am a Texan, then I am born in Houston."

rsion factor (p. 38) A ratio of two alent measures in different units.

Factor de conversión (p. 38) Razón de dos medidas equivalentes en unidades diferentes.

Example The ratio $\frac{1 \text{ ft}}{12 \text{ in.}}$ is a conversion factor.

English

Spanish

Coordinate(s) of a point (p. 451) The coordinate of a point is its distance and direction from the origin of a number line. The coordinates of a point on a coordinate plane are in the form (x, y), where x is the x-coordinate and y is the y-coordinate.

Coordenada(s) de un punto (p. 451) La coorde de un punto es su distancia y dirección desde el origen en una recta numérica. Las coordenadas un punto en un plano de coordenadas se expres como (x, y), donde x es la coordenada x, e y es la coordenada y.

Examples

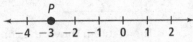

The coordinate of P is -3.

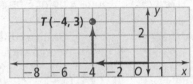

The coordinates of T are $(-4, 3)$.

Coordinate proof (p. 907) *See* **proof.**

Prueba de coordenadas (p. 907) *Ver* **proof.**

Coplanar points (p. 442) Coplanar points are points that lie in the same plane.

Puntos coplanarios (p. 442) Los puntos conplanarios son los puntos que éstan localiza en el mismo plano.

Correlation coefficient (p. 404) A number from -1 to 1 that tells you how closely the equation of the line of best fit models the data.

Coeficiente de correlación (p. 404) Número d 1 que indica con cuánta exactitud la línea de r encaje representa los datos.

Example

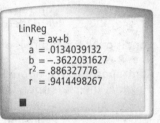

The correlation coefficient is approximately 0.94.

Corresponding angles (p. 655) Corresponding angles lie on the same side of the transversal t and in corresponding positions relative to ℓ and m.

Ángulos correspondientes (p. 655) Los ángul correspondientes están en el mismo lado de la transversal t y en las correspondientes posicio relativas a ℓ y m.

Example

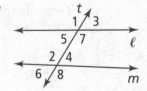

$\angle 1$ and $\angle 2$ are corresponding angles, as are $\angle 3$ and $\angle 4$, $\angle 5$ and $\angle 6$, and $\angle 7$ and $\angle 8$.

...terexample (p. 602) An example showing ...a statement is false.

Contraejemplo (p. 602) Ejemplo que demuestra que un enunciado es falso.

Example **Statement:** All apples are red.
Counterexample: A Granny Smith Apple is green.

...s products (of a proportion) (p. 53) In a ...ortion $\frac{a}{b} = \frac{c}{d}$, the products ad and bc. These ...ucts are equal.

Productos cruzados (de una proporción) (p. 53) En una proporción $\frac{a}{b} = \frac{c}{d}$, los productos ad y bc. Estos productos son iguales.

Example The cross products for $\frac{3}{4} = \frac{6}{8}$ are $3 \cdot 8$ and $4 \cdot 6$.

...root function (p. 356) A function containing ...e root with the independent variable in the ...and.

Función de la raíz cúbica (p. 356) Una función que contiene una raíz cúbica con la variable independiente en el radicando.

...ulative frequency table (p. 375) A table that ...s the number of data values that lie in or ...v the given intervals.

Tabla de frecuencia cumulativa (p. 375) Tabla que muestra el número de valores de datos que están dentro o por debajo de los intervalos dados.

Example

Interval	Frequency	Cumulative Frequency
0–9	5	5
10–19	8	13
20–29	4	17

D

...y factor (p. 312) 1 minus the percent rate of ...ge, expressed as a decimal, for an exponential ...situation.

Factor de decremento (p. 312) 1 menos la tasa porcentual de cambio, expresada como decimal, en una situación de reducción exponencial.

Example The decay factor of the function $y = 5(0.3)^x$ is 0.3.

...ctive reasoning (p. 622) Deductive reasoning ...rocess of reasoning logically from given facts ...onclusion.

Razonamiento deductivo (p. 622) El razonamiento deductivo es un proceso de razonamiento lógico que parte de hechos dados hasta llegar a una conclusión.

Example Based on the fact that the sum of any two even numbers is even, you can deduce that the product of any whole number and any even number is even.

Dependent system (p. 233) A system of equations that does not have a unique solution.

Sistema dependiente (p. 233) Sistema de ecuaciones que no tiene una solución única.

Example The system $\begin{cases} y = 2x + 3 \\ -4x + 2y = 6 \end{cases}$ represents two equations for the same line, so it has many solutions. It is a dependent system.

Dependent variable (p. 103) A variable that provides the output values of a function.

Variable dependiente (p. 103) Variable de la dependen los valores de salida de una función

Example In the equation $y = 3x$, y is the dependent variable.

Direct variation (p. 176) A linear function defined by an equation of the form $y = kx$, where $k \neq 0$.

Variación directa (p. 176) Una función lineal definida por una ecuación de la forma $y\ kx$, do $k \neq 0$, representa una variación directa.

Example $y = 18x$ is a direct variation.

Discrete graph (p. 119) A graph composed of isolated points.

Gráfica discreta (p. 119) Una gráfica discreta compuesta de puntos aislados.

Example

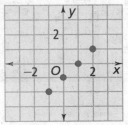

Distance between two points on a line (p. 451) The distance between two points on a line is the absolute value of the difference of the coordinates of the points.

Distancia entre dos puntos de una linea (p. 451) Ladistancia entre dos puntos de una lfnea es el valor absoluto de la diferencia de la coordenadas de los puntos.

Example

$$AB = |a - b|$$

Distance from a point to a line (p. 798) The distance from a point to a line is the length of the perpendicular segment from the point to the line.

Distancia desde un punto hasta una recta (p. 798) La distancia desde un punto hasta u recta es la longitud del segmento perpendicul que va desde el punto hasta la recta.

Example

The distance from point P to a line ℓ is PT.

Spanish

...ributive Property (p. 3) For every real number ... and *c*:

... + c) = ab + ac

c)a = ba + ca

... − c) = ab − ac

c)a = ba − ca

Propiedad Distributiva (p. 3) Para cada número real *a*, *b* y *c*:

$a(b + c) = ab + ac$

$(b + c)a = ba + ca$

$a(b − c) = ab − ac$

$(b − c)a = ba − ca$

Examples $3(19 + 4) = 3(19) + 3(4)$

$(19 + 4)3 = 19(3) + 4(3)$

$7(11 − 2) = 7(11) − 7(2)$

$(11 − 2)7 = 11(7) − 2(7)$

...ain (of a relation or function) (p. 135) The ...ble values for the input of a relation or ...tion.

Dominio (de una relación o función) (p. 135) Posibles valores de entrada de una relación o función.

Example In the function $f(x) = x + 22$, the domain is all real numbers.

 E

...nation method (p. 247) A method for solving ...tem of linear equations. You add or subtract ...quations to eliminate a variable.

Eliminación (p. 247) Método para resolver un sistema de ecuaciones lineales. Se suman o se restan las ecuaciones para eliminar una variable.

Example

$3x + y = 19$

$\underline{2x − y = 1}$ Add the equations to get $x = 4$.

$5x + 0 = 20$

$2(4) − y = 1 \rightarrow$ Substitute 4 for x in the second equation.

$8 − y = 1$

$y = 7 \rightarrow$ Solve for y.

...ngular triangle or polygon (p. 852) An ...ngular triangle (polygon) is a triangle ...gon) whose angles are all congruent.

Triángulo o polígono equiángulo (p. 852) Un triángulo (polígono) equiángulo es un triángulo (polígono) cuyos ángulos son todos congruentes.

Example

 Each angle of the pentagon is a 108° angle.

...ateral triangle or polygon (p. 852) An ...ateral triangle (polygon) is a triangle ...gon) whose sides are all congruent.

Triángulo o polígono equilátero (p. 852) Un triángulo (polígono) equilátero es un triángulo (polígono) cuyos lados son todos congruentes.

Example

 Each side of the quadrilateral is 1.2 cm long.

English

Spanish

Equivalent statements (p. 610) Equivalent statements are statements with the same truth value.

Enunciados equivalentes (p. 610) Los enuncia equivalentes son enunciados con el mismo valo verdadero.

Example The following statements are equivalent: If a figure is a square, then it is a rectangle. If a figure is not a rectangle, then it is not a square.

Even function (p. 144) A function f is an even function if and only if $f(-x) = f(x)$ for all values of x in its domain.

Función par (p. 144) Una función f es una fun par si y solo si $f(-x) = f(x)$ para todos los valore x en su dominio.

Example $f(x) = x^2 + |x|$ is an even function because
$f(-x) = (-x)^2 + |-x| = x^2 + |x| = f(x)$

Explicit formula (p. 150) An explicit formula expresses the nth term of a sequence in terms of n.

Fórmula explícita (p. 150) Una fórmula explíc expresa el n-ésimo término de una progresión función de n.

Example Let $a_n = 2n + 5$ for positive integers n. If $n = 7$, then $a_7 = 2(7) + 5 = 19$.

Exponential decay (p. 312) A situation modeled with a function of the form $y = ab^x$, where $a > 0$ and $0 < b < 1$.

Decremento exponencial (p. 312) Para $a > 0$ y $0 < b < 1$, la función $y = ab^x$ representa decremento exponencial.

Example $y = 5(0.1)^x$

Exponential function (p. 291) A function that repeatedly multiplies an initial amount by the same positive number. You can model all exponential functions using $y = ab^x$, where a is a nonzero constant, $b > 0$, and $b \neq 1$.

Función exponencial (p. 291) Función que multiplica repetidas veces una cantidad inicial el mismo número positivo. Todas las funciones exponenciales se pueden representar mediante $y = ab^x$, donde a es una constante con valor distinto de cero, $b > 0$ y $b \neq 1$.

Example

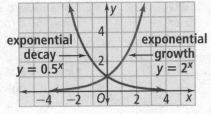

Exponential growth (p. 309) A situation modeled with a function of the form $y = ab^x$, where $a > 0$ and $b > 1$.

Incremento exponencial (p. 309) Para $a > 0$ y $b > 1$, la función $y = ab^x$ representa el incremento exponencial.

Example $y = 100(2)^x$

glish

rior angle of a polygon (p. 689) An exterior
e of a polygon is an angle formed by a side
an extension of an adjacent side.

Example

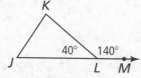

∠*KLM* is an exterior angle of △*JKL*.

---

apolation (p. 401) The process of predicting a
e outside the range of known values.

---

proof (p. 672) *See* **proof.**

---

ula (p. 31) An equation that states a
onship among quantities.

Example The formula for the volume *V* of a
cylinder is $V = \pi r^2 h$, where *r* is the
radius of the cylinder and *h* is its
height.

---

ency (p. 371) The number of data items in
terval.

---

ency table (p. 371) A table that groups a set
ta values into intervals and shows the
ency for each interval.

Example

Interval	Frequency
0–9	5
10–19	8
20–29	4

---

ion (p. 105) A relation that assigns exactly
alue in the range to each value of the
in.

Example Earned income is a function of
the number of hours worked. If
you earn $4.50/h, then your
income is expressed by the
function $f(h) = 4.5h$.

Spanish

Ángulo exterior de un polígono (p. 689) El
ángulo exterior de un polígono es un ángulo
formado por un lado y una extensión de un lado
adyacente.

Extrapolación (p. 401) Proceso que se usa para
predecir un valor por fuera del ámbito de los
valores dados.

F

Prueba de flujo (p. 672) *Ver* **proof.**

Fórmula (p. 31) Ecuación que establece una
relación entre cantidades.

Frecuencia (p. 371) Número de datos de un
intervalo.

Tabla de frecuencias (p. 371) Tabla que agrupa un
conjunto de datos en intervalos y muestra la
frecuencia de cada intervalo.

Función (p. 105) La relación que asigna
exactamente un valor del rango a cada valor del
dominio.

Visual **Glossary**

English

Spanish

Function notation (p. 137)   To write a rule in function notation, you use the symbol $f(x)$ in place of y.

Notación de una función (p. 137)   Para expresa una regla en notación de función se usa el símb $f(x)$ en lugar de y.

Example $f(x) = 3x - 8$ is in function notation.

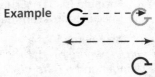

Geometric sequence (p. 329)   A number sequence formed by multiplying a term in a sequence by a fixed number to find the next term.

Progresión geométrica (p. 329)   Tipo de sucesi numérica formada al multiplicar un término de secuencia por un número constante, para halla siguiente término.

Example 9, 3, 1, $\frac{1}{3}$,.... is an example of a geometric sequence.

Glide reflection (p. 536)   A glide reflection is the composition of a translation followed by a reflection across a line parallel to the direction of translation.

Reflexión deslizada (p. 536)   Una reflexión po deslizamiento es la composición de una traslac seguida por una reflexión a través de una línea paralela a la dirección de traslación.

Example

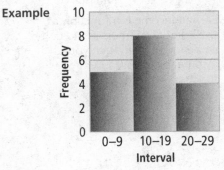

The blue G in the diagram is a glide reflection image of the black G.

Growth factor (p. 309)   1 plus the percent rate of change for an exponential growth situation.

Factor incremental (p. 309)   1 más la tasa porcentual de cambio en una situación de incremento exponencial.

Example The growth factor of $y = 7(1.3)^x$ is 1.3.

Height   *See* **parallelogram; trapezoid; triangle.**

Altura   *Ver* **parallelogram; trapezoid.**

Histogram (p. 372)   A special type of bar graph that can display data from a frequency table. Each bar represents an interval. The height of each bar shows the frequency of the interval it represents.

Histograma (p. 372)   Tipo de gráfica de barra muestra los datos de una tabla de frecuencia. barra representa un intervalo. La altura de cad barra muestra la frecuencia del intervalo al qu representa.

Example

glish	Spanish

otenuse (p. 753) *See* **right triangle.**

Hipotenusa (p. 753) *Ver* **right triangle.**

othesis (p. 607) In an *if-then* statement ditional), the hypothesis is the part that ws *if*.

Hipótesis (p. 607) En un enunciado *si . . . entonces . . .* (condicional), la hipótesis es la parte del enunciado que sigue el *si*.

Example In the conditional "If an animal has four legs, then it is a horse," the hypothesis is "an animal has four legs."

I

e (p. 495) *See* **transformation.**

Imagen (p. 495) *Ver* **transformation.**

ity (p. 24) An equation that is true for value.

Identidad (p. 24) Una ecuación que es verdadera para todos los valores.

Example $5 - 14x = 5\left(1 - \frac{14}{5}x\right)$ is an identity because it is true for any value of x.

ter of a triangle (p. 806) The incenter of a gle is the point of concurrency of the angle ors of the triangle.

Incentro de un triángulo (p. 806) El incentro de un triángulo es el punto donde concurren las tres bisectrices de los ángulos del triángulo.

Example

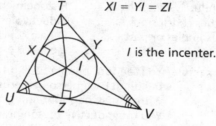

$XI = YI = ZI$

I is the incenter.

sistent system (p. 233) A system of ions that has no solution.

Sistema incompatible (p. 233) Un sistema incompatible es un sistema de ecuaciones para el cual no hay solución.

Example $\begin{cases} y = 2x + 3 \\ -2x + y = 1 \end{cases}$ is a system of parallel lines, so it has no solution. It is an inconsistent system.

endent system (p. 233) A system of linear ons that has a unique solution.

Sistema independiente (p. 233) Un sistema de ecuaciones lineales que tenga una sola solución es un sistema independiente.

Example $\begin{cases} x + 2y = -7 \\ 2x - 3y = 0 \end{cases}$ has the unique solution $(-3, -2)$. It is an independent system.

Visual **Glossary**

Independent variable (p. 103) A variable that provides the input values of a function.

Example In the equation $y = 3x$, x is the independent variable.

Variable independiente (p. 103) Variable de l que dependen los valores de entrada de una función.

Indirect proof (p. 820) *See* **indirect reasoning; proof.**

Prueba indirecta (p. 820) *Ver* **indirect reasoni proof.**

Indirect reasoning (p. 820) Indirect reasoning is a type of reasoning in which all possiblities are considered and then all but one are proved false. The remaining possibility must be true.

Example Eduardo spent more than $60 on two books at a store. Prove that at least one book costs more than $30.
Proof: Suppose neither costs more than $30. Then he spent no more than $60 at the store. Since this contradicts the given information, at least one book costs more than $30.

Razonamiento indirecto (p. 820) Razonamier indirecto es un tipo de razonamiento en el qu consideran todas las posibilidades y se prueba todas son falsas, a excepción de una. La posibi restante debe ser verdadera.

Inductive reasoning (p. 599) Inductive reasoning is a type of reasoning that reaches conclusions based on a pattern of specific examples or past events.

Example You see four people walk into a building. Each person emerges with a small bag containing food. You use inductive reasoning to conclude that this building contains a restaurant.

Razonamiento inductivo (p. 599) El razonam inductivo es un tipo de razonamiento en el cu llega a conclusiones con base en un patrón de ejemplos específicos o sucesos pasados.

Input (p. 103) A value of the independent variable.

Example The input is any value of x you substitute into a function.

Entrada (p. 103) Valor de una variable independiente.

Inscribed in (p. 806) A circle is inscribed in a polygon if the sides of the polygon are tangent to the circle. A polygon is inscribed in a circle if the vertices of the polygon are on the circle.

Inscrito en (p. 806) Un círculo está inscrito e polígono si los lados del polígono son tanger círculo. Un polígono está inscrito en un círcu los vértices del polígono están en el círculo.

Example

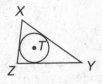

⊙*T* is inscribed in △*XYZ*.

ABCD is inscribed in ⊙*J*.

polation (p. 401)   The process of estimating
ue between two known quantities.

Interpolación (p. 401)   Proceso que se usa para estimar el valor entre dos cantidades dadas.

quartile range (p. 392)   The interquartile
e of a set of data is the difference between
hird and first quartiles.

Intervalo intercuartil (p. 392)   El rango intercuartil de un conjunto de datos es la diferencia entre el tercero y el primer cuartiles.

Example   The first and third quartiles of the data set 2, 3, 4, 5, 5, 6, 7, and 7 are 3.5 and 6.5. The interquartile range is $6.5 - 3.5 = 3$.

section (p. 444)   The intersection of two or
geometric figures is the set of points the
es have in common.

Intersección (p. 444)   La intersección de dos o más figuras geométricas es el conjunto de puntos que las figuras tienen en común.

Example
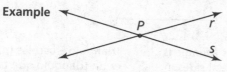
The intersection of lines r and s is point P.

val notation (p. 74)   A notation for describing
terval on a number line. The interval's
oint(s) are given, and a parenthesis or bracket
d to indicate whether each endpoint is
led in the interval.

Notación de intervalo (p. 74)   Notación que describe un intervalo en una recta numérica. Los extremos del intervalo se incluyen y se usa un paréntesis o corchete para indicar si cada extremo está incluido en el intervalo.

Example   For $-2 \leq x < 8$, the interval notation is $[-2, 8)$.

e (p. 610)   The inverse of the conditional
then q" is the conditional "if not p, then
"

Inverso (p. 610)   El inverso del condicional "si p, entonces q" es el condicional "si no p, entonces no q".

Example   **Conditional:** If a figure is a square, then it is a parallelogram. **Inverse:** If a figure is not a square, then it is not a parallelogram.

tric drawing (p. 433)   An isometric drawing
a corner view of a three-dimensional figure.
ually drawn on isometric dot paper. An
tric drawing allows you to see the top, front,
de of an object in the same drawing.

Dibujo isométrico (p. 433)   Un dibujo isométrico muestra la perspectiva de una esquina de una figura tridimensional. Generalmente se dibuja en papel punteado isométrico. Un dibujo isométrico permite ver la cima, el frente, y el lado de un objeto en el mismo dibujo.

Example
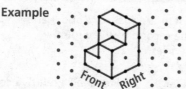

English

Spanish

Isometry (p. 532)   An isometry, also known as a *congruence transformation*, is a transformation in which an original figure and its image are congruent.

Isometría (p. 532)   Una isometría, conocida también como una *transformación de congrue* es una transformación en donde una figura original y su imagen son congruentes.

Example   The four isometries are reflections, rotations, translations, and glide reflections.

Isosceles trapezoid (p. 483, 894)   An isosceles trapezoid is a trapezoid whose nonparallel sides are congruent.

Trapecio isósceles (p. 483, 894)   Un trapecio isósceles es un trapecio cuyos lados opuestos no paralelos son congruentes.

Example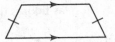

Isosceles triangle (p. 744)   An isosceles triangle is a triangle that has at least two congruent sides. If there are two congruent sides, they are called *legs*. The *vertex angle* is between them. The third side is called the *base* and the other two angles are called *base angles*.

Triángulo isosceles (p. 744)   Un triángulo isos es un triángulo que tiene por lo menos dos lac congruentes. Si tiene dos lodos congruentes, é se llaman *catetos*. Entre ellos se encuentra el *ángulo del vértice*. El tercer lado se llama *base* otros dos ángulos se llaman *ángulos de base*.

Example

Vertex angle

Base angle — Leg / \ Leg — Base angle

Base

J

Joint frequency (p. 414)   A joint frequency is an entry in the body of a two-way frequency table.

Frecuencia conjunta (p. 414)   Una frecuencia conjunta es una entrada en el cuerpo de una de frecuencias de doble entrada.

Example

	Male	Female	Totals
Juniors	3	4	7
Seniors	3	2	5
Totals	6	6	12

3 and 4 in the first row, and 3 and 2 in the second row are joint frequencies.

Joint relative frequency (p. 416)   A joint relative frequency is a joint frequency in a two-way frequency table divided by the grand total of the entries in the table. It is also an entry in the body of a two-way relative frequency table.

Frecuencia relativa conjunta (p. 416)   Una frecuencia relativa conjunta es una frecuencia conjunta en una tabla de frecuencias de dobl entrada dividido por el total de las entradas (tabla. Es también una entrada en el cuerpo d tabla de frecuencias relativas de doble entrac

glish

K

(p. 483) A kite is a quadrilateral with two
s of consecutive sides congruent and no
osite sides congruent.

Example

L

See **isosceles triangle; right triangle;**
ezoid.

terms (p. 7) Terms with exactly the same
ble factors in a variable expression.

Example $3\sqrt{7}$ and $25\sqrt{7}$ are like radicals.

(pp. 441) In Euclidean geometry, a line is
fined. You can think of a line as a straight
that extends in two opposite directions
out end and has no thickness. A line contains
tely many points. In spherical geometry, you
hink of a line as a great circle of a sphere.

Example

of best fit (p. 404) The most accurate trend
n a scatter plot showing the relationship
een two sets of data.

Example

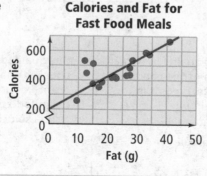

Calories and Fat for Fast Food Meals

f reflection (p. 508) *See* **reflection.**

f symmetry (p. 523) *See* **reflectional symmetry.**

Spanish

Cometa (p. 483) Una cometa es un cuadrilatero
con dos pares de lados congruentes consecutivos
y sin laods opuestos congruentes.

Cateto *Ver* **isosceles triangle; right triangle;
trapezoid.**

Radicales semejantes (p. 7) Expresiones radicales
con los mismos radicandos.

Recta (pp. 441) En la geometría euclidiana, una
recta es indefinida. Se puede pensar en una recta
como un camino derecho que se extiende en
direcciones opuestas sin fin ni grosor. Una recta
tiene un número infinito de puntos. En la
geometría esférica, se puede pensar en una recta
como un gran círculo de una esfera.

Recta de mayor aproximación (p. 404) La línea de
tendencia en un diagrama de puntos que más se
acerca a los puntos que representan la relación
entre dos conjuntos de datos.

Eje de reflexión (p. 508) *Ver* **reflection.**

Eje de simetría (p. 523) *Ver* **reflectional symmetry.**

English

Spanish

Line plot (p. 382) A line plot is a graph that shows the shape of a data set by stacking X's above each data value on a number line.

Diagrama de puntos (p. 382) Un diagrama de puntos es una gráfica que muestra la forma de conjunto de datos agrupando X sobre cada va de una recta numérica.

Example

Company A

```
        X   X
        X   X   X   X
    X   X   X   X   X   X
    50  51  52  53  54  55
```

**Monthly Earnings
(thousands of dollars)**

Line symmetry (p. 523) *See* reflectional symmetry.

Simetría axial (p. 523) *Ver* reflectional symm

Linear equation (p. 186) An equation whose graph forms a straight line.

Ecuación lineal (p. 186) Ecuación cuya gráfica una línea recta.

Example

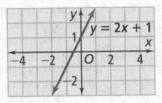

Linear function (p. 105) A function whose graph is a line is a linear function. You can represent a linear function with a linear equation.

Función lineal (p. 105) Una función cuya grá es una recta es una función lineal. La función se representa con una ecuación lineal.

Example

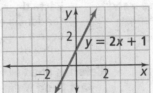

Linear inequality (p. 263) An inequality in two variables whose graph is a region of the coordinate plane that is bounded by a line. Each point in the region is a solution of the inequality.

Desigualdad lineal (p. 263) Una desigualdad lineal es una desigualdad de dos variables cuy gráfica es una región del plano de coordenad delimitado por una recta. Cada punto de la re es una solución de la desigualdad.

Example

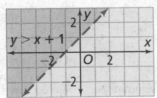

glish

Spanish

ar pair (p. 469) A linear pair is a pair of cent angles whose noncommon sides are osite rays.

Par lineal (p. 469) Un par lineal es un par de ángulos adjuntos cuyos lados no comunes son semirrectas opuestas.

Example

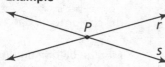

The intersection of lines *r* and *s* is point *P*.

ar parent function (p. 186) The simplest form inear function.

Función lineal elemental (p. 186) La forma más simple de una función lineal.

Example $y = x$

al equation (p. 29) An equation involving or more variables.

Ecuación literal (p. 29) Ecuación que incluye dos o más variables.

Example $4x + 2y = 18$ is a literal equation.

M

inal frequency (p. 414) A marginal ency is an entry in the Total row or Total nn of a two-way frequency table.

Frecuencia marginal (p. 414) Una frecuencia marginal es una entrada en la fila Total o columna Total de una tabla de frecuencias de doble entrada.

Example

	Male	Female	Totals
Juniors	3	4	7
Seniors	3	2	5
Totals	6	6	12

6 and 6 in the Total row and 7 and 5 in the Total column are marginal frequencies.

inal relative frequency (p. 416) A marginal ve frequency is a marginal frequency in a vay frequency table divided by the grand for the table.

Frecuencia relativa marginal (p. 416) Una frecuencia relativa marginal es una frecuencia marginal en una tabla de frecuencias de doble entrada dividido por el total de la tabla.

(p. 379) To find the mean of a set of data , find the sum of the data values and divide m by the number of data values. The mean is $\frac{\text{of the data values}}{\text{umber of data values}}$.

Media (p. 379) Para hallar la media de un conjunto de datos, halla la suma de los valores de los datos y divide la suma por el total del valor de los datos. La media es $\frac{\text{la suma de los datos}}{\text{el número total de valores de datos}}$.

Example In the data set 12, 11, 12, 10, 13, 12, and 7, the mean is $\frac{12 + 11 + 12 + 10 + 13 + 12 + 7}{7} = 11$.

English | Spanish

Mean absolute deviation (MAD) (p. 388) Mean absolute deviation is a measure of the spread of a data set. For data values $x_1, x_2, \ldots x_n$, the mean absolute deviation is given by $\frac{|x_1 - \bar{x}| + |x_2 - \bar{x}| + \ldots + |x_n - \bar{x}|}{n}$, where $\bar{x}$ is the mean of the data set.

Desviación absoluta media (p. 388) Desviació absoluta media es una medida de la dispersión un conjunto de datos. Para los datos $x_1, x_2, \ldots$ la desviación absoluta media es igual a $\frac{|x_1 - \bar{x}| + |x_2 - \bar{x}| + \ldots + |x_n - \bar{x}|}{n}$, donde $\bar{x}$ es la me del conjunto de datos.

Measure of an angle (p. 460) Consider $\overrightarrow{OD}$ and a point C on one side of $\overrightarrow{OD}$. Every ray of the form $\overrightarrow{OC}$ can be paired one to one with a real number from 0 to 180. The measure of $\angle COD$ is the absolute value of the difference of the real numbers paired with $\overrightarrow{OC}$ and $\overrightarrow{OD}$.

Medida de un ángulo (p. 460) Toma en cuent $\overrightarrow{OD}$ y un punto C a un lado de $\overrightarrow{OD}$. Cada semirrecta de la forma $\overrightarrow{OC}$ puede ser empareja exactamente con un número real de 0 a 180. L medida de $\angle COD$ es el valor absoluto de la diferencia de los números reales emparejados $\overrightarrow{OC}$ y $\overrightarrow{OD}$.

Example

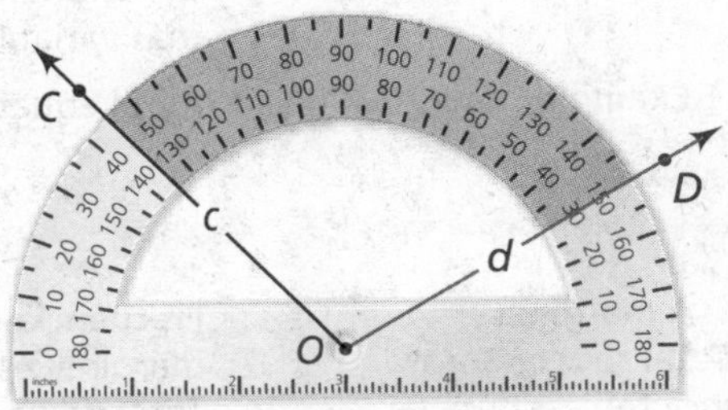

$m\angle COD = 105$

Measure of central tendency (p. 379) Mean, median, and mode. They are used to organize and summarize a set of data.

Medida de tendencia central (p. 379) La mec mediana y la moda. Se usan para organizar y resumir un conjunto de datos.

Example For examples, see *mean*, *median*, and *mode*.

Measure of dispersion (p. 382) A measure that describes how dispersed, or spread out, the values in a data set are. Range is a measure of dispersion.

Medida de dispersión (p. 382) Medida que describe cómo se dispersan, o esparecen, los valores de un conjunto de datos. La amplitud una medida de dispersión.

Example For an example, see *range*.

Median (p. 379) The middle value in an ordered set of numbers.

Mediana (p. 379) El valor del medio en un conjunto ordenado de números.

Example In the data set 7, 10, 11, 12, 12, 12, and 13, the median is 12.

Median of a triangle (p. 811) A median of a triangle is a segment that has as its endpoints a vertex of the triangle and the midpoint of the opposite side.

Mediana de un triángulo (p. 811) Una medi de un triángulo es un segmento que tiene en extremos el vértice del triángulo y el punto m del lado opuesto.

Example

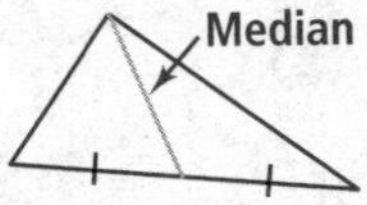

egment of a trapezoid (p. 896)   The
egment of a trapezoid is the segment that
the midpoints of the nonparallel opposite
of a trapezoid.

Segmento medio de un triángulo (p. 896)   Un
segmento medio de un triángulo es un segmento
que une los puntos medios de dos lados del
triángulo.

Example

oint of a segment (p. 454)   A midpoint of a
ent is the point that divides the segment into
ongruent segments.

Punto medio de un segmento (p. 454)   El punto
medio de un segmento es el punto que divide el
segmento en dos segmentos congruentes.

Example   Midpoint of $\overline{AB}$

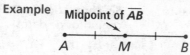

egment of a triangle (p. 787)   A midsegment
iangle is a segment that joins the midpoints
o sides of the triangle.

Segmento medio de un triángulo (p. 787)   Un
segmento medio de un triángulo es un segmento
que une los puntos medios de dos lados del
triángulo.

Example

(p. 379)   The mode is the most frequently
ing value (or values) in a set of data. A data
y have no mode, one mode, or more than
ode.

Moda (p. 379)   La moda es el valor o valores que
ocurren con mayor frequencia en un conjunto de
datos. El conjunto de datos puede no tener moda,
o tener una o más modas.

Example   In the data set 7, 7, 9, 10, 11, and
13, the mode is 7.

N

on (p. 610)   The negation of a statement
e opposite meaning of the original
ent.

Negación (p. 610)   La negación de un enunciado
tiene el sentido opuesto del enunciado original.

Example   The angle is obtuse.
Negation: The angle is not obtuse.

ve correlation (p. 399)   The relationship
en two sets of data, in which one set of data
ses as the other set of data increases.

Correlación negativa (p. 399)   Relación entre dos
conjuntos de datos en la que uno de los conjuntos
disminuye a medida que el otro aumenta.

Example

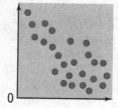

English

Spanish

Net (p. 431)   A net is a two-dimensional pattern that you can fold to form a three-dimensional figure.

Plantilla (p. 431)   Una plantilla es una figura bidimensional que se puede doblar para forma una figura tridimensional.

Example

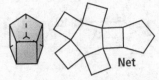

Net

The net shown can be folded into a prism with pentagonal bases.

No correlation (p. 399)   There does not appear to be a relationship between two sets of data.

Sin correlación (p. 399)   No hay relación entre conjuntos de datos.

Example

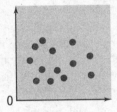

Nonlinear function (p. 110)   A function whose graph is not a line or part of a line.

Función no lineal (p. 110)   Función cuya gráfi es una línea o parte de una línea.

Example

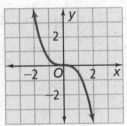

Obtuse angle (p. 460)   An obtuse angle is an angle whose measure is between 90 and 180.

Ángulo obtuso (p. 460)   Un ángulo obtuso e ángulo que mide entre 90 y 180 grados.

Example

147°

Odd function (p. 144)   A function f is an odd function if and only if $f(-x) = -f(x)$ for all values of x in its domain.

Función impar (p. 144)   Una función f es una función impar si y solo si $f(-x) = -f(x)$ para t los valores de x en su dominio.

Example   The function $f(x) = x^3 + 2x$ is odd because $f(-x) = (-x)^3 + 2(-x) = -x^3 - 2x = -f(x)$

osite angles (p. 858) Opposite angles of a
~rilateral are two angles that do not share
~e.

Ángulos opuestos (p. 858) Los ángulos opuestos de un cuadrilátero son dos ángulos que no comparten lados.

Example

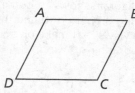

∠A and ∠C are
opposite angles,
as are ∠B and ∠D.

~site rays (p. 443) Opposite rays are collinear
~with the same endpoint. They form a line.

Semirrectas opuestas (p. 443) Las semirrectas opuestos son semirrectas colineales con el mismo extremo. Forman una recta.

Example

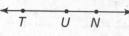

$\overrightarrow{UT}$ and $\overrightarrow{UN}$ are opposite rays.

~site reciprocals (p. 214) A number of the
~$-\frac{b}{a}$, where $\frac{a}{b}$ is a nonzero rational number.
~roduct of a number and its opposite
~ocal is −1.

Recíproco inverso (p. 214) Número en la forma $-\frac{b}{a}$, donde $\frac{a}{b}$ es un número racional diferente de cero. El producto de un número y su recíproco inverso es −1.

Example $\frac{2}{5}$ and $-\frac{5}{2}$ are opposite reciprocals
because $\left(\frac{2}{5}\right)\left(-\frac{5}{2}\right) = -1$.

~site sides (p. 858) Opposite sides of a
~ilateral are two sides that do not share a
~.

Lados opuestos (p. 858) Los lados opuestos de un cuadrilátero son dos lados que no tienen un vértice en común.

Example

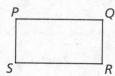

$\overline{PQ}$ and $\overline{SR}$ are
opposite sides,
as are $\overline{PS}$ and $\overline{QR}$.

~center of a triangle (p. 814) The orthocenter
~iangle is the point of concurrency of the lines
~ning the altitudes of the triangle.

Ortocentro de un triángulo (p. 814) El ortocentro de un triángulo es el punto donde se intersecan las alturas de un triángulo.

Example

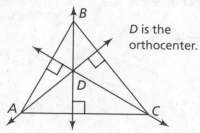

D is the
orthocenter.

Orthographic drawing (p. 435) An orthographic drawing is the top view, front view, and right-side view of a three-dimensional figure.

Dibujo ortográfico (p. 435) Un dibujo ortográ... es la vista desde arriba, la vista de frente y la v... del lado derecho de una figura tridimensional.

Example The diagram shows an isometric drawing (upper right) and the three views that make up an orthographic drawing.

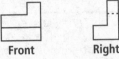

Top

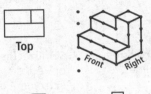

Front   Right

Front

Right

Outlier (p. 379) An outlier is a data value that is much higher or lower than the other data values in the set.

Valor extremo (p. 379) Un valor extremo es e... valor de un dato que es mucho más alto o mu... más bajo que los otros valores del conjunto de datos.

Example For the set of values 2, 5, 3, 7, 12, the data value 12 is an outlier.

Output (p. 103) A value of the dependent variable.

Salida (p. 103) Valor de una variable dependiente.

Example The output of the function $f(x) = x^2$ when $x = 3$ is 9.

P

Paragraph proof (p. 639) *See* **proof.**

Prueba de párrafo (p. 639) *Ver* **proof.**

Example The output of the function $f(x) = x^2$ when $x = 3$ is 9.

Parallel lines (p. 212, 653) Two lines are parallel if they lie in the same plane and do not intersect. The symbol ∥ means "is parallel to".

Paralle lines (p. 212, 653) Dos rectas son par... si están en el mismo plano y no se cortan. El símbolo ∥ significa "es paralelo a".

Example $\ell \parallel m$

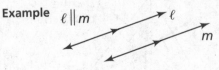

The red symbols indicate parallel lines.

elogram (p. 483, 858) A parallelogram is a ilateral with two pairs of parallel sides. You oose any side to be the *base*. An *altitude* is gment perpendicular to the line containing se drawn from the side opposite the base. *eight* is the length of an altitude.

Paralelogramo (p. 483, 858) Un paralelogramo es un cuadrilátero con dos pares de lados paralelos. Se puede escoger cualquier lado como la *base*. Una *altura* es un segmento perpendicular a la recta que contiene la base, trazada desde el lado opuesto a la base. La *altura*, por extensión, es la longitud de una altura.

Example

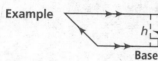

Altitude

Base

l planes (p. 653) Parallel planes are planes o not intersect.

Planos paralelos (p. 653) Planos paralelos son planos que no se cortan.

Example

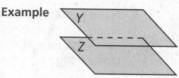

Planes *Y* and *Z* are parallel.

function (p. 186) A family of functions is a of functions with common characteristics. A function is the simplest function with these teristics.

Función elemental (p. 186) Una familia de funciones es un grupo de funciones con características en común. La función elemental es la función más simple que reúne esas características.

Example $y = x$ is the parent function for the family of linear equations of the form $y = mx + b$.

tile (p. 395) A value that separates a data ⊃ 100 equal parts.

Percentil (p. 395) Valor que separa el conjunto de datos en 100 partes iguales.

tile rank (p. 395) The percentage of data that are less than or equal to a given value.

Rango percentil (p. 395) Porcentaje de valores de datos que es menos o igual a un valor dado.

ter of a polygon (p. 545) The perimeter of gon is the sum of the lengths of its sides.

Perímetro de un polígono (p. 545) El perímetro de un polígono es la suma de las longitudes de sus lados

Example

4 in.

4 in.   3 in.

5 in.

$P = 4 + 4 + 5 + 3$
$= 16$ in.

dicular bisector (p. 593) The perpendicular r of a segment is a line, segment, or ray that endicular to the segment at its midpoint.

Mediatriz (p. 593) La mediatriz de un segmento es una recta, segmento o semirrecta que es perpendicular al segmento en su punto medio.

Example

$\overleftrightarrow{YZ}$ is the perpendicular bisector of $\overline{AB}$. It is perpendicular to $\overline{AB}$ and intersects $\overline{AB}$ at midpoint *M*.

Visual **Glossary**

English

Spanish

Perpendicular lines (pp. 213, 593) Perpendicular lines are lines that intersect and form right angles. The symbol ⊥ means "is perpendicular to". Two lines are perpendicular if the product of their slopes is −1.

Rectas Perpendiculars (pp. 213, 593) Las rect perpendiculars son recta sue se cortan y frma angulos rectos. El símbolo ⊥ significa "es perpendicular a". Dos rectas son perpendicula el producto de sus pendientes es −1.

Example

Piecewise function (p. 357) A piecewise function has different rules for different parts of its domain.

Función de fragmentos (p. 357) Una funció fragmentos tiene reglas diferentes para difer partes de su dominio.

Plane (p. 441) In Euclidean geometry, a plane is undefined. You can think of a plane as a flat surface that extends without end and has no thickness. A plane contains infinitely many lines.

Plano (p. 441) En la geometría euclidiana, u plano es indefinido. Se puede pensar en un p como una superficie plana sin fin, ni grosor. U plano tiene un número infinito de rectas.

Example

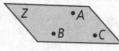

Plane *ABC* or plane *Z*

Point (p. 441) In Euclidean geometry, a point is undefined. You can think of a point as a location. A point has no size

Punto (p. 441) En la geometría euclidiana, u punto es indefinido. Puedes imaginarte a un como un lugar. Un punto no tiene dimensión

Example • *P*

Point of concurrency (p. 803) *See* **concurrent lines.**

Punto de concurrencia (p. 803) *Ver* **concurre lines.**

Point-slope form (p. 195) A linear equation of a nonvertical line written as $y - y_1 = m(x - x_1)$. The line passes through the point (x_1, y_1) with slope *m*.

Forma punto-pendiente (p. 195) La ecuació lineal de una recta no vertical que pasa por punto (x_1, y_1) con pendiente m está dada po $y - y_1 = m(x - x_1)$.

Example An equation with a slope of $-\frac{1}{2}$ passing through $(2, -1)$ would be written $y + 1 = -\frac{1}{2}(x - 2)$ in point-slope form.

Point symmetry (p. 523) Point symmetry is the type of symmetry for which there is a rotation of 180° that maps a figure onto itself.

Simetría central (p. 523) La simetría central tipo de simetría en la que una figura se ha r 180° sobre sí misma.

Polygon (p. 483) A polygon is a closed plane figure formed by three or more segments. Each segment intersects exactly two other segments, but only at their endpoints, and no two segments with a common endpoint are collinear. The *vertices* of the polygon are the endpoints of the sides. A *diagonal* is a segment that connects two non-consecutive vertices.

Polígono (p. 483) Un polígono es una figur plana compuesta or tres o más semgentos. C segmento intersecta los otros dos segments exactamente, pero únicamente en sus punto extremos y ningúno de los segmentos extrer comunes son colineales. Los *vértices* del polí son los extremos de los lados. Una *diagonal* segmento que conecta dos vértices no consecutivos.

Example

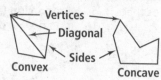

Vertices — Diagonal — Sides

Convex   Concave

---

ve correlation (p. 399) The relationship
en two sets of data in which both sets of
ncrease together.

Correlación positiva (p. 399) La relación entre dos
conjuntos de datos en la que ambos conjuntos
incrementan a la vez.

Example

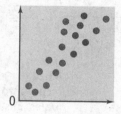

0

---

ate (p. 444) A postulate, or *axiom*, is an
ed statement of fact.

Postulado (p. 444) Un postulado, o *axioma*, es un
enunciado que se acepta como un hecho.

Example Through any two points there is
exactly one line.

---

ge (p. 495) *See* **transformation.**

Preimagen (p. 495) *Ver* **transformation.**

(pp. 632, 639, 672, 907) A proof is a
cing argument that uses deductive
ing. A proof can be written in many forms.
o-column proof, the statements and reasons
gned in columns. In a paragraph proof, the
ents and reasons are connected in
ces. In a flow proof, arrows show the logical
tions between the statements. In a
nate proof, a figure is drawn on a
nate plane and the formulas for slope,
nt, and distance are used to prove
ties of the figure. An indirect proof involves
e of indirect reasoning.

Prueba (pp. 632, 639, 672, 907) Una prueba es un
argumento convincente en el cual se usa el
razonamiento deductivo. Una prueba se puede
escribir de varias maneras. En una *prueba de dos
columnas*, los enunciados y las razones se alinean
en columnas. En una *prueba de párrafo*, los
enunciados y razones están unidos en oraciones. En
una *prueba de flujo*, hay flechas que indican las
conexiones lógicas entre enunciados. En una
prueba de coordenadas, se dibuja una figura en un
plano de coordenadas y se usan las fórmulas de la
pendiente, punto medio y distancia para probar las
propiedades de la figura. Una *prueba indirecta*
incluye el uso de razonamiento indirecto.

Example

E

F G

Given: $\triangle EFG$, with right angle $\angle F$
Prove: $\angle E$ and $\angle G$ are complementary.

Paragraph Proof: Because $\angle F$ is a right angle,
$m\angle F = 90$. By the Triangle Angle-Sum
Theorem, $m\angle E + m\angle F + m\angle G = 180$. By
substitution, $m\angle E + 90 + m\angle G = 180$.
Subtracting 90 from each side yields $m\angle E + m$
$\angle G = 90$. $\angle E$ and $\angle G$ are complementary by
definition.

English

Spanish

Proportion (p. 52) An equation that states that two ratios are equal.

Example $\frac{7.5}{9} = \frac{5}{6}$

Proporción (p. 52) Es una ecuación que estab que dos razones son iguales.

 Q

Quadrilateral (p. 483) A quadrilateral is a polygon with four sides.

Example

Cuadrilátero (p. 483) Un cuadrilátero es un polígono de cuatro lados.

Quartile (p. 392) A quartile is a value that separates a finite data set into four equal parts. The second quartile (Q_2) is the median of the data set. The first and third quartiles (Q_1 and Q_3) are the medians of the lower half and upper half of the data, respectively.

Example For the data set 2, 3, 4, 5, 5, 6, 7, 7, the first quartile is 3.5, the second quartile (or median) is 5, and the third quartile is 6.5.

Cuartil (p. 392) Un cuartil es el valor que sep un conjunto de datos finitos en cuatro partes iguales. El segundo cuartil (Q_2) es la mediana conjunto de datos. El primer cuartil y el tercer cuartil (Q_1 y Q_3) son medianas de la mitad inf y de la mitad superior de los datos, respectivamente.

 R

Radical expression (p. 344) Expression that contains a radical.

Example $\sqrt{3}$, $\sqrt{5x}$ and $\sqrt{x-10}$ are examples of radical expressions.

Expresión radical (p. 344) Expresiones que contienen radicales.

Range (of a relation or function) (p. 135) The possible values of the output, or dependent variable, of a relation or function.

Example In the function $y = |x|$, the range is the set of all nonnegative numbers.

Rango (de una relación o función) (p. 135) conjunto de todos los valores posibles de la s o variable dependiente, de una relación o fu

Range of a set of data (p. 382) The difference between the greatest and the least data values for a set of data.

Example For the set 2, 5, 8, 12, the range is $12 - 2 = 10$.

Rango de un conjunto de datos (p. 382) Diferencia entre el valor mayor y el menor en conjunto de datos.

Rate (p. 37) A ratio of a to b where a and b represent quantities measured in different units.

Example Traveling 125 miles in 2 hours results in the rate $\frac{125 \text{ miles}}{2 \text{ hours}}$ or 62.5 mi/h.

Tasa (p. 37) La relación que existe entre a y cuando a y b son cantidades medidas con dis unidades.

of change (p. 167) The relationship between quantities that are changing. The rate of ge is also called slope.

of change $= \dfrac{\text{change in the dependent variable}}{\text{change in the independent variable}}$

Tasa de cambio (p. 167) La relación entre dos cantidades que cambian. La tasa de cambio se llama también pendiente.

tasa de cambio $= \dfrac{\text{cambio en la variable dependiente}}{\text{cambio en la variable independiente}}$

Example Video rental for 1 day is \$1.99.
Video rental for 2 days is \$2.99.

$$\text{rate of change} = \frac{2.99 - 1.99}{2 - 1}$$
$$= \frac{1.00}{1}$$
$$= 1$$

(p. 37) A ratio is the comparison of two ities by division.

Razón (p. 37) Una razón es la comparación de dos cantidades por medio de una división.

Example $\frac{5}{7}$ and $7:3$ are ratios.

---

nalize the denominator (p. 349) To alize the denominator of an expression, e it so there are no radicals in any minator and no denominators in any radical.

Racionalizar el denominador (p. 349) Para racionalizar el denominador de una expresión, ésta se escribe de modo que no haya radicales en ningún denominador y no haya denominadores en ningún radical.

Example $\dfrac{2}{\sqrt{5}} = \dfrac{2}{\sqrt{5}} \cdot \dfrac{\sqrt{5}}{\sqrt{5}} = \dfrac{2\sqrt{5}}{\sqrt{25}} = \dfrac{2\sqrt{5}}{5}$

. 443) A ray is the part of a line that s of one *endpoint* and all the points of the n one side of the endpoint.

Semirrecta (p. 443) Una semirrecta es la parte de una recta que tiene un *extremo* de donde parten todos los puntos de la recta.

Example

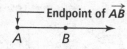

Endpoint of $\overrightarrow{AB}$

A B

---

gle (p. 483) A rectangle is a parallelogram our right angles.

Rectangle (p. 483) Un rectángulo es un paralelogramo con cuatro ángulos rectos.

Example

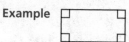

---

ive formula (p. 149) A recursive formula s the terms in a sequence by relating each o the ones before it.

Fórmula recursiva (p. 149) Una fórmula recursiva define los términos de una secuencia al relacionar cada término con los términos que lo anteceden.

Example Let $a_n = 2.5a_{n-1} + 3a_{n-2}$. If $a_5 = 3$ and $a_4 = 7.5$, then
$a_6 = 2.5(3) + 3(7.5) = 30$.

Reflection (p. 508) A reflection (*flip*) across line *r*, called the *line of reflection*, is a transformation such that if a point *A* is on line *r*, then the image of *A* is itself, and if a point *B* is not on line *r*, then its image *B′* is the point such that *r* is the perpendicular bisector of $\overline{BB'}$.

Reflexión (p. 508) Una reflexión (*inversión*) a través de una línea *r*, llamada el *eje de reflexión* una transformación en la que si un punto *A* es parte de la línea *r*, la imagen de *A* es sí misma, un punto *B* no está en la línea *r*, su imagen *B′* punto en el cual la línea *r* es la bisectriz perpendicular de $\overline{BB'}$.

Example

Reflectional symmetry (p. 523) Reflectional symmetry, or *line symmetry*, is the type of symmetry for which there is a reflection that maps a figure onto itself. The reflection line is the *line of symmetry*. The line of symmetry divides a figure with reflectional symmetry into two congruent halves.

Simetría reflexiva (p. 523) Simetría reflexiva, *simetría lineal*, es el tipo de simetría donde ha una reflexión que ubica una figura en sí misma eje de reflexión es el *eje de simetría*. El eje de simetría divide una figura con simetría reflexiva dos mitades congruentes.

Example

A reflection across the given line maps the figure onto itself.

Regular polygon (pp. 484, 852) A regular polygon is a polygon that is both equilateral and equiangular. Its *center* is the point that is equidistant from its vertices.

Polígono regular (pp. 484, 852) Un polígono regular es un polígono que es equilateral y equiangular. Su *centro* es el punto equidistan sus vértices.

Example

ABCDEF is a regular hexagon. Point *X* is its center.

Relation (p. 135) Any set of ordered pairs.

Relación (p. 135) Cualquier conjunto de pare ordenados.

Example {(0, 0), (2, 3), (2, −7)} is a relation.

Relative frequency (p. 416) The ratio of the number of times an event occurs to the total number of events in the sample space.

Freuencia relativa (p. 416) La razón del núm de veces que ocurre un evento número de eve en el espacio muestral.

Example

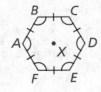

Archery Results				
Scoring Region	Yellow	Red	Blue	Black	White
Arrow Strikes	52	25	10	8	5

$$\text{Relative frequency of spinning 1} = \frac{\text{frequency of spinning 1}}{\text{total frequencies}}$$
$$= \frac{29}{100}$$

glish

ote interior angles (p. 689) Remote interior
es are the two nonadjacent interior angles
sponding to each exterior angle of a triangle.

Ángulos interiores remotos (p. 689) Los ángulos
interiores remotos son los dos ángulos interiores
no adyacentes que corresponden a cada ángulo
exterior de un triángulo.

---

ual (p. 411) The difference between the
ue of a data point and the corresponding
ue of a model for the data set.

Residuo (p. 411) La diferencia entre el valor de y
de un punto y el valor de y correspondiente a ese
punto en el modelo del conjunto de datos.

---

nbus (p. 483) A rhombus is a parallelogram
four congruent sides.

Rombo (p. 483) Un rombo es un paralelogramo
de cuatro lados congruentes.

Example

---

t angle (p. 460) A right angle is an angle
e measure is 90.

Ángulo recto (p. 460) Un ángulo recto es un
ángulo que mide 90.

Example $90°$

 This symbol
indicates a
right angle.

---

motion (p. 495) A transformation in the
e that preserves distance and angle measure.

Movimiento rígido (p. 495) Una transformación
en el piano que no cambia la distancia ni la medida
del ángulo.

Example Translations, reflections, and
rotations are rigid motions.

---

ion (p. 515) A rotation *(turn)* of $x°$ about a
R, called the *center of rotation*, is a
formation such that for any point V, its image
point V', where $RV = RV'$ and $m\angle VRV' = x$.
nage of R is itself. The positive number of
es x that a figure rotates is the *angle of
on*.

Rotación (p. 515) Una rotación *(giro)* de $x°$ sobre
un punto R, llamado el *centro de rotación*, es una
transformación en la que para cualquier punto V,
su imagen es el punto V', donde $RV = RV'$ y
$m\angle VRV' = x$. La imagen de R es sí misma. El
número positivo de grados x que una figura rota es
el *ángulo de rotación*.

Example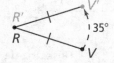

---

ional symmetry (p. 523) Rotational
etry is the type of symmetry for which there
tation of 180° or less that maps a figure
tself.

Simetría rotacional (p. 523) La simetría rotacional
es un tipo de simetría en la que una rotación de
180° o menos vuelve a trazar una figura sobre
sí misma.

Example The figure has 120°
rotational symmetry.

Visual **Glossary**

English

Same-side interior angles (p. 655) Same-side interior angles lie on the same side of the transversal *t* and between ℓ and *m*.

Example

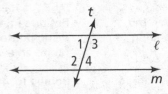

∠1 and ∠2 are same-side interior angles, as are ∠3 and ∠4.

Scatter plot (p. 399) A graph that relates two different sets of data by displaying them as ordered pairs.

Example

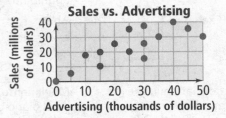

The scatter plot displays the amount spent on advertising (in thousands of dollars) versus product sales (in millions of dollars).

Segment (p. 443) A segment is the part of a line that consists of two points, called *endpoints*, and all points between them.

Example   Endpoints of $\overline{DE}$

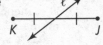

Segment bisector (p. 454) A segment bisector is a line, segment, ray, or plane that intersects a segment at its midpoint.

Example

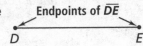

ℓ bisects $\overline{KJ}$.

Sequence (p. 146) An ordered list of numbers that often forms a pattern.

Example $-4, 5, 14, 23$ is a sequence.

Side *See* **angle.**

Spanish

Ángulos internos del mismo lado (p. 655) Lo ángulos internos del mismo lado están situado el mismo lado de la transversal *t* y dentro de ℓ

Diagrama de puntos (p. 399) Grafica que mu la relacion entre dos conjuntos. Los datos de a conjuntos se presentan como pares ordenados

Segmento (p. 443) Un segmento es la parte de una recta que tiene dos puntos, llamados *extremos*, entre los cuales están todos los pun de esa recta.

Bisectriz de un segmento (p. 454) La bisectri un segmento es una recta, segmento, semirre plano que corta un segmento en su punto me

Progresion (p. 146) Lista ordenada de nume que muchas veces forma un patron.

Lado *Ver* **angle.**

Visual **Glossary**

glish

Spanish

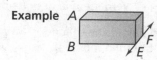

lines (p. 653)   Skew lines are lines that do
e in the same plane.

Rectas cruzadas (p. 653)   Las rectas cruzadas son
rectas que no están en el mismo plano.

Example $\overleftrightarrow{AB}$ and $\overleftrightarrow{EF}$ are skew.

(p. 168)   The ratio of the vertical change to
orizontal change.

$= \frac{\text{vertical change}}{\text{horizontal change}} = \frac{y_2 - y_1}{x_2 - x_1}$, where $x_2 - x_1 \neq 0$

Pendiente (p. 168)   La razón del cambio vertical al
cambio horizontal. pendiente cambio vertical cambio
horizontal. pendiente $= \frac{\text{cambio vertical}}{\text{cambio horizontal}} = \frac{y_2 - y_1}{x_2 - x_1}$,
donde $x_2 - x_1 \neq 0$

Example

The slope of the line above is $\frac{2}{4} = \frac{1}{2}$.

-intercept form (p. 186)   The slope-intercept
of a linear equation is $y = mx + b$, where m is
ope of the line and b is the y-intercept.

Forma pendiente-intercepto (p. 186)   La forma
pendiente-intercepto es la ecuación lineal
$y = mx + b$, en la que m es la pendiente de la
recta y b es el punto de intersección de esa
recta con el eje y.

Example $y = 8x - 2$

---

on of a system of linear equations (p. 231)
rdered pair in a system that makes all the
ions of that system true.

**Solución de un sistema de ecuaciones lineales
(p. 231)**   Todo par ordenado de un sistema que
hace verdaderas todas las ecuaciones de ese sistema.

Example   (2, 1) is a solution of the system
$y = 2x - 3$
$y = x - 1$
because the ordered pair makes
both equations true.

---

on of a system of linear inequalities
1)   Any ordered pair that makes all of
equalities in the system true.

**Solución de un sistema de desigualdades lineales
(p. 271)**   Todo par ordenado que hace verdaderas
todas las desigualdades del sistema.

Example

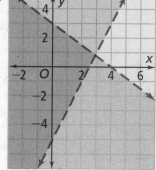

The dark shaded area shows the
solution of the system $y > 2x - 5$
$3x + 4y < 12$.

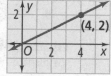

Visual Glossary

English

Spanish

Solution of an inequality (two variables) (p. 263) Any ordered pair that makes the inequality true.

Solución de una desigualdad (dos variables) (p. 263) Cualquier par ordenado que haga verdadera la desigualdad.

Example Each ordered pair in the shaded area and on the solid red line is a solution of $3x - 5y \le 10$.

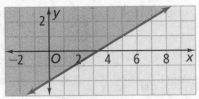

Space (p. 443) Space is the set of all points.

Espacio (p. 443) El espacio es el conjunto de los puntos.

Square (p. 483) A square is a parallelogram with four congruent sides and four right angles.

Cuadrado (p. 483) Un cuadrado es un paralelogramo con cuatro lados congruentes y cuatro ángulos rectos.

Example

Square root function (p. 354) A function that contains the independent variable in the radicand.

Función de raíz cuadrada (p. 354) Una funci◌ que contiene la variable independiente en el radicando.

Example $y = \sqrt{2x}$ is a square root function.

Standard deviation (p. 390) A measure of how data varies, or deviates, from the mean.

Desviación típica (p. 390) Medida de cómo ◌ datos varían, o se desvían, de la media.

Example Use the following formula to find the standard deviation.

$$\sigma = \sqrt{\frac{\Sigma(x - \overline{x})^2}{n}}$$

Standard form of a linear equation (p. 203) The standard form of a linear equation is $Ax + By = C$, where A, B, and C are real numbers and A and B are not both zero.

Forma normal de una ecuación lineal (p. 203) ◌ forma normal de una ecuación lineal es Ax By◌ donde A, B y C son números reales, y donde ◌ no son iguales a cero.

Example $6x - y = 12$

Step function (p. 358) A step function pairs every number in an interval with a single value. The graph of a step function can look like the steps of a staircase.

Función escalón (p. 358) Una función escaló◌ empareja cada número de un intervalo con u◌ valor. La gráfica de una función escalón se pu◌ parecer a los peldaños de una escalera.

Straight angle (p. 460) A straight angle is an angle whose measure is 180.

Ángulo llano (p. 460) Un ángulo llano es un◌ ángulo que mide 180.

Example

$m\angle AOB = 180$

ghtedge (p. 591) A straightedge is a ruler no markings on it.

Regla sin graduación (p. 591) Una regla sin graduación no tiene marcas.

itution method (p. 240) A method of solving em of equations by replacing one variable an equivalent expression containing the other ble.

Método de sustitución (p. 240) Método para resolver un sistema de ecuaciones en el que se reemplaza una variable por una expresión equivalente que contenga la otra variable.

Example If $y = 2x + 5$ and $x + 3y = 7$, then
$x + 3(2x + 5) = 7$.

ementary angles (p. 467) Two angles are ementary if the sum of their measures is 180.

Ángulos suplementarios (p. 467) Dos ángulos son suplementarios cuando sus medidas suman 180.

Example

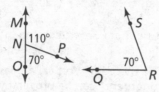

$\angle MNP$ and $\angle ONP$ are supplementary,
as are $\angle MNP$ and $\angle QRS$.

etry (p. 523) A figure has symmetry if there sometry that maps the figure onto itself. *See* oint symmetry; reflectional symmetry; onal symmetry.

Simetría (p. 523) Una figura tiene simetría si hay una isometría que traza la figura sobre sí misma. *Ver también* **point symmetry; reflectional symmetry; rotational symmetry.**

Example

A regular pentagon has reflectional symmetry and 72° rotational symmetry.

n of linear equations (p. 231) Two or more equations using the same variables.

Sistema de ecuaciones lineales (p. 231) Dos o más ecuaciones lineales que usen las mismas variables.

Example $y = 5x + 7$
$y = \frac{1}{2}x - 3$

n of linear inequalities (p. 271) Two or inear inequalities using the same variables.

Sistema de desigualdades lineales (p. 271) Dos o más desigualdades lineales que usen las mismas variables.

Example $y \le x + 11$
$y < 5x$

Term (p. 6) A number, variable, or the product or quotient of a number and one or more variables.

Término (p. 6) Un número, una variable o el producto o cociente de un número y una o m... variables.

Example The expression $5x + \frac{y}{2} - 8$ has three terms: $5x$, $\frac{y}{2}$, and -8.

Term of a sequence (p. 146) A term of a sequence is any number in a sequence.

Término de una progresión (p. 146) Un térm... de una secuencia es cualquier número de una secuencia.

Example -4 is the first term of the sequence $-4, 5, 14, 23$.

Theorem (p. 636) A theorem is a conjecture that is proven.

Teorema (p. 636) Un teorema es una conjetu... que se demuestra.

Example The theorem "Vertical angles are congruent" can be proven by using postulates, definitions, properties, and previously stated theorems.

Transformation (p. 495) A transformation is a change in the position, size, or shape of a geometric figure. The given figure is called the *preimage* and the resulting figure is called the *image*. A transformation *maps* a figure onto its image. *Prime notation* is sometimes used to identify image points. In the diagram, X' (read "X prime") is the image of X.

Transformación (p. 495) Una transformación... un cambio en la posición, tamaño o forma de... figura. La figura dada se llama la preimagen y figura resultante se llama la *imagen*. Una transformación *traza* la figura sobre su propi... imagen. La *notación prima* a veces se utilize p... identificar los puntos de la imagen. En el diag... de la derecha, X' (leído X prima) es la imagen...

Example Preimage   Image

$\triangle XYZ \rightarrow \triangle X'Y'Z'$

Translation of a graph (p. 219) A translation (*slide*) is a transformation that moves points the same distance and in the same direction.

Traslación (p. 219) Una traslación (*desplazamiento*) es una transformación en la... se mueven puntos la misma distancia en la m... dirección.

Example

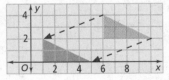

The blue triangle is the image of the red triangle under the translation $(-5, -2)$.

slation (p. 498) A translation is a sformation that moves points the same nce and in the same direction.

Traslación (p. 498) Una traslación es una transformación en la que se mueven puntos la misma distancia en la misma dirección.

Example

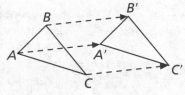

---

sversal (p. 655) A transversal is a line that sects two or more lines at distinct points.

Transversal (p. 655) Una transversal es una línea que interseca dos o más líneas en puntos precisos.

Example

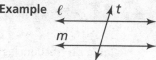

t is a transversal of ℓ and m.

---

ezoid (pp. 483, 894) A trapezoid is a rilateral with exactly one pair of parallel sides, *bases*. The nonparallel sides are called the *legs* e trapezoid. Each pair of angles adjacent to a are *base angles* of the trapezoid. An *altitude* rapezoid is a perpendicular segment from ase to the line containing the other base. Its h is called the *height* of the trapezoid.

Trapecio (pp. 483, 894) Un trapecio es un cuadrilátero con exactamente un par de lados paralelos, l, as *bases*. Los lados no paralelos se llaman los *catetos* del trapecio. Cada par de ángulos adyacentes a la base son los *ángulos de base* del trapecio. Una *altura* del trapecio es un segmento perpendicular que va de una base a la recta que contiene la otra base. Su longitud se llama, por extensión, la *altura* del trapecio.

Example

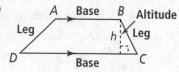

In trapezoid *ABCD*, $\angle ADC$ and $\angle BCD$ are one pair of base angles, and $\angle DAB$ and $\angle ABC$ are the other.

---

line (p. 401) A line on a scatter plot drawn the points. It shows a correlation.

Línea de tendencia (p. 401) Línea de un diagrama de puntos que se traza cerca de los puntos para mostrar una correlación.

Example

Positive

Negative

English

Truth value (p. 609) The truth value of a statement is "true" or "false" according to whether the statement is true or false, respectively.

Two-way frequency table (p. 414) A table that displays frequencies in two different categories.

Example

	Male	Female	Totals
Juniors	3	4	7
Seniors	3	2	5
Totals	6	6	12

Two-way relative frequency table (p. 416) A two-way relative frequency table shows joint relative frequencies and marginal relative frequencies for two categories of data.

U

Unit analysis (p. 39) Including units for each quantity in a calculation to determine the unit of the answer.

Example To change 10 ft to yards, multiply by the conversion factor $\frac{1 \text{ yd}}{3 \text{ ft}}$.

$$10 \text{ ft} \left(\frac{1 \text{ yd}}{3 \text{ ft}} \right) = 3\frac{1}{3} \text{ yd}$$

Unit rate (p. 37) A rate with a denominator of 1.

Example The unit rate for 120 miles driven in 2 hours is 60 mi/h.

V

Vertex *See* **angle**. The plural form of *vertex* is *vertices*.

Vertex angle (p. 744) *See* **isosceles triangle**.

Vertical angles (p. 466) Vertical angles are two angles whose sides form two pairs of opposite rays.

Example

Spanish

Valor verdadero (p. 609) El valor verdadero d enunciado es "verdadero" o "falso" según el enunciado sea *verdadero* o falso, respectivame

Table de frecuencias de doble entrada (p. 414) Una tabla de frecuencies que contiene dos categorias de datos.

Tabla de frecuencias relativas de doble entrad (p. 416) Una tabla de frecuencias relativas de doble entrada muestra las frecuencias relativa conjuntas y las frecuencias relativas marginale para dos categorías de datos.

Análisis de unidades (p. 39) Incluir unidades cada cantidad de un cálculo como ayuda para determinar la unidad que se debe usar para la respuesta.

Razón en unidades (p. 37) Razón cuyo denominador es 1.

Vértice *Ver* **angle**.

Ángulo del vértice (p. 744) *Ver* **isosceles tria**

Ángulos opuestos por el vértice (p. 466) Dos ángulos son ángulos opuestos por el vértice si lados son semirrectas opuestas.

$\angle 1$ and $\angle 2$ are vertical angles, as are $\angle 3$ and $\angle 4$.

cal line test (p. 136)   The vertical-line test is
thod used to determine if a relation is a
ion or not. If a vertical line passes through a
n more than once, the graph is not the graph
function.

Prueba de la recta vertical (p. 136)   La prueba de
recta vertical es un método que se usa para
determinar si una relación es una función o no. Si
una recta vertical pasa por el medio de una gráfica
más de una vez, la gráfica no es una gráfica de
una función.

Example

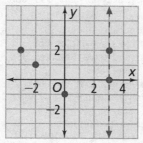

A line would pass through (3, 0)
and (3, 2), so the relation is not
a function.

rcept (p. 203)   The x-coordinate of a point
e a graph crosses the x-axis.

Intercepto en x (p. 203)   Coordenada x por donde
la gráfica cruza el eje de las x.

Example   The x-intercept of $3x + 4y = 12$
is 4.

rcept (p. 186)   The y-coordinate of a point
e a graph crosses the y-axis.

Intercepto en y (p. 186)   Coordenada y por donde
la gráfica cruza el eje de las y.

Example   The y-intercept of $y = 5x + 2$ is 2.

Visual Glossary

Index

W

X

Y

Z

Acknowledgments

Staff Credits

The people who made up the High School Mathematics team—representing composition services, core design digital and multimedia production services, digital product development, editorial, editorial services, manufacturing, marketing, and production management—are listed below.

Patty Fagan, Suzanne Finn, Matt Frueh, Cynthia Harvey, Linda Johnson, Roshni Kutty, Cheryl Mahan, Eve Melnechuk, Cynthia Metallides, Hope Morley, Michael Oster, Wynnette Outland, Brian Reardon, Matthew Rogers, Ann-Marie Sheehan, Kristen Siefers, Richard Sullivan, Susan Tauer, Mark Tricca, Oscar Vera, Paula Vergith

Additional Credits: Emily Bosak, Olivia Gerde, Alyse McGuire, Stephanie Mosely

Illustration

Jeff Grunewald: 101, 102, 134, 584, 613, 627, 643, 857, 872, 916; **Christopher Wilson:** 377; **Stephen Durke:** 439, 440, 450, 451, 464, 457, 479, 500, 556, 563, 674, 684, 690, 711, 720, 734, 741, 751, 768, 794, 797, 801, 805, 806, 810, 826, 835, 837, 839, 844; **Phil Guzy:** 525.

Technical Illustration

Aptara, Inc.; Datagrafix, Inc.; GGS Book Services

Photography

Every effort has been made to secure permission and provide appropriate credit for photographic material. publisher deeply regrets any omission and pledges to correct errors called to its attention in subsequent edit

Unless otherwise acknowledged, all photographs are property of Pearson Education, Inc.

35, Reuters/Corbis; **158**, John Glover/Alamy Images; **158**, Bob Gibbons/Alamy Images; **352**, Laurie Neish/iStockphoto; **446**, Kelly Redinger/Alamy Images; **465**, Stuart Melvin/Alamy Images; **474**, Richard Meng Fundamental Photographs; **514**, North Wind Picture Archives/Alamy Images; **522**, Alan Copson/City Pictur Alamy Images; **620**, Material courtesy of Bill Vicars an Lifeprint; **643**, Jenny Thompson/Fotolia; **657**, Kevin Fleming/Corbis; **669**, photo courtesy of Frank Adelste Ithaca, NY; **677**, Robert Llewellyn/Corbis; **690**, Peter C Iconica/Getty Images; **738**, Viktor Kitaykin/iStockphot **748**, John Wells/Photo Researchers, Inc; **759**, Image Source Black/Jupiter Images; **779 l**, M.C. Escher's "Symmetry E56" © 2009 The M.C. Escher Company-Holland. All rights reserved. www.mcescher.com; **779 r**, M.C. Escher's "Symmetry E18" © 2009 The M.C. Escher Company-Holland. All rights reserved. www.mcescher.com; **793**, Allen.B/Shutterstock; **853 l**, Laurie Strachan/Alamy Images; **853 r,** BestShot iStockphoto; **866**, Esa Hiltula/Alamy Images; **878 t**, C Cortes IV/Reuters/Landov LLC; **878 b**, Michael Jenner. Alamy Images; **892**, Rodney Raschke/Active Photo Se **902**, Colin Underhill/Alamy Images.